# CHEMICAL ANALYSIS

Vol. 1. **The Analytical Chemistry of Industrial Poisons, Hazards, and Solvents.** *Second Edition. By Morris B. Jacobs*

Vol. 2. **Chromatographic Adsorption Analysis.** By Harold H. Strain (*out of print*)

Vol. 3. **Colorimetric Determination of Traces of Metals.** *Third Edition.* By E. B. Sandell

Vol. 4. **Organic Reagents Used in Gravimetric and Volumetric Analysis.** By John F. Flagg (*out of print*)

Vol. 5. **Aquametry: Application of the Karl Fischer Reagent to Quantitative Analyses Involving Water.** By John Mitchell, Jr. and Donald Milton Smith (*temporarily out of print*)

Vol. 6. **Analysis of Insecticides and Acaricides.** By Francis A. Gunther and Roger C. Blinn (*out of print*)

Vol. 7. **Chemical Analysis of Industrial Solvents.** By Morris B. Jacobs and Leopold Scheflan

Vol. 8. **Colorimetric Determination of Nonmetals.** Edited by David F. Boltz

Vol. 9. **Analytical Chemistry of Titanium Metals and Compounds.** By Maurice Codell

Vol. 10. **The Chemical Analysis of Air Pollutants.** By Morris B. Jacobs

Vol. 11. **X-Ray Spectrochemical Analysis.** By L. S. Birks

Vol. 12. **Systematic Analysis of Surface-Active Agents.** By Milton J. Rosen and Henry A. Goldsmith

Vol. 13. **Alternating Current Polarography and Tensammetry.** By B. Breyer and H. H. Bauer

Vol. 14. **Flame Photometry.** By R. Herrmann and J. Alkemade

Vol. 15. **The Titration of Organic Compounds.** (*In two Parts*) By M. R. F. Ashworth

Vol. 16. **Complexation in Analytical Chemistry: A Guide for the Critical Selection of Analytical Methods Based on Complexation Reactions.** By Anders Ringbom

Vol. 17. **Electron Probe Microanalysis.** By L. S. Birks

Vol. 18. **Organic Complexing Reagents: Structure, Behavior, and Application to Inorganic Analysis.** By D. D. Perrin

Vol. 19. **Thermal Methods of Analysis.** By Wesley Wm. Wendlandt

Vol. 20. **Amperometric Titrations.** By John T. Stock

Vol. 21. **Reflectance Spectroscopy.** By Wesley Wm. Wendlandt and Harry G. Hecht

Vol. 22. **The Analytical Toxicology of Industrial Inorganic Poisons.** By the late Morris B. Jacobs

Vol. 23. **The Formation and Properties of Precipitates.** By Alan G. Walton

*other volumes in preparation*

# CHEMICAL ANALYSIS

## A SERIES OF MONOGRAPHS ON
## ANALYTICAL CHEMISTRY AND ITS APPLICATIONS

*Editors*

### P. J. ELVING • I. M. KOLTHOFF

Volume 23

### INTERSCIENCE PUBLISHERS
*A division of John Wiley & Sons, New York/London/Sydney*

# The Formation and Properties of Precipitates

### ALAN G. WALTON

*Department of Chemistry*
*Case and Western Reserve University*
*Cleveland, Ohio*

*with a contribution by Helga Füredi*

1967

INTERSCIENCE PUBLISHERS
*a division of John Wiley & Sons, New York/London/Sydney*

Copyright © 1967 by John Wiley & Sons, Inc.

Library of Congress Catalog Card Number 67-19727

PRINTED IN THE UNITED STATES OF AMERICA

# PREFACE

It has been said that there are more data relating to precip tation from solution in the chemical literature than for any other single subject. The reasons for this are fairly clear; historically, the separation and purification of compounds have been largely dependent upon their relative solubility, and experimentally, meaningful observations may be made without sophisticated apparatus. Unfortunately, the advantages of large quantities of data in this field are, to a large extent, counterbalanced by conflicting observations and conclusions. Furthermore, until this past decade or so, most information in the literature has been qualitative in nature since it relates mainly to solubility and precipitate morphology. Recent experimental and theoretical advances have, however, enabled a more quantitative approach to the mechanism of precipitate formation and development to be formulated. For these reasons an historical approach to the problem of writing a treatise on precipitation phenomena does not seem appropriate. I have chosen, therefore, to approach the features of precipitation, nucleation, growth, coprecipitation, surface properties and multicomponent systems from as quantitative a viewpoint as possible.

The molecular mechanism theme of precipitation extends through Chapters 1 to 5. Chapter 6 is a review of the work performed in the area of precipitation by the Jugoslav school and has been contributed by Dr. Furedi who is on leave from the Ruđer Bošković Institute in Zagreb. The approach, which is mainly empirical in nature, is included for two reasons. First, it represents a method or methods for tackling complex applied problems. Second, because many of the original papers were in Croatian journals and were not readily available in translated form, a review, in English, seems appropriate.

This book is directed toward those interested in the mechanism of precipitation from solution, whether it be in analytical or physical chemistry, physiology or geophysics, some examples being explored from each of these areas. It is hoped that not only the areas of extensive knowledge will be brought to the fore, but those also which are poorly understood. In spite of the prevalence of data many fundamental features of the precipitation process are not yet elucidated;

some of these are accessible to modern methods and techniques. Above all the formation and properties of precipitates should be regarded as interrelated phenomena which when separated are more or less intelligible but together form a very complicated picture. It is only by examination of each piece that the entire picture can conceivably be integrated and understood as a whole.

ALAN G. WALTON

## Acknowledgments

To my wife and family for their patience and encouragement during my nightly closeted sojourn, I give my official warm appreciation. My thanks also go particularly to Mr. M. E. Henstock, lecturer in Metallurgy at the University of Nottingham, for his word by word sifting of the text and to my research associate, Dr. Helga Füredi, for contributing Chapter 6.

I wish to acknowledge the permission of the various authors and journal editors for reproduction of many of the diagrams and to thank Drs. K. Jackson and T. Watanabe for the contribution of unpublished micrographs and Professor Kolthoff for helpful suggestions. To Helen Bircher, secretary and typist, thank you for efforts above and beyond the call of duty.

# CONTENTS

**1. Nucleation** . . . . . . . . . . . . . . . . . . . . . . . . . . . . . . . . . . . . . . . . . . . . . . . . . .   1
   1. Cluster Formation . . . . . . . . . . . . . . . . . . . . . . . . . . . . . . . . . . . . . . . . .   1
   2. Nature of the Nucleus . . . . . . . . . . . . . . . . . . . . . . . . . . . . . . . . . . . . . .   2
      A. Classical Formulation . . . . . . . . . . . . . . . . . . . . . . . . . . . . . . .   3
      B. Nonclassical Theory . . . . . . . . . . . . . . . . . . . . . . . . . . . . . . . .   6
   3. Heterogeneous Nucleation . . . . . . . . . . . . . . . . . . . . . . . . . . . . . . . . .   7
   4. Experimental Investigation of Heterogeneous Nucleation . . . . . . .  12
   5. Coherent and Incoherent Nucleation . . . . . . . . . . . . . . . . . . . . . . .  19
   6. Size Effects . . . . . . . . . . . . . . . . . . . . . . . . . . . . . . . . . . . . . . . . . . . .  20
   7. Nucleation Inhibition . . . . . . . . . . . . . . . . . . . . . . . . . . . . . . . . . . . .  23
   8. Precipitation Systems . . . . . . . . . . . . . . . . . . . . . . . . . . . . . . . . . . . .  24
   9. Nucleation from Homogeneous Solution . . . . . . . . . . . . . . . . . . . . .  26
  10. Homogeneous Nucleation . . . . . . . . . . . . . . . . . . . . . . . . . . . . . . . . .  29
  11. Induction Periods . . . . . . . . . . . . . . . . . . . . . . . . . . . . . . . . . . . . . . .  31
  12. Nucleation in Physiology . . . . . . . . . . . . . . . . . . . . . . . . . . . . . . . . .  32
  13. Morphological Considerations . . . . . . . . . . . . . . . . . . . . . . . . . . . . .  35
  14. Nucleation Kinetics . . . . . . . . . . . . . . . . . . . . . . . . . . . . . . . . . . . . . .  39
  15. Summary . . . . . . . . . . . . . . . . . . . . . . . . . . . . . . . . . . . . . . . . . . . . . .  41
      References . . . . . . . . . . . . . . . . . . . . . . . . . . . . . . . . . . . . . . . . . . .  42

**2. Precipitation and Growth Kinetics** . . . . . . . . . . . . . . . . . . . . . . . . . . . .  44
   1. Crystal Growth . . . . . . . . . . . . . . . . . . . . . . . . . . . . . . . . . . . . . . . . . .  45
   2. Crystal Growth Kinetics . . . . . . . . . . . . . . . . . . . . . . . . . . . . . . . . . .  49
      A. Screw Dislocation . . . . . . . . . . . . . . . . . . . . . . . . . . . . . . . . . .  49
      B. Two-Dimensional Nucleation . . . . . . . . . . . . . . . . . . . . . . . . . .  51
   3. Growth of Seed Crystals . . . . . . . . . . . . . . . . . . . . . . . . . . . . . . . . . .  54
   4. Effect of Impurities on Seed Growth Rates . . . . . . . . . . . . . . . . . . .  56
   5. Dissolution of Seed Crystals . . . . . . . . . . . . . . . . . . . . . . . . . . . . . . .  58
   6. Anomalies in Seed Crystal Growth . . . . . . . . . . . . . . . . . . . . . . . . . .  60
   7. Precipitation from Homogeneous Solution . . . . . . . . . . . . . . . . . . . .  61
   8. Precipitation of Organic Crystals and Ion–Chelate Compounds .  64
   9. Precipitation by Direct Mixing . . . . . . . . . . . . . . . . . . . . . . . . . . . . .  66
  10. Temperature Coefficients of Growth and Precipitation . . . . . . . . .  69
  11. Dissolution of Precipitates . . . . . . . . . . . . . . . . . . . . . . . . . . . . . . . .  70
  12. Secondary Growth . . . . . . . . . . . . . . . . . . . . . . . . . . . . . . . . . . . . . . .  71
  13. Techniques for Following Growth and Precipitation Kinetics . .  72
  14. Summary . . . . . . . . . . . . . . . . . . . . . . . . . . . . . . . . . . . . . . . . . . . . . .  74
      References . . . . . . . . . . . . . . . . . . . . . . . . . . . . . . . . . . . . . . . . . . .  76

**3. Coprecipitation** . . . . . . . . . . . . . . . . . . . . . . . . . . . . . . . . . . . . . . . . . . . . .  79
   1. Equilibrium Systems—Miscible Components . . . . . . . . . . . . . . . . . .  80
   2. Structural Principles of Mixed Crystal Formation . . . . . . . . . . . . .  86
   3. Intermediate Miscibility . . . . . . . . . . . . . . . . . . . . . . . . . . . . . . . . . .  89

    4.  Nonequilibrium Conditions.................................     91
    5.  Experimental Examination of Heterogeneous Distribution......     95
    6.  Distribution of Microcomponent in the Solid Phase...........     97
    7.  Rate of Precipitation.....................................     98
    8.  Adsorption Compounds.....................................    103
    9.  Coprecipitation of liquids...............................    107
   10.  Coprecipitation in Geochemistry and Physiology.............    108
        References...............................................    111

4.  Surface Properties..............................................    113
    1.  Energetics of Interfaces...................................    113
    2.  The Surface Energy of Solids..............................    114
        A.  Ionic Surfaces.........................................    115
        B.  Organic Crystals......................................    124
    3.  Liquid–Solid Interactions.................................    125
    4.  Evaluation of Interfacial Energies.........................    129
    5.  Thermodynamic Determination of Dispersive Forces..........    132
    6.  Polar Interfacial Forces...................................    133
    7.  Curved Surfaces............................................    135
    8.  Surface Enthalpy..........................................    137
    9.  Adsorption from Solution...................................    138
        A.  Adsorption of Ions....................................    140
        B.  Adsorption of Molecules................................    141
   10.  Real Surfaces.............................................    142
   11.  Rates of Adsorption and Surface Exchange...................    143
   12.  Aging of Precipitates.....................................    145
   13.  Estimation of Precipitate Surface Areas....................    146
   14.  Summary..................................................    148
        References...............................................    148

5.  Morphology......................................................    151
    1.  Solubility................................................    151
    2.  Rate of Growth............................................    156
    3.  Dendritic Growth..........................................    158
    4.  Instability of the Interface..............................    161
    5.  Fragmentation of Dendrites................................    163
    6.  Whisker Formation.........................................    165
    7.  Crystal Habit.............................................    166
    8.  Habit Modification by Solvent.............................    169
    9.  Habit Modification by Foreign Ions........................    170
   10.  Modification by Organic Materials and Dyes.................    173
   11.  Liquid Crystals...........................................    174
   12.  Agglomeration.............................................    175
   13.  Ionic Effect on Stability.................................    177
   14.  Solvent Effect on Stability...............................    180
   15.  Summary..................................................    182
        References...............................................    185

**6. Complex Precipitation Systems,** *by H. Füredi* ...................... **188**
  1. Experimental Methods and Techniques ..................... 188
  2. Evaluation of Equilibrium Constants ...................... 189
      A. Metal–Ligand Complex Formation ..................... 190
      B. Metal–Hydroxide Complex Formation .................. 191
      C. Proton Complexes .................................... 192
      D. Mixed Salt Formation ............................... 193
  3. The Solubility Curve .................................... 194
  4. The Precipitation Boundary .............................. 196
  5. Graphical Presentation of Precipitation Data ............... 197
      A. Evaluation of Coagulation Values from Kinetic Precipitation Data .................................................. 197
      B. Precipitation Curves ................................. 201
      C. Precipitation Diagrams—Two-Component Systems ....... 203
      D. Precipitation Diagrams—Three- and Multicomponent Systems .................................................. 206
  6. Applications ........................................... 209
      Acknowledgments ...................................... 213
      References ............................................ 213

Author Index ............................................... 217
Inorganic Compound Index ................................... 223
Organic Compound Index .................................... 227
Subject Index .............................................. 229

# CHAPTER 1

# NUCLEATION

Nucleation phenomena are important in many diverse areas of science. The generation of crystals from solution is of particular significance not only in analytical chemistry but also in physiology and in the geochemical sciences. In the field of physiology, nucleation occurs under normal conditions (e.g., bone growth) and under abnormal conditions (bladder, kidney and gall stones, gout, silicosis, etc.). In geochemistry the formation of sedimentary deposits, sometimes generated by bacterial nucleating action, may be singled out as an important nucleation problem.

Nucleation or the birth of crystals from solution is important both in its own right and as a process which, to a large extent, controls the number, size, structure, and morphology of precipitated crystals. Unfortunately, our understanding of the nature of such crystal formation processes is by no means complete. Part of the difficulty stems from the fact that crystal nuclei in the size range of mechanistic importance are of the order 5–20 Å in diameter and are thus too large to be treated by individual atomistic concepts and too small to be treated by bulk thermodynamic theories. They are too large to be fully characterized by techniques such as conductivity, but too small to be detected by light scattering or even most forms of electron microscopy. Furthermore, it is unlikely that they exist in any system for any but the merest transient moment of time.

Some other practical difficulties arising in the study of crystal nucleation from solution are concerned with the elucidation of the relative roles of crystallization, dissolution, and agglomeration in the overall precipitation scheme. For these and other reasons the mechanism of the primary processes in precipitation from solution is to some extent obscured, and, as a consequence, the interpretation of experimental data is often difficult.

## 1. Cluster Formation

The interaction between ions and between molecules which leads to cluster formation and eventually to the evolution of crystals has been

1

likened to a chemical reaction. In the chemical reaction the activation energy is a barrier which must be surmounted before products may be formed; similarly, the energy barrier to nucleation must be overcome before crystallization can occur. One result of this energy barrier is the necessary creation of some degree of supersaturation before spontaneous crystallization will occur.

In solutions at normal temperature the molecules or ions of solute are in constant motion and consequently are often within the sphere of influence of another molecule or ion. Hence, groups of molecules or ions are always present when the solute is present in any concentration other than trivial. There is, though, at the outset, a distinct difference between the clustering of ions and the clustering of molecules. Because of their ionic charge, ions tend to associate with neutral or oppositely charged groups, whereas uncharged molecules do not suffer from this restriction.

Prior to nucleation there is continuous formation and dissolution of ionic or molecular clusters in equilibrium with all other clusters. If the concentration of solute ions or molecules is high enough, the clusters become sufficiently large to become consolidated into small crystallites, whereupon the supposedly irreversible crystal growth ensues.

The largest cluster which may exist before spontaneous crystallization is usually referred to as the critical cluster, or nucleus, so that in terms of molecular aggregation the process may be represented as follows:

$$A \quad + A \rightleftharpoons A_2$$

$$A_2 \quad + A \rightleftharpoons A_3$$

$$A_{x-1} + A \rightleftharpoons A_x \text{ (critical cluster or nucleus)}$$

$$A_x \quad + A \xrightarrow{\text{nucleation}} A_{x+1}$$

$$A_{x+1} + A \rightarrow \text{crystal growth}$$

## 2. Nature of the Nucleus

In order to treat the nucleation phenomenon quantitatively, it is necessary to have some clear idea of the nature of the nucleus preceding crystal formation. Precipitation of organic crystals from solution undoubtedly involves straightforward molecular aggregation in the

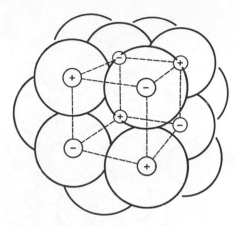

Fig. 1-1. In this model the formation of an ionic embryo involves a strong interaction between ions so that the internal lattice solvation is overcome and the configuration becomes that of a small piece of crystal in a solvent cavity (there is no particular significance in the number of ions demonstrated). The ions are in fact relaxed from their normal (bulk) lattice positions and, apart from the usual thermodynamic difficulties in dealing with small clusters, the ionic or molecular "volume" cannot strictly be identified with that of the bulk crystalline phase.

initial stages. Precipitation of ionic crystals, on the other hand, presents a somewhat ambiguous situation. Two extreme possibilities exist: either the initiating nucleus resembles a minute piece of bulk crystal and may be treated by the "embryo in a cavity" model, or, at the other extreme, the nucleus is diffuse with the solvated ions being virtually unchanged from their individual state. These conditions correspond to tight binding for strong interaction or weak binding for strong solvation, and are depicted in Figs. 1-1 and 1-2. The mathematical analysis of nucleation in these two situations will be quite different. The first case may be represented in terms of a classical formulation resembling that proposed by Volmer and others; the second requires a nonclassical analysis which might be treated by kinetic or thermodynamic reasoning.

## A. CLASSICAL FORMULATION (1–8)

If a small, stationary, spherical nucleus of diameter $l$ is created from stationary ions, the change in energy of the system is related

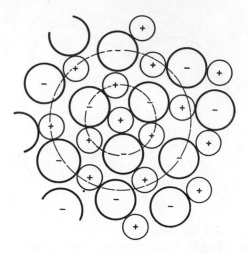

Fig. 1-2. A cross-sectional (schematic) diagram of a weakly interacting diffuse ionic cluster. Ionic interactions are not sufficient at this stage of embryonic development to overcome solvation forces.

to the ion "bonds" formed, leading to a heat of crystallization (negative) and the energy required to create the surface.

The standard free energy change may be represented approximately by

$$\Delta G^0 = \frac{\pi l^3}{6}\Delta G_v + \pi l^2 \sigma_{CL} \tag{1-1}$$

where $\Delta G_v$ is the volume free energy resulting from bond formation (and hence, by convention, is negative in sign) and $\sigma_{CL}$ is the interfacial energy per unit area of surface (Changes in the chemical composition of the system are usually deemed negligible.)

For large nuclei the volume term predominates; for small nuclei the surface term predominates. Consequently, the maximum $\Delta G^0$ with respect to $l$ is given for a cubic nucleus by

$$\Delta G^* = \frac{\pi l^2 \sigma_{CL}}{3} = \frac{16\pi\sigma_{CL}^3}{3\Delta G_v^2} \tag{1-2}$$

where $\Delta G^*$ is the activation energy barrier to the nucleation process.

The volume free energy, $\Delta G_v$, is obtained from the Gibbs-Kelvin equation as

$$\Delta G_v = \frac{mkT}{v} \ln s = \frac{4\sigma_{CL}}{l} \tag{1-3}$$

where $m$ is the number of ions in the neutral molecule, $v$ is the molecular volume, and $s$ is the supersaturation. Hence

$$\Delta G^* = \frac{16\pi \sigma_{CL}^3 v^2}{3(mkT \ln s^*)^2} \tag{1-4}$$

In this manner it is possible to relate the activation energy barrier to the supersaturation, $s$.

Some of the difficulties in applying this treatment to real situations are often glossed over. It is normally recognized that the interfacial energy $\sigma_{CL}$ is not necessarily independent of cluster size, but less familiar is the fact that extra thermodynamic terms involving rotation, vibration, and translation of the clusters become rather important for small clusters. Changes in chemical composition of the system should also be considered. For small clusters the Gibbs-Kelvin equation (Eq. 1-3) is modified to

$$\Delta G_v = \frac{4\sigma_{CL}}{l} - \frac{1}{n} \tag{1-5}$$

where $n$ is the number of molecules or ions in the cluster corresponding to $\Delta G^*$. Furthermore, it seems unlikely that very small clusters can maintain thermodynamic equilibrium without gross fluctuations in $\sigma_{CL}$. These criticisms will be seen to be of importance when experimental precipitation data are examined.

The rate of nucleation $dN/dt$ is usually written in the form (derived from the law of mass action)

$$\frac{dN}{dt} = J = A \exp(-\Delta G^0/kT) \tag{1-6}$$

or, from Eq. (1-4)

$$J = A \exp\left[\frac{16\pi \sigma_{CL}^3 v^2}{3k^3 T^3 (m \ln s^*)^2}\right] \tag{1-7}$$

If $J$ is plotted as a function of supersaturation, a curve like that in Fig. 1-3 is produced. It can be seen that there is in essence a critical

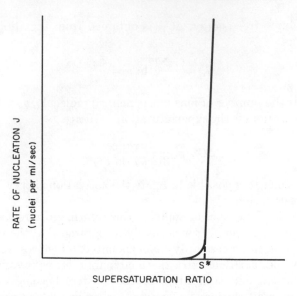

Fig. 1-3. The relation between the homogeneous nucleation rate, $J$ (nuclei per ml/sec) and the degree of supersaturation ($s$ = actual concentration/solubility).

supersaturation, $s^*$, below which nucleation is very slow and above which nucleation is extremely fast. This critical supersaturation is usually chosen to correspond to a rate of one nucleus being formed per second per unit volume, in which case Eq. 1-7 becomes

$$\ln s^* = \left[\frac{32\sigma_{CL}^3 v^2}{k^3 T^3 m^2 \ln A}\right]^{1/2} \tag{1-8}$$

If the preexponential factor $A$ is known, it is clear that the only unknown in Eq. 1-8 is the interfacial energy, $\sigma_{CL}$. Actually $A$ can be resolved into a fairly complicated expression, but for present purposes it can be taken to be equal to $10^{25}$.

The theory predicts, then, a critical supersaturation $s^*$ from which $\sigma_{CL}$ can be calculated. It will be seen in Chapter 4 that there are independent methods for determining the interfacial energy $\sigma_{CL}$ and, consequently, a real test of the theory is possible.

## B. Nonclassical Theory (9–11)

For weakly bonded clusters where no significant desolvation occurs, no surface is formed and other means of expressing the nucleation process must be found. Sears has attempted to treat ionic crystal nucleation by nonclassical means but there does not, as yet, seem to be much support for this particular application. Much wider cognizance has been given to the Christiansen-Nielsen kinetic theory (12,13), which can also be regarded as nonclassical. Christiansen and Nielsen proposed that reacting ions do form clusters, but that the precipitation rate, $R$, could be expressed in terms of the primary ion concentration, $c$, by

$$R = k_1 c^p \qquad (1\text{-}9)$$

where $p$ is the number of ions in the critical cluster.

They argued that, provided the precipitated phase becomes visible when $c \sim c_0$, then the induction time $\lambda$ could be related to $c$ by

$$\lambda^{-1} = k_2 c_0{}^{p-1} \qquad (1\text{-}10)$$

In the early 1950's several sparingly soluble salts were shown to follow this type of relation with $p$ in the range 2–6, and a considerable amount of effort was devoted to working on this hypothesis (14).

However, induction periods have been found to be strongly influenced by impurities and by the crystal growth rate. It seems, therefore, that little fundamental information regarding the nucleation process can be gleaned from the measurement of the period elapsing between the time of reactant mixing and the time at which precipitation becomes detectable.

## 3. Heterogeneous Nucleation

So far nucleation has been considered as a homogeneous process, that is, the influence of solids other than the precipitating phase has been ignored. In practice, however, the influence of impurities is strong. Again, there are two distinctly different models which can be assumed in a theoretical formulation of heterogeneous processes. The first, as before, assumes that the nucleus (critical) resembles a small piece of bulk phase. In Fig. 1-4 the influence of the substrate is shown to affect the coherence of the interface by causing dislocations. Turnbull and Vonnegut (15) have explored this model and conclude that the energy barrier to nucleation (Eq. 1-1) is modified in two ways. First, the deposited nucleus is distorted, affecting the interatomic forces and consequently modifying $\Delta G_v$, and second, the

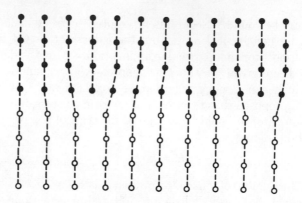

Fig. 1-4. Turnbull-Vonnegut model for the arrangement of atoms in the interfacial region. The lattice disregistry between deposit and substrate leads to distortion and dislocations in the deposit surface (15).

introduction of the solid–solid interface modifies the surface energy requirements. Thus, for a cylindrical nucleus, radius $r$, height $h$

$$\Delta G_{\text{het}}^{0} = \pi r^2 h (\Delta G_v + \chi) + 2\pi r h \sigma_e + \pi r^2 (\sigma_{\text{CL}} + \sigma_{\text{CS}} - \sigma_{\text{SL}}) \quad (1\text{-}11)$$

where $\sigma_{\text{CS}}$ is the crystal/substrate interfacial energy, $\sigma_{\text{SL}}$ is the substrate/solution interfacial energy, and $\sigma_e$ is the cluster-edge energy.

In almost every case the influence of the substrate is to lower the energy barrier to nucleation and hence catalyze the nucleation process. Furthermore, Turnbull and Vonnegut relate the term $\chi$ to the elastic modulus, $c'$, of the nucleus in the plane adjacent to the substrate and $\delta$, the misfit of the nucleus on the substrate, by

$$\chi = c' \delta^2 \quad (1\text{-}12)$$

For example, if the nucleus lattice parameter, $a_0^{\text{nuc}}$ lies adjacent to the substrate plane of parameter $a_0^{\text{sub}}$, then

$$\delta = \frac{a_0^{\text{sub}} - a_0^{\text{nuc}}}{a_0^{\text{sub}}} \quad (1\text{-}13)$$

Proceeding by maximum Equation 1-11 and substituting for

$\Delta G_v$ from Eq. 1-3, we find that the critical supersaturation (for cylindrical nuclei) is given by

$$m \ln s^* = \frac{v}{kT} c' \delta^2 + \frac{2\sigma_e v \pi^{1/2}}{kT} \left( \frac{\sigma_{\mathrm{CL}} + \sigma_{\mathrm{CS}} - \sigma_{\mathrm{SL}}}{kT \ln A} \right)^{1/2} \qquad (1\text{-}14)$$

where the symbols are those used in Eqs. 1-8 and 1-11.

Experimentally it is found that the degree of misfit does indeed affect the energy barrier to heterogeneous nucleation in qualitative accord with the Turnbull-Vonnegut theory. Consequently, it is to be expected that formation of precipitates will be catalyzed by impurities, one criterion of the effectiveness being the lattice match between precipitate crystal and impurity substrate.

The second model, proposed recently by Upreti and Walton (17), attempts to avoid several of the macroscopic parameters appearing in the Turnbull-Vonnegut theory. For example, most recent studies of ionic crystal nucleation lead to the conclusion that relatively few ions are involved in the critical cluster and hence the critical nucleus is unlikely to possess bulk crystal ion spacing, elastic moduli, or surface energy. Further, it is again not entirely certain that the ions in the cluster are desolvated. Figures 1-5a and 5b show two possible groupings of ions in which either the interaction is stronger between substrate and cluster ions, or vice versa.

The derivation of this latter theory assumes a sequence of diffusion, adsorption, surface diffusion (or diffusion through a surface layer), and clustering; it is derived as follows. The nucleation rate for surface nuclei may be written as

$$J = A'' N_n^* R'_{n^*} \qquad (1\text{-}15)$$

where $N_n^*$ is the number of critical clusters and $R'_{n^*}$ is the rate of addition of the postcritical ion by surface diffusion; $A'' = 4l^* Z'$, where $l^*$ is the edge length of the (square) cluster and $Z'$ is a two-dimensional Zeldovich factor.

$$R'_{n^*} = N_1 a_0 v' \exp \left( -Q_D / kT \right) \qquad (1\text{-}16)$$

where $a_0$ is the distance of separation between active sites, $v'$ is the frequency for jump diffusion, and $Q_D$ is the activation energy of sur-

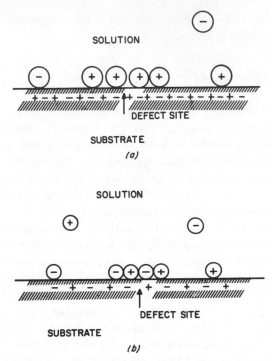

Fig. 1-5. (a) Model for the two-dimensional coherent nucleation of ions onto an ionic substrate. The clustering process follows a reversible sequence of adsorption, diffusion, and incorporation into the cluster. In this particular model the position of depositing ions is determined entirely by the substrate lattice configuration and would be applicable to the deposition of weakly interacting ions or molecules which are strongly adsorbed. Such a situation might, for example, apply to the deposition of (111) planes of oriented alkali halide crystals. (b) Model for the two-dimensional incoherent nucleation of strongly interacting ions. Clustering is determined by the lattice of the deposit rather than the substrate, although the most favorable energetic process still corresponds to a perfect lattice match between deposit and substrate. Such a situation might occur with (100) or (110) deposition of alkali halides.

face diffusion. From the Langmuir isotherm the surface concentration of primary species $N_1$ may be written

$$N_1 = \frac{R}{\nu''} \exp\ (Q_{\text{ads}}/kT) \qquad (1\text{-}17)$$

where $R$ is the rate of arrival of ions at the surface and $\nu''$ is the vibration frequency of adsorbed ions.

The number of critical clusters in terms of the primary species may be written as

$$N_n{}^* = N_1 \exp{(-\Delta G^*/kT)} \qquad (1\text{-}18)$$

(assuming a distribution between active sites). Combining Eq. 1-15, 1-16, 1-17, and 1-18,

$$J = A'' \left(\frac{R}{\nu''}\right)^2 a_0\nu' \exp{[(2Q_{ads} - Q_D - \Delta G^*)/kT]} \qquad (1\text{-}19)$$

The standard free energy of two-dimensional cluster formation is obtained by writing

$$\Delta G^0 = n\gamma E^\infty + \gamma\sigma' \qquad (1\text{-}20)$$

where $E^\infty$ is the interaction between one ion and all other ions in an infinite two-dimensional network, $\sigma'$ is the undistorted two-dimensional cluster-edge energy, and $\gamma$ is the ratio of the interionic distance in an undistorted cluster divided by the distorted distance (i.e., $\gamma = 1 - \delta$ where $\delta$ is the lattice mismatch). After maximization and application of a two-dimensional analog of the Gibbs-Kelvin equation to Eq. 1-20, the maximum Gibbs free energy for formation of a square two-dimensional cluster is

$$\Delta G^* = 4d^2\sigma_e^2/m\gamma kT \ln{s^*} \qquad (1\text{-}21)$$

where $d$ is the average ion diameter, $\sigma_e$ is the specific edge energy of the strained cluster, and $n$ is the number of ions forming a neutral molecule in the cluster. Hence, on substitution in Eq. 1-19 and putting $\ln J = 0$ (critical nucleation rate),

$$\ln{s^*} = \frac{4d^2\sigma_e^2}{m\gamma kT}[(2Q_{ads} - Q_D + BkT)^{-1}] \qquad (1\text{-}22)$$

where $B = \ln{4l^* A (R/\nu'')^2 a_0\nu'}$.

This final equation predicts that favorable nucleation sites will be those of high adsorption energy ($Q_{ads}$) and that the critical supersaturation will increase with lattice mismatch between nucleus and substrate. Further, the critical supersaturation will decrease with increase in temperature.

If the depositing ions interact weakly with the substrate and are clustered in the second configuration of Fig. 1-5$b$, a more complicated approach is necessary, but in simple form an equation similar to Eq. 1-22 is produced:

$$\ln s^* = \frac{4d^2\sigma_e^2}{mkT}\,[(2Q_{ads}\,f(\gamma,n) - Q_D + BkT)^{-1}] \qquad (1\text{-}23)$$

Equations 1-22 and 1-23 relate, therefore, to coherent and incoherent nucleation, respectively. If $\gamma = 1$ and $Q_D = 2Q_{ads}$ or $BkT \gg 2Q_{ads} - Q_D$, Eqs. 1-22 and 1-23 reduce to the form of nucleation implicated in crystal growth (Chap. 2). Nucleation from concentrated solutions may involve direct addition of ions to the cluster, removing the surface diffusion criterion. A further (unexplored) possibility is that in some cases nucleation may occur from instability of adsorbed multilayers.

### 4. Experimental Investigation of Heterogeneous Nucleation

Before examining the complex situation existing in most precipitation systems, it is necessary to attempt to evaluate the validity of the theoretical concepts by using model systems. In this respect the heterogeneous nucleation of crystals from solution is more readily studied. The requirements for such a model heterogeneous system are that the substrate is of a known lattice arrangement, well defined in terms of surface structure (a plane surface with no defects would be most suitable); the nucleating material should also be of a known lattice arrangement, which preferably should be simple. The onset of nucleation should be accurately definable in terms of a critical supersaturation, and the structural relationship between substrate and deposit should be known. This last requirement virtually limits the ideal study to a system where epitaxy, i.e., oriented overgrowth, is observable. Fortunately, many such systems are known; some, with their relative orientation and degree of mismatch $\delta$ are given in Table 1-1. Figure 1-6 shows a typical orientation of rubidium chloride on a mica substrate; in this case the (111) plane lies adjacent to the (100) plane of the mica. Because of its cleavage properties and ability to form a well-defined surface, mica has been the most popular substrate for heterogeneous nucleation studies.

TABLE 1-1a
Epitaxial Growth of Inorganic Crystals on Some Insoluble Substrates[a]

| Substrate | Deposit | Lattice misfit, % | Orientation | |
|---|---|---|---|---|
| | | | Substrate | Deposit |
| PbS | KI | 18 | (001), (100) | (001), (100) |
| | RbBr | 15 | | |
| | RbCl | 10 | | |
| | KBr | 10 | | |
| | NaI | 8 | | |
| | KCl | 5 | | |
| | NaBr | −1 | | |
| | AgBr | −4 | | |
| | NaCl | −6 | | |
| | AgCl | −7 | | |
| CaCO₃ | KI | 10 | (100), (010) | (100), (010) |
| | RbBr | 7 | | |
| | RbCl | 3 | | |
| | KBr | 3 | | |
| | NaI | 1 | | |
| | KCl | −2 | | |
| | NaBr | −7 | | |
| | NaCl | −12 | | |
| CaF₂ | KBr | 21 | (111), (1̄10) | (111), (1̄10) |
| | KCl | 14 | | |
| | NaBr | 8 | | |
| | NaCl | 3 | | |
| | LiBr | 0 | | |
| | LiCl | −6 | | |

[a] Data from J. H. van der Merwe, *Discussions Faraday Soc.*, **5**, 201 (1949).

Bradley (18) was among the first to attempt such measurements with the nucleation of ammonium iodide on a muscovite (mica) substrate. A saturated solution of ammonium iodide in contact with a mica substrate was slowly cooled until it nucleated; rapid crystal growth then occurred and the critical supersaturation could be evaluated. Newkirk and Turnbull (16) refined the experimental technique somewhat and chose a series of mica substrates with different lattice parameters to attempt an evaluation of the Turnbull-Vonnegut theory. The relationship between the orientation of

TABLE 1-1b

Epitaxial Growth of Some Organic Crystals upon Inorganic Substrates[a]

| Substrate | Deposit | Lattice misfit, % | Orientation | |
|---|---|---|---|---|
| | | | Substrate | Deposit |
| ZnS | Thiourea | 12,2 | $(110),(1\bar{1}0)$ | $(011),(001)$ |
| | | 0, −6 | | $(101),(010)$ |
| | | 3, −8 | (001) | $(001),(100)$ |
| Mica | Thiourea | −4, 6 | (010) | $(010),(001)$ |
| | Urea | | (100) | Various |
| NaCl, Mica, NaNO₃, BaSO₄ | p-Aminophenol | — | | |
| Mica, ZnS | p-Nitrobenzoic acid | | | |

[a] Data from J. H. van der Merwe, *Discussions Faraday Soc.*, **5**, 201 (1949).

ammonium iodide and the mica substrate is shown in Fig. 1-7, the (111) plane of ammonium iodide lying adjacent to the (100) mica plane.   Interpretation of the data for the nucleation of ammonium iodide by these mica substrates was attempted using Eq. 1-11. Hence, a plot of log critical supersaturation versus the square of the mismatch $\delta$ should be a line of slope related to the elastic modulus $c$ (provided the other energetic terms do not change).   As expected, the lattice parameter of the substrate affected the critical degree of supercooling (Fig. 1-8), but the elastic modulus calculated for ammonium iodide was inaccurate by two orders of magnitude.

An effective test of the alternative theory (Eq. 1-22) is not directly possible from the preceding data, though if approximate $\sigma_e$ values ($\sim 10^{-5}$ erg/cm) are substituted along with the experimental data, adsorption energies of approximately $10^{-12}$ to $10^{-14}$ erg are obtained, which seem fairly reasonable.   Equation 1-22, however, can be more thoroughly tested if nucleation data is available over a range of temperatures.

Fig. 1-6. Micrograph of the epitaxial growth of RbCl crystals on mica. The RbCl crystals show (111) orientation (× 20).

Recently, careful experimentation on the nucleation of alkali halide crystals onto a mica substrate has been carried out. In these experiments alkali halide crystals were deposited from solution onto supercooled muscovite substrates, the apparatus being shown in Fig. 1-9. Control of the substrate temperatures was effected by a thermoelectric cooler, quite precise data ($s^* = \pm 0.010$) being obtained (17). The onset of crystal nucleation was determined visually as the first crystal appeared. In most of the cases examined, it was possible to obtain different degrees of supercooling for the appearance of the first and subsequent crystals; ammonium iodide, however, was an exception because a large number of crystals appeared simultaneously. Repeated experiments using the same substrate showed the appearance of crystals in the same position,

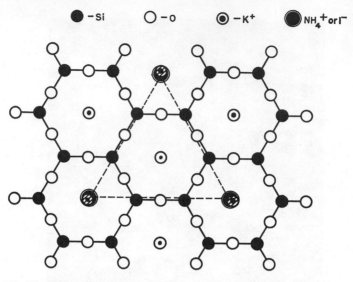

Fig. 1-7. The surface structure of muscovite, which induces (111) orientation of alkali halide crystals because of the unicharged cation ($K^+$) (or anion $OH^-$) lattice net.

with the same orientation at the same degree of supercooling, bearing out the fact that there are active sites even in the most carefully prepared mica substrates. The data obtained from this series of experiments are shown in Table 1-2 and Fig. 1-10. One interesting feature of these data is that, in agreement with theoretical prediction, the most favorable lattice registry does not necessarily lead to the most favorable energetic process. Dunning et al. (19) have observed that the epitaxial formation of ammonium iodide and rubidium iodide crystals first involves the growth of thin crystal layers adjacent to the surface. It is only when these layers impinge upon a step that the three-dimensional "pyramids" erupt. Whether this is a general phenomenon in epitaxial growth of alkali halides on mica is not possible to say with the limited availability of observational data. The qualitative correctness of Eq. 1-22 seems to suggest that the appropriate function parameters have been incorporated.

Without a detailed knowledge of the change of cluster-edge energy with the number of ions in the cluster, it is not possible to fully evaluate the individual parameters in Eq. 1-22. The values of $\sigma_e$

and $Q_{ads}$, though, are again of the order $10^{-5}$ erg/cm and $10^{-12}$ erg per ion, respectively, which is in reasonable accord with expectations for these parameters.

TABLE 1-2

Critical Supersaturation for the Heterogeneous Nucleation of Alkali Halide Crystals upon Mica as a Function of Lattice Match and Saturation Temperature[a]

| Deposit | 9.6°C | 19.8°C | 30.C° | 40°C | $\delta$, % |
|---------|-------|--------|-------|------|-------------|
| KCl | 1.125 | 1.081 | 1.038 | 1.010 | −14 |
| KBr | 1.110 | 1.049 | 1.036 | 1.016 | −10 |
| KI | 1.038 | 1.011 | 1.007 | [b] | −4 |
| $NH_4I$ | 1.016 | 1.006 | 1.002 | [b] | −1 |
| RbCl | — | 1.082 | — | — | −10 |
| RbBr | — | 1.003 | — | — | −6 |

[a] Data from ref. 17.
[b] Solutions decompose.

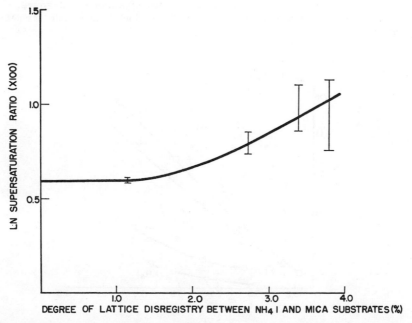

Fig. 1-8. Maximum stable supersaturation for ammonium iodide crystals nucleated upon various natural and synthetic micas. (After Newkirk and Turnbull, ref. 16)

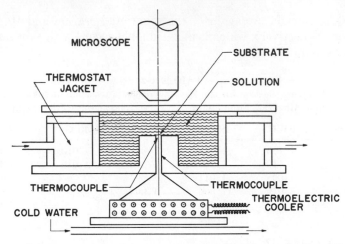

Fig. 1-9. Cell for examining heterogeneous nucleation from solution.  The substrate is mounted upon a thermoelectrically cooled cold finger and the critical supersaturation detected visually by the sudden appearance and growth of crystals deposited from the solution, the bulk of which is maintained at near saturation temperature (17).

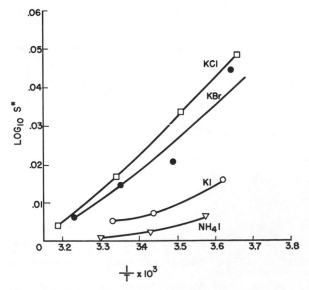

Fig. 1-10. The critical supersaturation ratio $s^*$ as a function of (crystallization temperature)$^{-1}$ for four alkali halide crystals depositing on muscovite (17).

Equation 1-22 predicts satisfactorily (qualitatively) the dependence of critical stable supersaturation upon lattice mismatch and temperature, and the presence of active sites is accounted for in terms of sites of strong adsorption. Another important point which may be realized from Eq. 1-22 is that the edge energy is related to the strength of ionic bonding and the lattice energy of the depositing crystal (20). Hence, materials of high lattice energy will often supersaturate considerably, even in the presence of ideally matched substrates.

The following general principles may thus be enunciated for the heterogeneous nucleation of precipitates from solution where the substrate is not well defined.

*1.* Fairly soluble salts will not supersaturate to a large degree because of a high rate of arrival of ions at the active sites and a high concentration of adsorbed material upon the active impurities.

*2.* Sparingly soluble salts will supersaturate to a high degree, particularly if the lattice energy is large (e.g., $BaSO_4$, $CaCO_3$, $PbCrO_4$).

*3.* Favorable precipitation sites in the substrate will be those where strong adsorption occurs, particularly if bonding with the substrate is possible.

## 5. Coherent and Incoherent Nucleation

Figures 1-5a and b show the physical situation corresponding to incoherent and coherent nucleation, respectively. It seems worthwhile to attempt to determine under what circumstances these two types of nucleation occur. The preceding data for the nucleation of alkali halides on mica suggest strongly that nucleation in this particular case is coherent, that is, the positions of ions in the initiating nucleus are determined by the lattice arrangement of the substrate. This fact is particularly reasonable when it is realized that the ions in a (111) lattice plane of an alkali halide crystal carry a common electrostatic charge and are mutually repelling. Such a circumstance is not repeated in the (100) or (110) planes where strong cohesive forces are at play. It would seem at first sight that the mutual interaction forces for the (100) and (110) planes would be likely to cause clustering which would be less susceptible to substrate influence. Without experimental evidence, this particular system is open to conjecture. Similarly, the relation between ice nucleation and the degree of coherence with the substrate is debatable. The effectiveness of silver iodide in nucleating ice crystals has traditionally been ascribed to lattice matching, but recently observations of ice nucleation at surface defects and steps have led to conjecture that the lattice arrangement may not be as important as was originally supposed. The solidification of liquids is a well-explored area, having a relatively satisfactory correlation with theory. It is not particularly germane to a discussion of the precipitation of crystals from solution, except as an indication of the influence of interfacial forces in determining the nucleation of organic polar and nonpolar crystals. The polar nature of water molecules represents an intermediate between the strongly interacting ionic clusters, which under certain circumstances certainly nucleate coherently, and nonpolar molecules, metal atoms, etc., which probably do not. A decisive experiment described recently by Evans (21) has provided strong evidence that the substrate lattice is a decisive factor in nucleating ice. In this experiment, ice was nucleated by silver iodide under high external pressure. At high pressures a different crystallographic form of ice is usually formed (hexagonal ice I changes to tetragonal ice III). In the presence of silver iodide substrates, however, this phase (ice III) did not form, clearly indicating the configurational influence of the substrate.

The principles governing the formation of coherent nucleation layers are as follows:

*1.* Ionic crystals nucleate coherently with ionic substrates, particularly if the crystallographic orientation is favorable.

*2.* Polar molecular crystals nucleate coherently with ionic substrates, particularly if strong polarization is involved.

*3.* Nonpolar molecules (polymers, Fig. 1-17) apparently do not nucleate coherently upon ionic substrates, lattice mismatch being relatively unimportant in determining epitaxial deposition.

## 6. Size Effects

Heterogeneous nucleation upon a plane surface serves to define many of the basic thermodynamic parameters. Generally, however, the analytical chemist is concerned with systems in which the nucleating agent is a small suspended particle. In cloud physics it is well known that the size of the initiating particle strongly affects its nucleating capabilities. Fletcher (22) has found that, on a theoretical basis, spherical particles of a radius less than 1000 Å decrease in nucleation efficiency. Westwater (23) reports that, experimentally, particles of a size ~1 $\mu$ are the most suitable initiators for vapor condensation, both larger and smaller particles being less efficient. There does not seem to be pertinent data in the literature for a thorough study of size effects in nucleation from solution, but the increase in stable supersaturation which can be achieved by careful filtration suggests that solid particles of a size <1000 Å also are generally less efficient nucleators. On the other hand, colloidal silica (radius ~300 Å) is a much better nucleating agent for glycine than is granular sand (see Figs. 1-11a and b), possibly because of surface hydroxylation. Also, ground crystalline powders are better nucleating agents for benzene and water solidification processes than are larger crystals. For example, it is possible to supercool benzene approximately 14°C in the presence of crystalline sodium iodide, but only 3°C with thoroughly ground material. Nucleation efficiency, substrate size effects, lattice matching parameters, surface polarization and solvent structure, and field effects would seem to constitute a promising, and thus far relatively unexplored, field for experimentation. The fact that normal heterogeneities may be "blanked out" is shown by the nucleating effects of various substrates as demonstrated in Tables 1-3 and 1-4.

TABLE 1-3

Critical Degrees of Water Supercooling in the Presence of Powdered Substrates

| Substrate | Critical supercooling, °C |
|-----------|---------------------------|
| Teflon | >16 |
| Benzophenone | >16 |
| Thallium iodide | 6.2 |
| Lead iodide | 4.1 |
| Silver iodide | 2.5 |
| Silver chloride | 4.5 |
| Mercuric sulfide | 5.6 |
| Cadmium sulfide | 6.5 |

Fig. 1-11 *a*. Crystals of glycine precipated by adding ethanol to an aqueous solution ($\times$ 100).

TABLE 1-4

Critical Degrees of Benzene Supercooling in the Presence of Powdered Substrates

| Substrate | Critical supercooling, °C |
|-----------|---------------------------|
| KCl | 12.0 |
| KBr | 8.0 |
| KI | 5.5 |
| NaCl | 12.0 |
| NaBr | 3.5? |
| NaI | 5.3 |
| AgCl | 9 |
| AgBr | 8 |
| AgI | 5 |

Fig. 1-11 *b*. Crystals of glycine produced under the same conditions as *a*, but with two drops of colloidal silica added ($\times$ 100). The silica particles act as heterogeneous nuclei.

The limited amount of data available suggests then that the best nucleators are of a physical size in the region 0.1–1 $\mu$.

## 7. Nucleation Inhibition

Whereas nucleation from low degrees of supercooling or supersaturation are desirable in certain circumstances, e.g., the artificial seeding of clouds and the deposition of crystals from solution, it is undesirable in others. Examples of the latter situation are scaling in commercial distillation equipment and precipitation in oil, gasoline, and other products where deposits are undesirable. In the physiological area, too, it would be very convenient if nucleation inhibitors could be produced to prevent stone and sediment formation. There is, in fact, evidence that compounds do exist which greatly hinder the formation of crystals and hence lead to a situation where normally unstable supersaturations become stable. Very small quantities of these materials inhibit nucleation—for example, 0.3 ppm of poly-acrylic acid hinders the formation of calcium sulfate crystals (24)— and patents have been issued for methods of prevention of calcium carbonate deposition by polymeric compounds having two carboxylic groups adjacent to one another and spaced along the polymeric chain (25). Howard and co-workers (26) have also recently reported the isolation of a polypeptide which, in very small quantities, in-hibits the formation of calcium oxalate crystals and hence kidney and bladder stones. The mechanism of this inhibition does not seem to have been studied; however, it would appear that the most likely mode of operation is the adsorption of the inhibitor by active sites on impurity particles and/or heterogeneous substrate which then cannot catalyze the onset of nucleation.

## 8. Precipitation Systems

Since there are always impurities of various types in aqueous solu-tions, it is to be expected that nucleation will in general be hetero-geneous. Although the effectiveness of individual impurity particles will differ, it is clear that a precipitate can contain no more particles than the original number of impurity particles. The upper limit to the number of heteronuclei normally present in aqueous solu-tion appears to be between $10^6$ and $10^8$ nuclei/ml. Consequently, precipitation processes yielding fewer particles in the product than this can be suspected of having undergone heterogeneous nucleation. It is comparatively simple to show that nucleation is generally initiated by impurities, for example, barium sulfate, precipitated by mixing less than $10^{-2}M$ barium chloride and sodium sulfate, generally yields about $10^6$ particles/ml. If, however, rigorous steps are taken to remove impurity particles, this number can be reduced to ap-proximately 10 particles/ml (27). As yet no method has been found which entirely eliminates impurities from aqueous solution, so it is probably fair to say that no precipitation system has yet been devised in which heterogeneous nucleation has been absent.

The source of impurities which act as nuclei is of some interest. In direct mixing experiments most of the active nuclei appear to come from the solvent, although a few come also from the reaction vessel and reagents. Therefore, in a fixed volume of solution one can expect a virtually constant number of impurity nuclei and, hence, a constant number of precipitate particles independent of the initial reactant concentration, provided that heterogeneous nucleation is the dominant initiation mechanism. Several observations in the literature bear out this assertion (28,29). On the other hand, if some material is precipitated, either by supercooling or by first dissolving in one solvent and then changing the solvent composition (by addition of a second solvent), then most of the nuclei originate in the original material. In this case an approximately linear increase in particle numbers with solute concentration is to be expected. Data in Fig. 1-12 show this latter effect in the precipitation of cholesterol from mixed solvents (30).

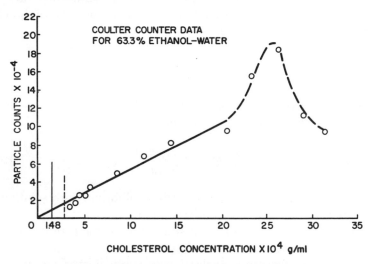

Fig. 1-12. The number of cholesterol particles precipitated from aqueous ethanolic solution. Particle numbers were established by dilution $\times$ 100 after precipitation and then using a Coulter counter. Nucleation is heterogeneous up to a supersaturation ratio of approximately 15, the source of impurity nuclei being the cholesterol itself. Above $s = 15$ the number of particles increases suddenly, but the size drops below the threshold of the counter. The onset of homogeneous nucleation at $s = 15$ leads to an interfacial energy for cholesterol vs. solution of 15 ergs/cm².

Precipitation by direct mixing is then usually initiated by hetero-geneous nucleation. Side effects caused by inhomogeneous mixing and particle agglomeration render most systems unsuitable for a quantitative study of heterogeneous nucleation, though useful data relating to homogeneous nucleation may sometimes be obtained. A controlled buildup of supersaturation can be achieved by several straightforward methods: evaporation, supercooling (or superheat-ing for materials with negative solubility coefficients), or chemical means are the three most common. The production of well-formed crystals in nature attests to the fact that slow precipitation from homogeneous solution is commonplace.

## 9. Nucleation from Homogeneous Solution

Supersaturation of soluble salt solutions is usually achieved either by supercooling or by evaporation. The supersaturation ratio, $s$, produced by supercooling is related to the molar heat of solution for saturated solutions, $\lambda_s$, and the supercooling, $\Delta T$, by

$$\ln s = \frac{\lambda_s}{R}\left(\frac{\Delta T}{TT_s}\right) \tag{1-24}$$

where $T_s$ is the saturation temperature and $T$ the operating tempera-ture. From the Gibbs-Kelvin relation (Eq. 1-3)

$$\Delta T = \frac{2v\sigma_{CL}T_sN}{m\lambda_s r_c} \tag{1-25}$$

where $r_c$ is the radius of the crystal in equilibrium with solution at temperature $T$, and $N$ is Avogadro's number.

One notes that for *homogeneous* nucleation at temperature $T$, $r_c$ is the critical cluster size (assuming a nonsolvated cluster). Un-fortunately, homogeneous nucleation is rarely if ever produced by supercooling aqueous solutions, though in quenched silicate glass and polymeric melts homogeneous nucleation is sometimes attained. Consequently, the considerable effort which has gone into corre-lating supercooling of aqueous solutions with the properties of the crystallizing phase has been rather fruitless. The evidence that nucleation in this type of system is heterogeneous is overwhelming.

It can be shown quite simply that if the solution is dispersed into a number of drops, each of which is supercooled, a spectrum of critical supercooling values is obtained. The impurities present in aqueous solutions have a spectrum of nucleating ability; hence, the process is clearly heterogeneous.

The same is true of systems in which the supersaturation is produced by evaporation or by chemical means. The advantages of precipitation from homogeneous solution in the production of well-formed crystals is widely known, but until recently the fact that it is heterogeneous and not homogeneous nucleation which initiates the precipitation was not fully appreciated. Again, filtration and removal of active impurities increases the maximum stable supersaturation, i.e., the metastable limit is increased. It seems unlikely that precipitation from homogeneous solution can give useful quantitative information unless seed crystals are introduced as model substrates.

Although quantitative data are usually not obtainable by precipitation from homogeneous solution, there is a certain amount of important nucleation information which can be derived from the metastable limit, i.e., the maximum stable supersaturation before precipitation. Of course, the metastable limit is in no way a fundamental parameter since its value is established only in terms of temporary stability and the particular impurities present in the system. Usually, however, it is possible to determine with some accuracy the onset of precipitation by techniques such as light scattering or conductivity measurements, and hence define a metastable limit for the particular system. Three of the better known studies of this type are by LaMer and Dinegar (31) (nucleation of sulfur, light scattering), Collins and Leineweber (32) (barium sulfate, light scattering, and conductivity), and Klein and Gordon (33) (silver chloride, conductivity). The chemical reactions generating the supersaturation in these three cases were:

(A) $S_2O_3^{2-} + H^+ \rightarrow HS_2O_3^- \longrightarrow$ sulfur $\downarrow$

(B) $S_2O_8^{2-} + S_2O_3^{2-} \rightarrow$ sulfate $\xrightarrow{Ba^{2+}} BaSO_4\downarrow$

(C) $CH_3CH{=}CHCl + H_2O \rightarrow$ chloride $\xrightarrow{Ag^+} AgCl \downarrow$

One notes that the maximum stable supersaturation before the onset of precipitation is characteristic of the nucleation of the precipitant upon the impurities in solution. This information, in itself, is not particularly meaningful, although it does define the conditions in which supersaturations might normally be expected. Many supersaturated solutions are found in nature, including body fluids (calcium phosphates, oxalate, and urates) and most lakes and oceans (calcium carbonate and phosphate). However, as far as the mechanism of nucleation is concerned, many additional data are required. Such data might be acquired by changing the solvent environment or the ionic environment. For example, addition of $Sr^{2+}$ ions to the precipitating barium sulfate system might well lead to changes in the initiating nucleus, with $Sr^{2+}$ replacing $Ba^{2+}$ and hence yielding different characteristic supersaturations. Unfortunately, these suggestions are entirely speculative since there are absolutely no data of this type in the literature. However, in an experiment of a similar type Black et al. (34) have found, using the Klein-Gordon method (reaction C), that when silver chloride is precipitated from homogeneous solution, the maximum stable supersaturation changes at the isoelectric point. This effect is demonstrated in Fig. 1-13 and is indicative of structural changes in the initiating nucleus. We see then that, potentially, straightforward measurements of supersaturation can yield useful atomistic information.

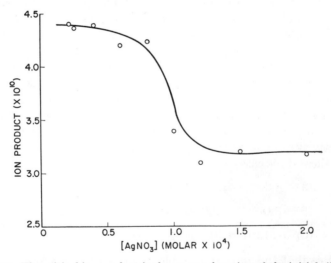

Fig. 1-13. The critical ion product is shown as a function of the initial silver ion concentration for the precipitation of silver chloride from homogeneous solution. The zero point of charge (isoelectric point) occurs at $|Ag^+| \sim 10^{-4}M$. (After Black, Insley, and Parfitt, ref. 34)

## 10. Homogeneous Nucleation

Since heterogeneous nucleation occurs at a supersaturation lower that that required for homogeneous nucleation, the latter process is to be expected only when a technique is used which produces considerable supersaturation. Since heterogeneous nucleation occurs at any supersaturation above the metastable limit, it too will be occurring simultaneously. The homogeneous process can be delineated, though, since it alone involves the generation of vast numbers of new particles. Hence, the relation between initial supersaturation and final particle numbers is crucial to the disentanglement of homogeneous and heterogeneous nucleation processes. (It is assumed that either coalescence does not occur or the agglomerate can be redispersed.) On this basis the relation between particle numbers and supersaturation should resemble that in Fig. 1-14 and the size supersaturation relation is shown in Fig. 1-15. The relation between particle size and supersaturation, of course, has been known for well over half a century, but it is only in the past few years that such precipitation data have been interpreted in terms of nucleation

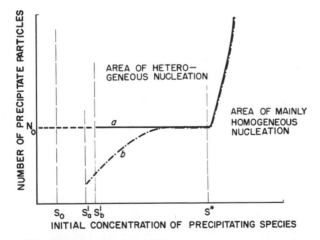

Fig. 1-14. Typical curves for the number of precipitate particles produced as a function of the initial precipitant concentration. Curve $a$ is for a system of $N_0$ impurity particles, each equally efficient in catalyzing heterogeneous nucleation. Curve $b$ corresponds to the precipitation onto $N_0$ impurities of varying nucleation efficiency. Heterogeneous nucleation occurs at a supersaturation $s'$ and homogeneous nucleation occurs at a much higher (critical) supersaturation $s^*$; $s_0$ is the solubility of the precipitant.

theory.    Nielsen (35) first identified a curve of the type shown in
Fig. 1-14 for barium sulfate precipitation and from Eq. 1-8 (assuming
$A = 10^{25}$ and spherical nuclei) has deduced that the interfacial
energy of the barium sulfate/water interface is approximately 125
ergs/cm$^2$, in good agreement with the value obtained by Walton (36)
from the particle size data of Suito and Takiyama (29) and Težak
(37).    Subsequently, several other salts have been investigated in
terms of the supersaturation-number or size relationships (38).
Interfacial energies calculated from these and older data (39) and
Eq. 1-8 are shown in Table 1-5.    Although there are as yet few direct
thermodynamic data with which to compare these values, it seems
likely that such data will become available in the near future when
the reliability of nucleation theory will be more thoroughly tested.

TABLE 1-5

Interfacial Energies (against aqueous solution) and Critical Cluster
Sizes Calculated from Homogeneous Nucleation Data
(assuming compact spherical nuclei of diameter $l^*$)

| Precipitate | Critical supersaturation ratio, $s^*$ | | Interfacial energy, ergs/cm$^2$ | Critical size $l^*$, Å | Ref[a] |
|---|---|---|---|---|---|
| BaSO$_4$ | 1000 (35) | 500 (29) | 116 | 11 | 35,29 |
| PbSO$_4$ | 28 (36) | 40 (40) | 74 | 13 | 36,40 |
| SrSO$_4$[b] | 39 | | 81 | 12 | 36 |
| PbCO$_3$ | 106 | | 105 | 11 | 36 |
| SrCO$_3$ | 30 | | 86 | 12 | 36 |
| CaF$_2$ | 80 | | 140 | 9 | 49 |
| MgF$_2$ | 30 | | 129 | 9 | 49 |
| AgCl | 5.5[c] | | 72 | 15 | 38 |
| AgBr | 3.7 | | 56 | 15 | 50 |
| Ag$_2$SO$_4$ | 19 | | 62 | 14 | 39 |
| Ca(C$_2$O$_4$) | 31 | | 67 | 13 | 36 |
| CH$_2$(NH$_2$)COOH[b] | 2.1 | | 40 | 30 | 51 |
| Cholesterol[b] | 13 | | 17 | 28 | 52 |

[a] This table is compiled from particle size data listed in the references using
Eqs. 1-3 and 1-8.    Corrections have not been made for ionic activities.

[b] These data apply to aqueous ethanol solutions.

[c] The critical supersaturation for silver chloride changes with ionic environment (38); the maximum value is quoted.

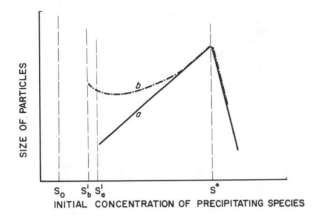

Fig. 1-15. Average precipitate particle size as a function of initial precipitant concentration. Curves *a* and *b* correspond to those in Fig. 1-14. A maximum particle size is usually found at or about the concentration corresponding to that causing homogeneous nucleation.

## 11. Induction Periods

As previously noted, the time elapsing before the appearance of a precipitate (independent of the observation technique) is a function of both nucleation and growth processes, the emphasis probably being upon the latter. If induction times are measured over a range of precipitant concentrations, an empirical relation of the form of Eq. 1-10 may be expected to apply, provided that both nucleation and growth mechanisms are consistently the same over this concentration range. If either mechanism should change, this may well be reflected in the measured induction times. In most inorganic systems three distinct regions of initiation and growth can be detected: these are, in order of increasing precipitant concentration, heterogeneous nucleation and discrete growth leading to compact particles, heterogeneous nucleation and rapid dendritic growth, and homogeneous nucleation plus controlled growth. Kolthoff and Van't Riet (40) have noted three induction regions, which correlate well with morphological observations, for the precipitation of lead sulfate. Their data are shown in Fig. 1-16. To the author's knowledge these are the only data which have been analyzed in the preceding manner, though undoubtedly many more will follow. It seems fairly likely that similar principles will unfold for organic systems.

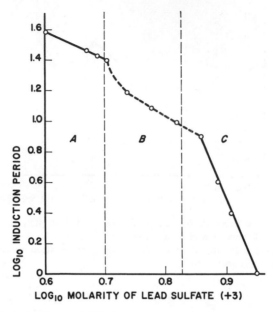

Fig. 1-16. The induction period before onset of precipitation is shown as a function of initial lead sulfate concentration.   In section $A$ the particles are compact and increase in size with increase in lead sulfate concentration.   A similar increase in size is observed in section $B$ but there is evidence of dendritic growth. In sections $A$ and $B$ nucleation is probably entirely heterogeneous.   In section $C$ homogeneous nucleation probably competes with crystal growth, and particle size decreases with increase in concentration.   (After Kolthoff and Van't Riet, ref. 40)

## 12. Nucleation in Physiology

We have seen so far that homogeneous nucleation occurs only under the extreme condition of high supersaturations and that heterogeneous nucleation is the usual initial precipitation process.   On the basis of physical adsorption, good nucleators are generally found to be those of fairly low adsorption energy but with strongly adsorbing sites.   A good lattice match between substrate and deposit also aids nucleation.   Nature, however, conspires to add a few more variables in its nucleation processes.   Invariably, phase changes within the body such as bone and tooth calcification and kidney stone formation occur by precipitation from homogeneous solution and are initiated by heterogeneous impurities.   Commonly, inorganic crystals are deposited upon or within a protein substrate, as in some forms of gout and also in bone growth. (Extraskeletal calcification is another interesting example; see Fig. 1-19.) A summary of physiological situations involving heterogeneous nucleation is given in Table 1-6. Knowledge of the nature and mechanism of these processes is important because it may lead to a better understanding of the control of diseased conditions. If we are allowed to extrapolate the data from the preceding sections, it would seem that the protein substrate would not be a particularly good initiator because of lack of strong adsorption, but could possibly act by means of good lattice match. As it turns out, probably neither of these deductions is valid since chemical bonding may well be involved. In Fig. 1-17a, b, and c are shown models of three possibilities for the mineralization of a polymeric substrate. The first shows physical alignment while the second and third show possible chemical binding processes. Since the latter processes involve chemical accretion which can occur from undersaturated solution, at least in the very initial stages, they cannot be termed nucleation in the classical physicochemical sense. It seems probable that chemical accretion processes initiate several physiological phase changes, and at present some effort is being devoted to the intermediate involved in this "biological glue" (41).

In model systems, nucleation of organic materials, including polymers, by inorganic substrates is known and the nature of this process throws further light on physiological precipitation. Fisher (42) was among the first to discover a structural relation between

TABLE 1-6

Some Examples of Heterogeneous Nucleation, in Physiological Systems

| Condition | Crystals | Substrate |
|---|---|---|
| Arthritis (gout) | Urates, calcium phosphate | Collagen |
| Gallstones | Cholesterol, calcium phosphate bile pigments | Bilirubinates, proteins |
| Kidney stones | Calcium oxalate and phosphate | Mucoid |
| Bladder stones | Calcium oxalate, uric acid | Mucoid |
| Sclerosis | Cholesterol, phospholipids | — |
| Silicosis | Amino acids, polypeptides, proteins | Silaceous materials |
| Bone growth | Calcium phosphate | Collagen |

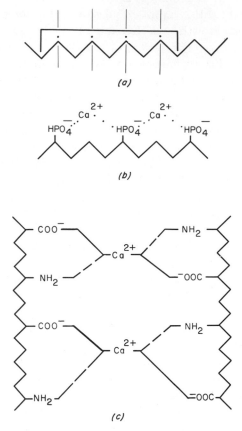

*(a)*

*(b)*

*(c)*

Fig. 1-17. (a) In this model, which might be typical of an inorganic crystal formed on a polymeric substrate, there is a relation between the configuration of substrate atoms and the orientation of the inorganic crystal. In practice it has *not* yet been shown that heterogeneous nucleation, for this type of system, is favored by lattice matching requirements. (b and c) Heterogeneous nucleation on a polymeric substrate by chemical accretion. These initial ions are bound covalently to the substrate or entities associated with the substrate and form anchors for subsequent complexing and cluster formation. This type of nucleation may be regarded as nonactivated, i.e., it is not necessary for the solution to be supersaturated for clusters to form. This type of nucleation may be involved in many physiological processes, including bone and tooth formation. Some bone defects may be associated with the blocking or absence of these active sites. In cases where more than one bound group is the basis for an embryonic site, the configuration of these groups and, hence, the physical and chemical configuration of the substrate will be important.

polyethylene precipitated onto sodium chloride crystals and ascribed this to lattice matching. However, recent results have shown that a number of polymers, e.g., polyethylene, Penton, polypropylene, and nylon, may be crystallized onto various single crystal substrates (43) epitaxial crystal growth of these materials is shown in Figs. 1-18 *a* and *b*. These polymers are polar and nonpolar and have linear, folded, and helical configurations; for none of them has any relationship been found between substrate nucleating ability and lattice matching. Orientation of these polymers is always along the (110) plane of the substrate alkali halide crystal. It seems most probable that the orientation effect is caused by polar and induced dipoles with the uniformly positive or negative directional charge in the substrate. It may be concluded, therefore, that there is essentially no lattice matching requirement for the heterogeneous nucleation of polymers upon ionic crystal substrates, or presumably for ionic crystals on polymeric materials.

Very recently attention has been directed toward the ability of certain complexing agents to induce calcification (48). The mechanism and the intriguing possibilities for such a process are not yet fully explored but it is evident that physiological nucleation must involve similar steps.

It would appear, then, that chemical bonding between substrate and one or both of the ions in the depositing phase can be important in heterogeneous nucleation. The nucleation of amino acids by colloidal silica has been mentioned previously (Fig. 1-11). The nucleation of glycine and alanine from solution is catalyzed by silica (51). Seifert (44) has suggested that this process is a fundamental cause of silicosis, colloidal silica replacing the template which usually forms body proteins. Undoubtedly the efficiency of silica as a substrate is influenced by the hydrogen bonding between amino acid and substrate hydroxyl groups. It would seem that, where bonding to the substrate occurs, the surface arrangement will lead to very specific nucleation features.

## 13. Morphological Considerations

Although it is usual to calculate interfacial energies from homogeneous nucleation data, it is also of interest to inquire further into the size and significance of the critical nucleus. Most of the evidence

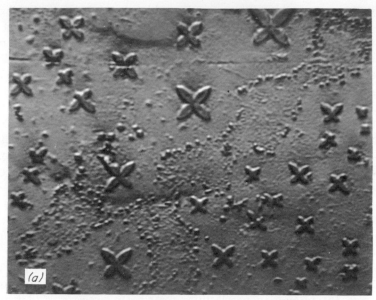

Fig. 1-18. (a) Epitaxial nucleation and growth of polyethylene crystals upon sodium chloride. The polyethylene is oriented along (110) planes with the chain folds lying along the surface. Other alkali halide crystals cause orientation in the same direction, with modified morphology.

which can be cited to elucidate the properties of the critical nucleus suggest that it is small and contains relatively few ions or molecules. None of these methods of deduction are free from criticism. Certainly, thermodynamic theory is severely strained in attempting to deal satisfactorily with the crystal nucleus, but it seems unlikely that sparingly soluble salts for which the concentration of ion pairs is extremely small could involve nuclei consisting of a large number of ions. Similarly, for the chemically induced calcification of bone it seems unlikely that extensive chemical binding occurs at the active site. There does not seem to be much reasonable doubt, therefore, that critical ion clusters, and probably molecular clusters, in solution contain few of the basic building blocks. This situation leads to some interesting features in the final precipitate. If, as Sears (11) has pointed out, the critical nucleus size is less than one unit cell, the crystallite must start growing without "knowing" what configuration

Fig. 1-18. (*b*) Epitaxy of polypropylene upon sodium chloride. Although the deposit appears to be directed in (100) direction, the polymer molecules probably lie diagonally across the square-shaped crystallites (magnification approximately 1000×, ref. 43).

it is finally to assume. Under these conditions amorphous or partially crystalline material is produced. The parameters which lead to an amorphous phase are then (*A*) high supersaturation where a small nucleus is to be expected (via Eq. 1-3) and (*B*) a large unit cell. In this second category hydroxyapatite (45) (bone mineral) and cholesterol (46) are two physiologically active materials which, when precipitated from a solution at very slight supersaturation, pass through a metastable, partially crystalline phase and eventually, by

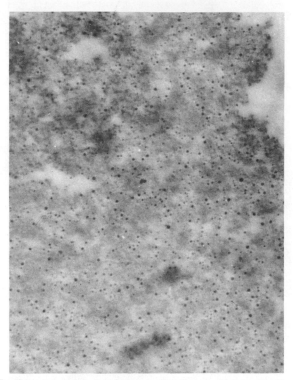

Fig. 1-19. In this remarkable micrograph (kindly supplied by T. Watanabe and M. Wilbur) the initial stages of biological matrix calcification are demonstrated. Wire grids coated with collodion and carbon were inserted between the mantle and shell of the American oyster, *Crassostrea virginica* and left for about 20 hours. During this period the oyster laid down an organic matrix and commenced calcification. The resulting electron micrograph shows the presence of minute calcite crystals (determined by electron diffraction), the smallest of which are less than 20 Å in diameter.

recrystallization, form more well-defined crystals. These processes may be followed by x-ray analysis. Figure 1-20 shows x-ray diffraction maxima for hydroxyapatite $(A)$ freshly precipitated and $(B)$ aged. Hydroxyapatite, $Ca_5(OH)(PO_4)_3$, has 18 ions per unit cell and cholesterol, 32 molecules. We may also expect other crystals to form amorphous precipitates, this condition being particularly applicable at high concentration where not only do the individual crystallites suffer

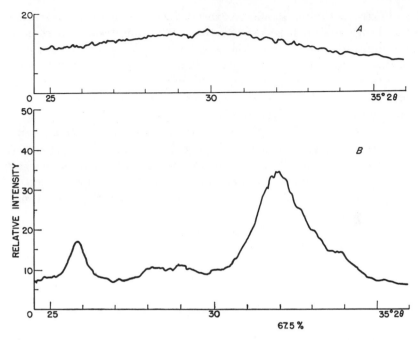

Fig. 1-20. Calcium phosphate precipitated from solution undergoes aging, changing from an amorphous to a more crystalline (67.5%) form. The upper curve (A) shows the x-ray diffraction pattern of calcium phosphate directly after precipitation (pH 10.5) and (B) after aging in solution for some hours. The stoichiometry changes from a calcium/phosphate ratio of approximately 1.5 initially to 1.67 (hydroxyapatite) after about two weeks. (Figure by Eanes, Gillesen, and Posner, ref. 45)

from rather haphazard growth, but agglomeration of the small crystallites into larger aggregates also favors an amorphous precipitate.

## 14. Nucleation Kinetics

So far, nucleation has been defined in terms of a limiting supersaturation which produces one new nucleus per second. Of course, the majority of precipitation data are obtained under dynamic rather than quasi-stationary conditions. We have already seen that thermodynamics are hardly capable of handling the latter situation and extreme caution should be exercised when attempting to stretch the theory still further to satisfy the kinetic condition.   Apart from the difficulties of applying the appropriate nucleation theory, it is necessary to combine this generation rate with a growth rate. Analyses of this type have been quite popular in chemical engineering practice, but evaluation of the parameters involved has added little to our understanding of the fundamental process.   Recently Nielsen (47) has solved the nucleation-rate law (Eq. 1-6) simultaneously with his precipitation kinetic laws (see Chap. 2).   The results are phrased in terms of the total number of precipitate particles produced by homogeneous nucleation and crystal growth at a supersaturation, $s$.

In terms of the energy barrier to nucleation, $\Delta G^*$, the equations may be expressed:

1. For diffusion-controlled growth:

$$N = 10^{22.2} \exp\left(\frac{-3 \, \Delta G^*}{5 \, kT}\right) \tag{1-26}$$

2. For mononuclear-controlled growth:

$$N = 10^{22.7} \exp\left(\frac{-4 \, \Delta G^*}{3 \, kT}\right) \tag{1-27}$$

3. For polynuclear-controlled growth:

$$N = 10^{22.4} \exp\left(\frac{-3 \, \Delta G^*}{4 \, kT}\right) \tag{1-28}$$

In terms of the supersaturation $s$, then,

$$\ln N = \log_{10} K_N - B\left(\frac{\sigma^3_{\mathrm{CL}} v^2}{k^3 T^3 \ln^2 s}\right) \tag{1-29}$$

where $B$ is a factor depending upon the geometry of the nucleus and the type of growth process.

Nielsen has reported an experimental evaluation of Eq. 1-29 and has derived kinetic factors and interfacial energy data from this equation (48); the results are given in Table 1-7.   It can be seen that in spite of all the theoretical flaws, the numerical data are consistent with expectation.   (The low kinetic constants $K_N$ for $SrSO_4$ and $CaF_2$ are attributed by Nielsen to solvation effects.)

TABLE 1-7

Kinetic Constants from Eq. 1-29 for Sparingly Soluble Salts, Assuming Cubic Nuclei (after Nielsen)

| | $\log_{10} K_N$ | $\sigma$, ergs/cm$^2$ |
|---|---|---|
| BaSO$_4$ | 22.3 | 151 |
| PbSO$_4$ | 20.0 | 119 |
| SrSO$_4$ | 11.8 | 70 |
| CaF$_2$ | 13.5 | 140 |

The values of Nielsen's kinetic constants are important because they show that, at least for the homogeneous nucleation of crystals from solution, nucleation is a very rapid process with very short induction periods. It seems doubtful from the evidence at hand, then, that a true induction period to homogeneous ionic crystal nucleation has ever been measured. Most of the literature concerned with induction periods in precipitation almost certainly pertains to the rate of crystal growth.

## 15. Summary

Of the two primary forms of precipitate nucleation, heterogeneous nucleation is by far the most common. Factors affecting the substrate efficiency are surface adsorption, diffusion, lattice matching, and particle size. For physically adsorbed materials, the best nucleators have a low energy barrier to surface diffusion but have strongly adsorbing active sites. Good lattice match between substrate and precipitate helps. Chemically adsorbed materials are nucleated only when a very specific surface arrangement is achieved. Methods of study are by supercooling solutions in the presence of well-defined substrates. Other methods of generating supersaturation are useful, provided the critical nucleation concentration is accessible.

Homogeneous nucleation occurs only at high supersaturation. Useful thermodynamic parameters may be evaluated if the concentration corresponding to the onset of homogeneous nucleation can be determined. The nature of the initiating nucleus affects the structural morphology of the product. The kinetics of nucleation, thus far, have not been studied in any detail.

Theories of nucleation are not yet entirely satisfactory but account semiquantitatively for most observations.

## References

1. M. Volmer, *Kinetic der Phasenbildung*, Steinkopff, Dresden, 1939.
2. R. Becker and W. Döring, *Ann. Physik*, **24**, 719 (1935).
3. R. Becker, *Discussions Faraday Soc.*, **5**, 55 (1949).
4. J. Frenkel, *Kinetic Theory of Liquids*, Oxford Univ. Press, New York, 1946, Chap. VII.
5. R. S. Bradley, *Quart. Rev. London*, **5**, 315 (1951).
6. V. K. LaMer, *Ind. Eng. Chem.*, **44**, 1270 (1952).
7. W. J. Dunning, in *Chemistry of the Solid State*, W. E. Garner, Ed., Butterworths, London, 1955.
8. A. G. Walton, *Science*, **148**, 601 (1965).
9. J. W. Cahn and J. E. Hilliard, *J. Chem. Phys.*, **28**, 258 (1958).
10. J. W. Cahn and J. E. Hilliard, *J. Chem. Phys.*, **31**, 688 (1959).
11. G. W. Sears, in *Physics and Chemistry of Ceramics*, C. Klingsberg, Ed., Gordon and Breach, New York, 1963.
12. J. A. Christiansen and A. E. Nielsen, *Acta Chem. Scand.*, **5**, 673 (1951).
13. J. A. Christiansen, *Acta Chem. Scand.*, **8**, 909, 1665 (1954).
14. A. E. Nielsen, *J. Colloid Sci.*, **10**, 576 (1955).
15. D. Turnbull and B. Vonnegut, *Ind. Eng. Chem.*, **44**, 1292 (1952).
16. J. B. Newkirk and D. Turnbull, *J. Appl. Phys.*, **26**, 579 (1955).
17. M. C. Upreti and A. G. Walton, Heterogeneous Nucleation of Crystals, presented at the 150th meeting of the American Chemical Society, Atlantic City, N. J., 1965; *J. Chem. Phys.*, **44**, 1936 (1966).
18. R. S. Bradley, *J. Chem. Soc.*, **1952**, 4530.
19. W. J. Dunning, P. G. Fox, and D. W. Parker, *Crystal Growth*, H. S. Peiser, Ed., Pergamon Press, New York, 1967, p. 509.
20. A. G. Walton, *J. Am. Ceram. Soc.*, **48**, 151 (1965).
21. L. F. Evans, *Nature*, **206**, 822 (1965).
22. N. Fletcher, *J. Chem. Phys.*, **29**, 572 (1958); **31**, 1136 (1959).
23. J. W. Westwater, *Proc. Intern. Symp. Nucleation Phenomena, Cleveland, 1965*, p. 35.
24. E. R. McCartney and A. E. Alexander, *J. Colloid Sci.*, **13**, 383 (1958); also ref. 26.
25. C. E. Johnson, U.S. Pat. 2,723,956.
26. J. F. Howard, Transcript of the First Conference on the Biology of Hard Tissue, New York Academy of Science (in press).
27. R. Weiss, Ph.D. thesis, Columbia University, 1962.
28. R. A. Johnson and J. D. O'Rourke, *Anal. Chem.*, **27**, 1699 (1953).
29. E. Suito and K. Takiyama, *Bull. Chem. Soc. Japan*, **27**, 121 (1954).
30. A. G. Walton, *Proc. Intern. Symp. Nucleation Phenomena, Cleveland, 1965*, p. 24.
31. V. K. LaMer and R. H. Dinegar, *J. Am. Chem. Soc.*, **72**, 4847 (1950).
32. F. C. Collins and J. P. Leineweber, *J. Phys. Chem.*, **60**, 389 (1956).
33. L. Gordon, D. H. Klein, and T. H. Walnut, *Talanta*, **3**, 177 (1959).
34. J. J. Black, M. J. Insley, and G. D. Parfitt, *J. Phot. Sci.*, **12**, 86 (1964).
35. A. E. Nielsen, *Acta Chem. Scand.*, **15**, 441 (1961).

36. A. G. Walton, *Mikrochim. Acta*, **3**, 422 (1963).

37. B. Težak et al., *Discussions Faraday Soc.*, **18**, 63 (1954.)

38. A. G. Walton, *Anal. Chim. Acta*, **29**, 434 (1963).

39. P. P. von Weimarn, *Chem. Rev.*, **2**, 217 (1925).

40. I. M. Kolthoff and B. Van't Riet, *J. Phys. Chem.*, **63**, 817 (1959).

41. See for example E. Schiffmann, A. G. Walton, and M. Urist, Transcript of the First Conference on the Biology of Hard Tissue, New York Academy of Science (in press).

42. E. W. Fisher, *Discussions Faraday Soc.*, **25**, 204 (1957); J. Willems, *ibid.*, **25**, 111 (1957); J. Willems, *Experimentia*, **13**, 465 (1957).

43. J. A. Koutsky, E. Baer and A. G. Walton, *J. Polymer Sci.*, **4**, 611 (1966); *Proc. Intern. Symp. Nucleation Phenomena, Cleveland, 1965*, p. 22.

44. H. Seifert, *Naturwissenschaften*, **42**, 13 (1955).

45. J. M. Stutman, J. D. Termine, and A. S. Posner, *Trans. N.Y. Acad. Sci.*, **27**, 669 (1965); E. D. Eanes, I. Gillesen, and A. S. Posner, *Nature*, **208**, 365 (1965).

46. H. Roth and D. Niederhiser, personal communication.

47. A. E. Nielsen, *Proc. Intern. Symp. Nucleation Phenomena, Cleveland, 1965*, p. 17.

48. E. Schiffmann, B. A. Corcoran, and G. R. Martin, *Arch. Biochem. Biophys.*, **115**, 87 (1966).

49. B. Cernicki and B. Težak, *Croat. Chem. Acta*, **28**, 175 (1956).

50. E. Matijević, *Chimia Aarau*, **9**, 287 (1955).

51. H. H. Lo, M.S. thesis, Case Institute of Technology, 1965.

52. A. G. Walton, unpublished data.

Since most of the recent developments in nucleation theory have occurred for vapor nucleation or liquid solidification processes, these might be regarded as clues to the future development of solution nucleation theory. Recent reviews for this type of material are:

1. Symposium on Nucleation Phenomena, Washington, D.C., June 21 and 22, 1965, Proceedings reprinted in *Ind. Eng. Chem.* (1965–6).

2. J. P. Hirth and G. M. Pound, *Condensation and Evaporation*, (*Progr. Mater. Sci. Part II*), Macmillan, New York, 1963.

3. J. Christian, *Theory of Transformations in Metals and Alloys*, Pergamon, New York, 1965.

4. M. E. Fine, *Introduction to Phase Transformations in Condensed Systems*, Macmillan, New York, 1965.

# CHAPTER 2

# PRECIPITATION AND GROWTH KINETICS

At first sight it would seem that reactions between ions to form precipitates might proceed extremely rapidly and be controlled entirely by the diffusion of ions to an appropriate reaction site. In fact, however, many precipitation reactions occurring at moderate degrees of supersaturation are easily followed with conventional techniques. Methods of study could clearly be based upon the rate of appearance of solid phase or upon the rate of disappearance of material from the solution phase. Many published articles report studies based on these concepts, but before these studies are outlined in more detail, it is worthwhile to consider the magnitude of the problem at hand.

Initiation of most precipitation processes is, as discussed in Chapter 1, a heterogeneous nucleation process involving deposition of the solute upon impurity particles. It is usually assumed that this primary nucleation stage is complete within a very short time after the onset of precipitation and for this reason can often be ignored in terms of the measurements which can be conveniently made upon the precipitation kinetics. The mode of initiation does, nevertheless, cause irregularities in morphology which are of direct importance in attempts to perfect a quantitative approach. The problem is then to formulate the overall rate of crystal growth of a large number of crystallites of irregular form and size from supersaturated solution. Evidently, there is little hope of treating such a complex process unambiguously unless the integral parts of the overall scheme are understood. These parts comprise crystal growth and the relationships among diffusion in solution, adsorption at the solid–liquid interface, surface diffusion, and the incorporation of solute material into the crystal lattice. Further complications, including competing dissolution and agglomeration processes, may also tend to obscure the normal growth process. The first consideration must be to simplify such a system and the most natural step, that of studying the growth of a single crystal, has in fact attracted a great deal of attention for many years.[*]

[*] Recent reviews of precipitation and crystallization studies have been published by J. A. Palermo and G. F. Bennett, and D. A. Blackadder (1).

### 1. Crystal Growth

If we consider the growth of a molecular crystal from a pure solution, it is evident that a cluster of molecules, adsorbed on a flat surface, will grow or dissociate, according to much the same rules that applied to heterogeneous nucleation. Crystal growth can, under certain circumstances, be regarded as a special form of heterogeneous nucleation in which the interfacial energy of the cluster–crystal interface is approximately zero. Two-dimensional nucleation of this type has been treated by Burton and Cabrera (2) and others, and appears to lead to a plausible growth mechanism. However, as with other forms of heterogeneous nucleation, surface nucleation is a process involving an activation energy, in this case, caused by the edge energy of the cluster. This energy barrier can, once again, be translated into a critical supersaturation below which crystal growth cannot occur. The model leads, therefore, to the rather unsatisfactory situation of stable solute supersaturation in the presence of the parent solute crystal. The growth rate would then be a function of supersaturation which shrank to zero at a well-defined supersaturation ratio, as shown in Fig. 2-1.

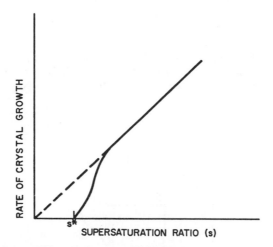

Fig. 2-1. The theoretical, surface-nucleation-controlled growth rate of a crystal is shown as a function of the supersaturation ratio, $s$. As with homogeneous and heterogeneous nucleation, there is a critical ratio $s^*$ below which the growth rate is negligible.

A closer look at the surface-nucleation model, Fig. 2-2, shows that once a step is present and the nucleus is of greater than critical size, growth should proceed readily until the surface layer is complete. A new nucleus is then required. Experimental observation establishes that, in general, crystals grow quite satisfactorily from solutions of quite low supersaturation, lower in fact than that indicated by the two-dimensional nucleation theory.

The solution to this problem, originally proposed by Frank (3), was that a growth pattern initiated by a screw dislocation would avoid the necessity of the critical supersaturation encountered in the nucleation theory. A schematic diagram of such a screw dislocation is given in Fig. 2-3.

 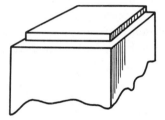

Fig. 2-2. A schematic representation of the development of a surface nucleus. Once surface nucleation has occurred, the surface nucleus extends over the crystal face, completing a new layer; renucleation is then necessary to initiate a new layer.

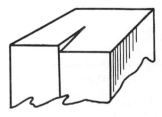

Fig. 2-3. A model screw dislocation which might, for example, be caused by an occluded impurity particle.

The development of the screw dislocation occurs either by addition of material directly from solution or, more likely, by addition of molecules diffusing across the crystal surface. Since both mechanisms lead to a constant rate of advancement of the step across the crystal surface, it can be seen that the step will move through a greater arc near the center of the crystal than at the edge, where it will lag behind. Consequently, the screw dislocation winds itself into a spiral as shown in Figs. 2-4a, b, and c.

Although the original concept of screw dislocations at the molecular level is not easy to substantiate for most crystals, the existence of spiral growth patterns with a step height equal to the height of one unit cell has been demonstrated by Dawson (4) for normal hectane crystals. Since this discovery, molecular steps in spiral growth patterns have been determined by electron miscroscopy for several materials. For example, studies of the relationship between step heights and the thermodynamics of single polymer-crystal formation represent a currently active area of research.

Spiral growth patterns are not limited to molecular dimensions; they may frequently be observed by conventional light microscopy. The step height in these crystals is an integral multiple of the unit cell height and the screw dislocation is probably initiated by the presence of an occluded impurity particle. Once a screw dislocation of any size is initiated, the crystal may grow with the spiral configuration without inhibition until the supersaturation is exhausted. Crystal growth by the screw mechanism is by now well substantiated for many different types of crystals. Examples shown in Figs. 2-5a and b are for a polymer (polyoxymethylene) and an ionic crystal (cadmium iodide). Initiation of dislocations usually comes about by nucleation upon an imperfect substrate, although other mechanisms are available (5).

It will be seen later on that the morphology of crystals grown from solution is often a direct indication of the growth mechanism. For example, crystals growing from pure solution at low supersaturations are generally well formed and of a shape which is directly related to the unit-cell structure. This feature comes about because of the relation between the screw dislocation and the regular buildup of the crystal lattice. The spiral growth pattern is also often representative of the molecular pattern, as can be seen from the cadmium iodide micrograph (Fig. 2-5b). Cadmium iodide has a hexagonal

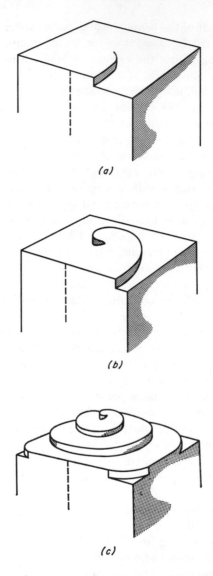

*(a)*

*(b)*

*(c)*

Fig. 2–4. Deposition of new material at the screw dislocation edge occurs at a uniform rate but the anchor dislocation center causes the relative rate of "winding" to be larger at the origin. Consequently, the screw dislocation winds into a growth spiral (see ref. 16).

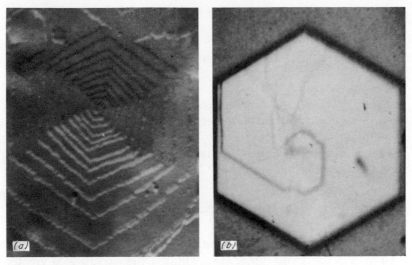

Fig. 2-5. (a) A characteristic growth spiral in polyoxymethylene (magnification ca. 20,000×) (by P. H. Geil). (b) Spiral growth pattern on cadmium iodide (magnification 50×).

crystal structure, a correlation being evident both with the crystal shape and spiral pattern. Many other crystals of different symmetry exhibit characteristic spiral growth patterns.

The discussion of single-crystal growth kinetics can then be divided into two sections, corresponding to growth at low supersaturations where screw dislocation predominate, and at higher supersaturations where two-dimensional surface nucleation may control growth. At still higher concentrations the rate of arrival of material from solution, i.e., diffusion, becomes the rate-limiting step.

## 2. Crystal Growth Kinetics

### A. SCREW DISLOCATION

In Figs. 2-4a, b, c is demonstrated the sequence of events leading from the formation of a step to the production of growth spirals. The velocity of movement of the step across the surface may be represented in terms of molecules striking the surface within a distance $x$ of the step and diffusing to it by

$$v_\infty = 2x_s(s - 1)\nu \exp(-W/kT) \tag{2-1}$$

where $x_s$ is the distance of mean surface diffusion, $s$ is the supersaturation ratio (surface), $\nu$ is the surface frequency factor (related to the mean lifetime of an absorbed molecule), and $W$ is the total energy of evaporation.

As soon as the step has wound itself into a spiral, Eq. 2-1 loses its validity and, according to Burton, Cabrera, and Frank (6), is modified to

$$v_\infty = 2x_s(s - 1)\nu \exp(-W/kT) \tanh(y_0/2x_s) \tag{2-2}$$

where $y_0$ is the distance between steps.

Growth of the spiral center ensues only if the curvature is greater than that of the critical surface cluster $r_c$. In accordance with a two-dimensional Gibbs-Kelvin relation, this critical radius at low supersaturation ratios is inversely proportional to the supersaturation ratio.

The theoretical linear growth rate $R$ perpendicular to the surface is given by the number of spiral turns passing a fixed point in unit time multiplied by the step height. Thus

$$R = v_\infty \delta/4\pi r_c = \left[\frac{(s-1)^2}{(s'-1)}\right] \delta\nu \exp(-W/kT) \tanh\left[\frac{s-1}{s'-1}\right] \tag{2-3}$$

where $s' - 1 = (2\pi r_c/x_s)(s - 1)$.

This final equation predicts, then, that for $s \ll s'$ the growth rate should be proportional to $(s - 1)^2$, i.e., the square of the super saturation. For $s \gg s'$ the growth rate should be proportional to $(s - 1)$.

The theory was originally developed for growth from the vapor, but it is believed to apply also to growth from solution. Frank has, however, suggested that $x_s$, the mean surface-diffusion distance, should be replaced by $x_L$, the thickness of the boundary layer adjacent to the crystal surface. This boundary layer concept will be expounded in greater detail in Chapter 4.

## B. Two-Dimensional Surface Nucleation

Perfect crystal surfaces contain no steps or screw dislocations and consequently cannot grow by the Frank mechanism. Surface or secondary nucleation is possible, though, on these surfaces leading to crystal growth. The principles of growth by surface two-dimensional nucleation are essentially the same as those outlined for heterogeneous nucleation in Chapter 1. As in Chapter 1, the surface cluster can be treated as a coherent piece of crystal rigidly related to the substrate structure, or as noncoherent and unmatched with the lattice substrate. The former treatment has been explored by Gibbs (7), Volmer (8), Kossel (9), Stranski (10), Becker and Döring (11), Frenkel (12), and Burton and Cabrera (2). Noncoherent nucleation has been treated by Sears (13).

The surface-nucleation rate equation is usually given in the form analogous to Eq. 1-7, Chapter 1:

$$J = A \exp\left(\frac{-\pi\sigma_e^2 v}{hk^2 T^2 \ln s}\right) \tag{2-4}$$

In this case $\sigma_e$ is the cluster–solution edge energy and $h$ is the cluster height. For organic crystals with the major molecular interaction arising from nearest-neighbor (London-van der Waals) forces, Eq. 2-4 may be modified to

$$J = A \exp\left[-\pi\phi^2/(kT)^2 \ln s\right] \tag{2-5}$$

where $\phi$ is the nearest-neighbor binding energy. Since the preexponential factor $A$ (the frequency of molecular arrival at the surface) is of the order $10^{20}$, Eq. 2-5 predicts the rate of growth of an organic crystal from supersaturation $s$ of 1.25 to be approximately 1 $\mu$ per month, much slower than growth by screw dislocation at the same supersaturation   Growth resulting from two-dimensional growth does become quite rapid at higher supersaturations and may become dominant under such conditions. It is to be noted that Eq. 2-5 does not apply to ionic crystals with long-range interaction forces. Furthermore, the derivation of Eq. 2-4 involves all the traditional errors of thermodynamic nucleation treatment to an acute degree. The two-dimensional edge energy is assumed to be independent of cluster size, which, although acceptable for molecular crystals, is

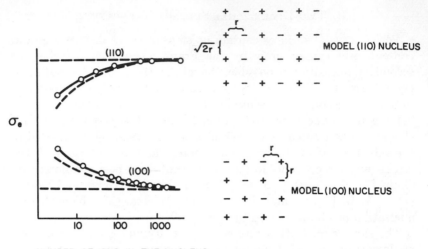

Fig. 2-6. The change of edge energy $\sigma_e$ with cluster size is shown for a two-dimensional sodium chloride-type ionic lattice net. The cluster is assumed to be held in its regular lattice positions and only electrostatic interactions have been considered in the calculations. Upper full curves apply, at the points indicated, to square clusters containing an even number of ions in a side, i.e., 2, 4, 6, etc. These clusters are consequently neutral. The lower dotted curves apply to square clusters containing 3, 5, 7, etc., ions per side and hence carry a net charge. This charge evidently lowers the effective edge energy of the cluster. The curves may only be regarded as linking the calculated values rather than representing a smooth change of edge energy with size.

probably invalid for ionic clusters. The variation of edge energy with number and arrangement of ions in the cluster is shown in Figs. 2-6a, b, and c. Actually, a correction factor can be added to the nucleation treatment which allows for this change. Whereas normally the Gibbs free energy barrier to the formation of a square nucleus of height $h$ and side $l$ would be

$$\Delta G^* = 2lh\sigma_e \qquad (2\text{-}6)$$

the variation of edge energy $\sigma_e$ with cluster size produces

$$\Delta G^* = 2l \left( h\sigma_e - \frac{\partial \sigma_e}{\partial l} \right) \qquad (2\text{-}7)$$

The latter correction term is quite important, and in some cases leads to preferential nucleation of normally unexpected (high-energy) crystal planes. Figure 2-7 shows the activation energy barrier $\Delta G^*$ in terms of critical cluster size when the edge energy correction is applied.

Both screw dislocation and surface-nucleation growth mechanisms lead to a specific dependence of growth rate upon supersaturation, but at constant supersaturation the growth rate is linear with time. Although the linear growth rate is a general conclusion, it is not to be expected that any one crystal will necessarily have a *characteristic* growth rate. Clearly, the growth rate by the screw mechanism is dependent upon the height of the growth step and this is an uncontrollable parameter. In consequence, the art of growing large crystals is still dependent upon the addition of surfactants, impurities, etc. which probably modify the growth mechanism. Individual crystals then cannot be expected to grow at a rate which is simply dependent upon the supersaturation at the crystal–solution interface.

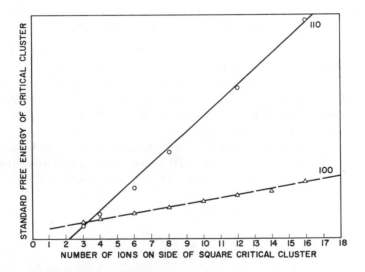

Fig. 2-7. Assuming that the cluster edge energy is a smooth function of its size, it is possible to calculate the standard free energy barrier to surface cluster formation via Eq. 2-7. The energy barrier to cluster formation is a function of both the cluster size and the internal configuration. Hence, the morphological development through surface nucleation is dependent upon the external conditions of supersaturation and temperature.

In support of this assertion, Bunn and Emmett (14) have surveyed a large number of crystals and have found no correlation between the net rate of growth of a particular crystal face and the supersaturation at that face.  The relation between growth rates, step heights, and supersaturation, however, is by now fairly well established (15,16). The necessity of observing growth morphology in relation to growth rates is therefore evident.

Unfortunately in precipitation processes it is not possible to examine the individual crystal morphology as the precipitate forms and it is, consequently, a statistical-average process with which we shall be concerned.  One notes that all the previous reasoning has been related to growth from pure solutions.  In practice there is often sufficient impurity present to modify the growth mechanism. Under such circumstances the best basis for further study seems to be the use of model systems for which essentially empirical equations have been developed.   The first of these model systems, a logical step from single crystals, is the study of seed-crystal growth kinetics.

### 3. Growth of Seed Crystals

The theories of growth kinetics may broadly be divided into two categories: those describing the rate-limiting process in terms of transport to the crystal surface, and others relating the rate control to processes occurring in the interface region.   The former classification will be referred to as diffusion-controlled, and the latter, as interface-controlled growth.

Diffusion-controlled growth has been a subject of continued interest throughout the past 60 to 70 years, starting perhaps with the old Noyes-Whitney (17) Nernst (18) equations and developing to the recent sophisticated approaches by Frisch (19,20) Ham (21), and others.   The general approach is to solve the diffusion equation

$$\frac{\partial c}{\partial t}(x,t) \;=\; D\nabla^2 \, c(x,t) \tag{2-8}$$

for appropriate boundary conditions.   It turns out that one fairly simple form of rate equation obtainable from a consideration of the diffusion process is

$$R \;=\; krD(c - c_0) \tag{2-9}$$

where $R$ is the rate of accumulation (e.g., g/sec) per particle of radius $r$. For seed crystals of any regular compact shape growing from supersaturated solutions, the overall rate of decrease in solute concentration is given by

$$\frac{dc}{dt} \sim -kn(c - c_0) \tag{2-10}$$

This equation is formulated on the basis that the final size of the seed crystals does not differ appreciably from the initial size. Such a criterion can be achieved by using fairly large seed crystals, by using many seed crystals, or by causing growth from low supersaturation. The growth of ionic crystals from electrolyte solutions has been studied extensively by Marc (22), Gapon, and others (23), most workers using conductivity measurements to characterize the change in electrolyte concentration with time. Quantitative measurements on the growth kinetics of seed crystals have, however, come relatively recently with the careful work of Davies (24) and Nancollas (25–28) and coworkers. The original work in this series of investigations showed that silver chloride seed crystals grew from supersaturated solution according to the following rate law:

$$\frac{dc}{dt} = -k'n(c - c_0)^2 \tag{2-11}$$

Thus, although the rate was dependent upon the number of seed crystals $n$, as expected, the kinetic order was 2 rather than 1, which might have been expected had growth been diffusion controlled.

In solutions where the silver and chloride ions are not in equivalent amounts the form of rate law could be identified further:

$$\frac{dm}{dt} = k'n(|Ag^+| - |Ag^+|_0)(|Cl^-| - |Cl^-|_0) \tag{2-12}$$

Davies and Jones (24) proposed therefore that the rate of growth of silver chloride crystals was controlled by an interface process and not by diffusion to the surface. Furthermore, the rate of deposition was found to be a function of the total surface area of the seeds.

The general growth rate of seed crystals from supersaturated solution has with subsequent work been shown to be

$$\frac{dc}{dt} = -k''s(c - c_0)^x \tag{2-13}$$

The kinetic order $x$ has been determined so far for silver chloride ($x = 2$), silver chromate ($x = 3$), magnesium oxalate ($x = 2$), and barium, lead, and strontium sulfates ($x = 2$). Various explanations have been proposed for the form of this equation. Doremus (29) suggested that a surface reaction between ions is rate controlling and that the subsequent steps of surface diffusion and inclusion into a surface site (probably a screw dislocation) are relatively fast. Walton (30) has extended this approach to take into account the appropriate adsorption processes with the conclusion that the kinetic order of Eq. 2-13 should always be the number of ions required to complete a neutral molecule upon the crystal surface. On this basis the kinetic order for organic or molecular crystals should be one, and for ionic crystals should be from two upwards.

### 4. Effect of Impurities on Seed Growth Rates

It has been known for many years that the presence of small amounts of soluble impurities alters both the growth rate and crystal habit of crystals formed in solution (31). Typically, the added impurity may consist of large organic molecules which coprecipitate with the growing substrate. Concentrations of $10^{-3}$ to $10^{-4}M$ are sufficient to produce considerable changes in growth rate and usually the growth rate is strongly inhibited, whereas dissolution is virtually unaffected. Another class of poisons has been reported by Sears et al. (32). The active species in this class are apparently complex inorganic ions which, when present in very small quantities ($10^{-5}$ to $10^{-6}M$), inhibit both growth and dissolution and are not incorporated into the crystal. Typical of this type of system is poisoning of lithium fluoride or potassium chloride crystal growth by ferric fluoride, the active species being postulated as $(FeF_6)^{3-}$; anions other than fluoride are equally effective. Sears concludes that the most probable mechanism of growth poisoning involves adsorption at the growth site (e.g., a surface step) rather than monolayer adsorption.

Growth and dissolution of organic crystals are also inhibited by active impurities. Higuchi and co-workers (33) have discovered recently that very small quantities of cholate salts modify both the growth and dissolution of cholesterol crystals; such evidence is of obvious physiological significance and undoubtedly there are many biological growth and dissolution processes in which surface-active impurities play an important part in controlling the overall rate.

Davies and Nancollas (34) have examined the effect of foreign ions on the growth rate of seed suspensions of silver chloride.   Their results may be summarized as follows:

*1.* Of the surfactants used, only the potassium salt of eosin (2,4,5,7-tetrabromofluorescein) completely prevented crystal growth.   Some retardation of dissolution of seed crystals was also observed in the presence of this material.   The other materials ($10^{-5}$ to $10^{-4}M$ potassium benzoate, potassium naphthalene-2-sulfonate, sodium dodecylsulfate, and cetyltrimethylammonium nitrate) inhibited growth but not dissolution.

*2.* The presence of soluble surface-active agents modifies the growth rate of silver chloride seeds but growth rates may still be expressed by the second-order equation (Eq. 2-11) with the exception of the potassium eosin poisoning.

*3.* The effectiveness of the poison is related to the surface charge of the seed, e.g., the cationic surfactant cetyltrimethylammonium nitrate is less effective with a positively charged substrate (achieved

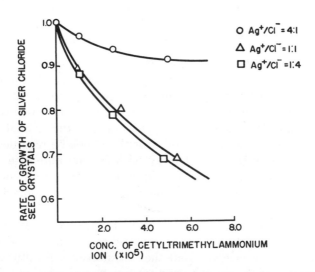

Fig. 2-8. Rate of growth of silver chloride seed crystals from supersaturated (I.P. = $2.57 \times 10^{-10}$) solutions in the presence of the surfactant cetyltrimethylammonium ion. In the lower curves the surface would carry a net negative charge in the absence of surfactant. The surface in the upper curve would probably have a very weak negative charge since the system is close to the isoelectric point. (After Davies and Nancollas, ref. 34)

by keeping silver ions in excess) than with a negative by charged substrate (chloride ions in excess). This effect is shown in Fig. 2-8.

Davies and Nancollas showed that the seed growth rates could be phrased in terms of a Langmuir adsorption process as follows. If $K_0$ is the rate constant for crystallization in the absence of contaminant and $bK_0$ is the limiting rate with contaminant present, then the actual rate constant $K$ is related to the amount of contaminant [A] and the rate constants for adsorption and desorption $k_1$ and $k_2$ by

$$K_0/(K_0 - K) = 1/(1 - b) + k_2(1 - b)k_1[A] \qquad (2\text{-}14)$$

In Fig. 2-9 the relation between $K_0/(K_0 - K)$ and [A] is shown to be a straight line. Strangely, $b$ is found to be dependent upon the excess of silver or chloride ions. Davies and Nancollas concluded that the configuration of surfactants and surface active sites may be important in establishing the value of $b$.

In a later work Nancollas and Purdie (35) found that eosin and dodecyl sulfate ions had essentially the same effect on the growth kinetics of magnesium oxalate as with silver chloride.

## 5. Dissolution of Seed Crystals

Dissolution kinetics are also conveniently examined by studies on seed crystals. The physical process of dissolution is more easily understood than are precipitation or growth since it can be conveniently phrased in terms of diffusion, a first-order equation of the form of Eq. 2-10 being found to fit most of the available data. Although dissolution and crystal growth cannot be regarded as reciprocal processes (as indicated by both the absolute rate and the kinetic form of growth and dissolution equations), the model used for dissolution processes has some relevance to coprecipitation phenomena (Chap. 3).

The theory originally proposed by Nernst (18) assumes that there is a linear concentration gradient confined to a thin layer of solution adhering to the surface and that the thickness of this diffusion layer is independent of the viscosity and temperature of solution. Though this assumption is debatable, the diffusion theory seems to be satisfactory, at least so far as it has been tested experimentally. Silver chloride and silver chromate seeds, which grow by second- and third-order relations, respectively, dissolve by a first-order relation.

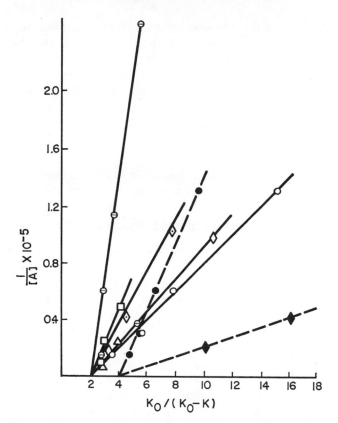

Fig. 2-9. The dependence of silver chloride seed crystal growth rates upon the concentration of adsorbed surfactant [A] in terms of Langmuir adsorption. $K_0$ and $K$ are the rate constants for crystallization in the absence and presence of surfactant, respectively. Surfactants were benzoate, $[Ag^+]/[Cl^-] = 1/1$ (△); dodecyl sulfate, 1/1 (⊖), 4/1 (●), 1/4 (○); naphthalene-2-sulfonate, 1/1 (□); cetyltrimethylammonium, 1/1 (◇), 4/1 (◆), 1/4 (◇). (After Davies and Nancollas, ref. 34)

Furthermore, the activation energy of dissolution $E_A$ given by

$$\ln k = \ln A - E_A/RT \qquad (2\text{-}15)$$

where $k$ is the dissolution rate constant, is found to be 5 kcal/mole for silver chloride dissolution (36), which is close to the normal activation energy for diffusion through solution.

The thickness of the diffusion layer surrounding a dissolving crystal is believed to be of the order $10^{-3}$ cm. Such layers are observable by diffraction microscopy, examples being shown with several different types of crystals in the work of Bunn and Emmett (14). Not surprisingly, the thickness of the diffusion layer is changed by stirring. The rate constant $k$ has been related to the stirring rate $w$ (rev/min) (37) by

$$k \propto w^a \tag{2-16}$$

with reported values of a range from 0.56 to 1.0. For silver chloride seeds the value of $a = 0.61$ has been reported (36).

## 6. Anomalies in Seed Crystal Growth

The growth of seed crystals of the 1:1 electrolytes, silver chloride and silver iodate, commences as soon as they are introduced into their stable supersaturated solutions, growth following the relationship given by Eq. 2-11. For 2:2 electrolytes, however, the normal growth of seed crystals is preceded either by an induction period, as with magnesium oxalate, or by a growth surge as in the case of barium, lead, and strontium sulfates. Such effects were noted early by several investigators and have been confirmed recently by Nancollas and Purdie. These authors suggest that the growth surge is caused by surface nucleation in the initial stages (28). Both the induction and surge are eliminated by introduction of larger quantities of seeding crystals. Evidently, the distribution and availability of solute to the seed surface is affected by the new inoculation and, consequently, the mutual interference of growing particles should be considered in a thorough theoretical approach (38).

The advantage of using seed crystals then is that the lack of reproducibility encountered in examining individual crystals is eliminated, probably through statistical averaging.

Growth kinetics, as investigated by this technique, will presumably be limited to sparingly soluble materials, mainly because of the difficulty of interpreting conductivity data at high concentrations. Fortunately it is sparingly soluble salts which are of major interest to analytical chemists concerned with precipitation processes, and we may now turn to investigations of analytical systems.

## 7. Precipitation from Homogeneous Solution

The method of precipitation from homogeneous solution or PFHS is well known in analytical chemistry as a good method for preparing coarse, crystalline precipitates (28). Essentially, the supersaturation required to cause nucleation and growth is generated by a chemical reaction. The nucleation stage, which is probably heterogeneous, as mentioned in Chapter 1, will only be of importance in growth considerations if nucleation is slow and extends over any period of time. Some workers have treated the collapse of supersaturation in PFHS runs as a joint growth and continuous nucleation process (39–41) but there is considerable evidence that such a process is very unlikely. If primary nucleations is a continuous process throughout the growth period, a wide spectrum of crystal sizes should be observed in the product. PFHS is, however, one of the best methods available for producing monodisperse precipitates. On a theoretical basis also it is not likely that primary nucleation will occur over long periods of time at successively lower degrees of supersaturation.

Since there are relatively few PFHS systems upon which quantitative growth measurements have been made, it is possible to look in some detail at these systems. LaMer (42) and co-workers were the first to examine such a process. They produced monodisperse sulfur sols by the decomposition of thiosulfate in acidic solutions.

$$4S_2O_3^{2-} \rightarrow 3SO_4^{2-} + 5S \tag{A}$$

Sulfur sols prepared by this method were highly monodisperse, such that under irradiation with "white" light they show higher-order Tyndall spectra. In other words, white incident light is split into its component colors which are diffracted at various angles to the incident path. The angle at which the primary color is generated is a function of the particle size. Hence, by making light-scattering measurements it proved possible to follow the growth kinetics.

These kinetics were found to be first order and were in accord with a diffusion-controlled mechanism. One of the difficulties in reproducing this type of experiment for inorganic precipitates is that the crystalline product is virtually always irregularly shaped, i.e., the particles have edges and corners. Sulfur sols are generally spherical and the extension of light scattering theory to nonspherical particles has proven rather difficult. For very small particles where Rayleigh theory is applicable, some of these difficulties are eliminated and the growth kinetics of silver iodide produced by the reaction B below have been studied by light scattering methods (43) and are also said to be diffusion controlled. This reaction is rather interesting because it seems to represent the only PFHS reaction studied in entirely nonaqueous solution.

$$2C_2H_5I + 2AgNO_3 + C_2H_5OH \xrightarrow{\text{ethanol}} 2AgI + (C_2H_5)_2O + HNO_3$$
$$+ C_2H_5NO_3 \quad \text{(B)}$$

At this point it seems worthwhile to look further into the difficulties of interpreting the data from PFHS reactions. The simple equations of form 2-9 and 2-10 become more complicated by addition of a "source function" term. This means that the total change in solute concentration with time is caused not only by the precipitation process, but also by the generation of new material. Hence

$$\frac{dc}{dt} = - f(r,s,D) + f(g) \quad (2\text{-}17)$$

where $g$ represents the generating reaction. Frisch and Collins (44) have examined this problem and Collins and Leineweber (45) have treated the precipitation kinetics of barium sulfate produced by generation of sulfate into excess barium ions by the persulfate–thiosulfate reaction:

$$S_2O_8^{2-} + 2S_2O_3^{2-} \rightarrow 2SO_4^{2-} + S_2O_6^{2-} \quad \text{(C)}$$

This reaction was followed by conductivity measurements and the results related to diffusion theory. The conductivity curve is shown in Fig. 2-10.

One interesting aspect of the diffusion equations as proposed by Frisch and Collins is the relationship between the particle size and time as given by the growth equation:

$$K_1[r(t) - r(0)] + \tfrac{1}{2}[r^2(t) - r^2(0)] = c_0K_2t \quad (2\text{-}18)$$

where $K_1$ and $K_2$ are both constants which incorporate the diffusion coefficient, $r(t)$ is the particle radius at time $t$, and $c_0$ is the concentration of solute in the bulk of solution. Equation 2-18 reveals a linear growth rate for small $r$ and for large $r$ a linear increase of $r^2$ with $t$.

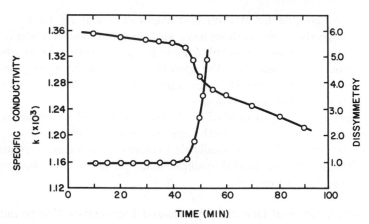

Fig. 2-10. The onset of precipitation and growth of precipitate particles ($BaSO_4$ by homogeneous reaction C) may be detected and followed by both conductivity and light scattering measurements. (After Collins and Leineweber, ref. 45)

In the light of the previous results, which are based upon the growth of seed crystals, it seems rather odd that diffusion theory should fit the growth rate of ionic crystals from solution at all. For example, the growth of barium sulfate precipitate particles under almost identical conditions of supersaturation is second order for seed crystals and first-order diffusion controlled from the Collins and Leineweber PFHS method. This brings us to a second difficulty in determining growth kinetics from PFHS methods, namely, that the generating reaction must be reliable and reproducible, and possess no interfering side reactions if the analysis is to be unambiguous. Unfortunately, neither reaction B nor reaction C falls in this category. Both reactions have been studied recently with the conclusion that side reactions and non-steady-state processes play an important part.

One other reaction which is of interest in this context has been studied rather fully. This PFHS reaction, originally examined by Gordon, Klein, and Walnut (46), can be caused for producing silver chloride crystals.

$$C_3H_5Cl + H_2O \rightarrow Cl^- + C_3H_5OH + H^+$$
$$Cl^- + Ag^+ \rightarrow AgCl \downarrow$$

The growth kinetics of silver chloride produced by this reaction

have been studied by Walton and Klein (47) and by Parfitt and
Insley (48); the latter authors have also made an extensive study of
the reaction kinetics and morphology of the precipitate.   Both sets of
of authors concluded that the growth kinetics were second-order
interface controlled, which is in agreement with the seed crystal
observations of Davies and Jones.

It cannot be said, in view of the limited number of available data,
that the development of growth kinetics for PFHS systems is yet at
a satisfactory level.   The available evidence does suggest, though,
that for carefully controlled systems some correlation will be found
with seed-growth kinetics.

## 8. Precipitation of Organic Crystals and Ion–Chelate Compounds

Many examples of metalloorganic precipitates, which are of importance in analytical separation procedures, are known.   For example,
zirconium may be separated in the form of its tetramandelate, and
nickel dimethylglyoximate is a familiar material.   Very little is
known of the mechanism of precipitation in such systems, though
much active interest has centered recently around the glyoxime
systems.

Work on the precipitation of tetraphenylarsonium perchlorate
crystals (a separatory method for perchlorate) indicated (49) that the
number of crystals, produced by mixing perchloric acid and tetraphenylarsonium chloride, increases with reactant concentration.
The morphology of the precipitate indicates that nucleation was
probably initiated upon impurities stemming from both reagents.
Similar studies with nickel dioxime crystals (49) also indicated that
nuclei originate from the reaction solutions.

The precipitation of dimethylglyoximes from homogeneous solution has been achieved (50) by reaction between biacetyl and hydroxylamine

Since the rates of the formation reactions involved in the precipitation process may often be followed spectrophotometrically, it is a

relatively simple matter to detect the onset of precipitation and changes in solution concentration in the initial states of precipitation. Using this method, Salesin, Abrahamson, and Gordon (51) have reported that more than one nucleation burst is observable in the precipitation of nickel dimethylglyoxime. This curious feature seems to indicate that crystal growth is slower than the generation of new material. In consequence, the supersaturation can increase even after heterogeneous nucleation has been initiated. The reason for slow crystal growth may stem from one of several causes—e.g., adsorption of reactants on the crystal surface may inhibit growth, or crystal growth in the metalloorganic systems may be inherently slow.

X-ray crystallographic studies of nickel and palladium dioximates have shown (52) that metal–metal bonding probably exists along the $c$ axis of the crystal, contributing approximately 10 kcal/mole to the binding energy. The metal–metal bonding arises because the chelate molecules are planar and are stacked directly above one another, each unit being rotated 90° at an interplanar distance of 3.24 Å. Other crystal studies (53) have shown that there is a very significant difference in the structures of the nickel chelates of the higher dioxime homologs of dimethylglyoxime, for example, ethylmethylglyoxime. The strong symmetrical hydrogen bonds, shown in reaction D, are present throughout the series. However, the completely different crystal packing which exists precludes any possibility of metal–metal bonding.

Thus, from a consideration of the known crystal data for these metal dioximates it seems that the formation of metal–metal bonding may play an important part in the nucleation and growth of nickel dimethylglyoximate, whereas it cannot do so in nickel ethylmethylglyoximate.

It is probable that the specific configuration of molecular units required for formation of these chelates, along with the rather weak interaction involved in the formation of the metal–metal bonds, would lead to high degrees of supersaturation prior to nucleation. Indeed, in the few studies of glyoximate nucleation, very large critical supersaturation ratios have been reported [23 for the palladium salt (54) and many hundreds for the nickel salt (55)]. Under such circumstances it must be concluded that the impurities normally present in solution are not particularly efficient nucleators for this type of precipitate.

## 9. Precipitation by Direct Mixing

By far the most complicated precipitation process for which a kinetic analysis has been attempted is that produced by direct mixing of reactants. Although the source function is eliminated from a theoretical consideration, the effect of inhomogeneous mixing and the resultant production of a wide spectrum of particle morphologies lead to rather irreproducible kinetics. In spite of these difficulties several analyses of this type of precipitation have been published. Probably the first such analysis was by Turnbull (56) in 1954 for barium sulfate.

In all precipitation experiments there is an induction period before the detection of precipitation; the duration of the induction period is a function of the precipitant concentration, impurity level, and sensitivity of the detecting technique. Typical precipitation curves are given in Fig. 2-11. It is usual to express results in terms of the fraction of the total precipitate formed at time $t$, i.e., $\alpha = (c - c_f)/(c_f - c_i)$, where $c_i$ and $c_f$ are the initial and final concentrations of reactants; $c$ is the solubility. Turnbull found that the method of mixing affected the overall rate of precipitation, but that the shape of

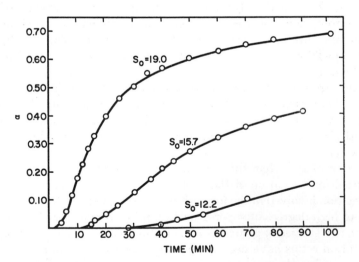

Fig. 2-11. Precipitation curves for barium sulfate produced by direct mixing; $s_0$ refers to the initial supersaturation ratio of barium sulfate. (After Turnbull, ref. 56)

the precipitation curves was unaltered. Evidence of the latter fact was demonstrated by the superimposition of the curves when modified by a numerical factor. Turnbull deduced from the diffusion equations that the radius of a spherical growing particle $r$ should change according to the relation

$$r^2/2D + r/G = mKt \qquad (2\text{-}19)$$

where $D$ is the diffusion coefficient, $G$ is the interface transfer coefficient, $m$ is the concentration of precipitant in the bulk of solution, and $K$ is the rate constant. Equation 2-19 is clearly similar to that developed by Frisch and Collins (Eq. 2-18) and leads to the conclusion that for small $r$

$$r \sim (mKG)t \qquad (2\text{-}20)$$

and the process is interface controlled. For large $r$

$$r^2 \rightarrow (2mKD)t \qquad (2\text{-}21)$$

and the process is diffusion controlled.

Comparing these relations with those stated previously for crystal growth, it can be seen that the linear increase in radius with time for the interface controlled process ($m$ kept constant) is the same as might be expected for screw dislocation or surface-nucleation controlled growth, though the assumptions have been quite different.

The diffusion equation (Eq. 2-9) yields for constant $c$, $r^2 = k'Dt$, and as a result the linear or square relation between particle size and time is often taken to be indicative of interface- or diffusion-controlled precipitation, respectively.* Perhaps the most significant point brought out by Turnbull is that barium sulfate and, as it turns out, most other inorganic salts precipitated from aqueous solution grow by an interface-controlled process, at least in the early stages. Turnbull's work also served to point out some shortcomings of the Christiansen-Nielsen theory (57) relating to nucleation and the induction period before precipitation. The development of precipitation kinetics from that time (1953) to the present is not by any means

* The Frisch-Collins relation (Eq. 2-18) suggests that the linear growth rate is not necessarily associated with interface reaction to the exclusion of diffusion.

all that could be desired.  The diffusion-controlled growth equation (Eq. 2-9) expressed in terms of the fraction precipitated is

$$\frac{d\alpha}{dt} = k\alpha^{1/3}(1 - \alpha) \qquad (2\text{-}22)$$

Johnson and O'Rourke (58) (1954) concluded from their conductometric measurements that the precipitation of barium sulfate could be represented best by an empirical equation of the form

$$\frac{d\alpha}{dt} = k\alpha^{2/3}(1 - \alpha)^p \qquad (2\text{-}23)$$

where $p$ was found to be 4.

Since Eq. 2-20 is identical in form with the growth equations found for seed crystals by Davies, Nancollas, and co-workers, there seems to be some justification for this relation.  It should be noted, however, that Johnson and O'Rourke treated the induction period and growth stage separately.

Neilsen (59) (1955) further developed and applied the precipitation equation (Eq. 2-20), finding $p = 3$ or 4 for barium sulfate, strontium sulfate, silver chromate, and calcium oxalate.  Doremus (29) (1958) also analyzed barium sulfate data and again reached the conclusion that $p$ lay between 3 and 4, giving a surface-reaction theory in partial explanation.  With all this concentrated effort directed particularly toward barium sulfate, it might have been expected that the potentialities of this system had been exhausted. However, all the preceding data have been obtained by conductivity techniques using platinum electrodes and Weiss (60) has shown that platinum actually catalyzes the precipitation.  The fact is that under similar conditions surface-reaction controlled growth has now been reported, with the reaction order varying from 0 to 4 (61–64), and in some cases diffusion from bulk solution has been found to be rate determining (45,60).  This confusing situation undoubtedly arises from a combination of the complexity of the system and difficulties with techniques.  It is possible that the anomalies present in the initiation of seed crystal growth are considerably magnified in the direct precipitation scheme where the total numbers of particles and precipitate surface area are not directly controllable.  It is also impossible to follow precipitation and growth of particles quantitatively because conductivity gives no information relating to size, shape, or numbers of precipitated particles, and whereas light scattering methods may be used to follow the precipitation process, the interpretation of data is extremely complicated. In an attempt to circumvent the difficulties with the conductivity technique, Walton (65) attempted an interpretation of turbidity data for silver chloride precipitation, finding a reaction order of approximately 2, in agreement with the seed-crystal data of Davies and Jones. Later work (66) on the more complicated barium sulfate system also yielded a kinetic order close to 2, in agreement with the seed crystal data.

In view of the wide discrepancies in reported data, it is perhaps worthwhile to mention that one important reason for attempting to understand precipitation kinetics is related to coprecipitation problems. Dynamic coprecipitation systems involve the incorporation of trace ions or molecules into the host lattice, and coprecipitation is an important method of concentrating trace elements. If a quantitative relation is to be established, it is necessary to know the relative rates of precipitation, the mechanism of incorporation, and a kinetic scheme which represents these processes.

## 10. Temperature Coefficients of Growth and Precipitation

It is pertinent to examine the temperature coefficient for growth kinetics for much the same reasons as reaction kinetic data are examined for temperature variance, i.e., the energy barrier to the rate process gives an insight into the mechanistic pathway.

In terms of an Arrhenius-type activation energy $E_c$, one has the usual relation

$$\ln k_c = \ln A_c - E_c/RT \qquad (2\text{-}24)$$

The preexponential factor $A_c$ has not been examined in any detail because its evaluation requires a knowledge of the surface area of the growing precipitate particles or seed crystals. Davies and Nancollas (34) report $E_c \sim 0$ for silver chloride seed crystals. Lichstein and Brescia (67) have found $E_c = 3$ kcal/mole for magnesium oxalate precipitation and Nielsen (68) finds $E_c = 5.0 \pm 0.5$ kcal/mole for barium sulfate precipitation. It would seem that the energy barrier is small and this can, perhaps, be interpreted in terms of temperature-insensitive process in the surface or interfacial layer. More extensive interpretation will require further careful experimentation.

## 11. Dissolution of Precipitates

The rate of dissolution of crystals is generally believed to be controlled by the diffusion rate of material leaving the surface. Under these circumstances the rate of increase in solution concentration is given by

$$\frac{dc}{dt} = \frac{DA}{V\delta}(c_0 - c) \tag{2-25}$$

where $A$ is the area of crystal in contact with volume $V$ of solution. As before, $c_0$ is the equilibrium (saturation) concentration. In early work Noyes and Whitney (17) found that Eq. 2-25 applied to the dissolution of benzoic acid and lead chloride crystals.

Although the dissolution of seed crystals is usually found to be first order with respect to undersaturation (i.e., diffusion controlled), it has been suggested (34,36) that at high degrees of undersaturation the order increases to between 1.5 and 2. It has been theorized that this high kinetic order was indicative of non-diffusion-controlled dissolution. Other suggestions have also been made by Pohl (69)

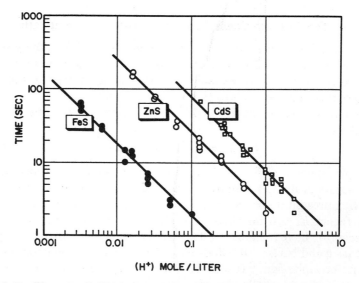

Fig. 2-12. The rate of dissolution of three sulfides in acidic solution. A fixed amount of sulfide dissolves in excess acid, showing first-order dependence upon the acid concentration. (After Pohl, ref. 69)

for the dissolution of iron, zinc, and cadmium sulfides in acid
solution.  He found that the dissolution rate was first order in the
acid concentration shown in Fig. 2-12.  Pohl's suggestion is that
hydrogen ions combine with the surface of the sulfides to form $HS^-$
ions which then pass into the bulk of solution.  If the formation of
$HS^-$ is rate determining in dissolution processes, the reverse process
could be involved in precipitation of sulfides.  Although it could be
argued that the solubility of the sulfides is a function of the acidity,
it is not easy to see how the dissolution can be rationalized in terms
of simple diffusion.  It may be, therefore, that dissolution reactions
which result in formation of a complex by one or more of the components of the solid phase in solution are controlled by the rate of
formation of that complex.

## 12. Secondary Growth

A system of suspended heterodisperse particles can undergo two
different types of secondary growth, both of which are spontaneous
in that they lower the total energy of the system by lowering the
interfacial free energy.  This is achieved by decreasing the total
precipitate surface area either by agglomeration and recrystallization
or by Ostwald ripening.  This latter process is a result of the different
solubility "pressure" exerted by particles of different sizes and is
summarized thermodynamically by the Gibbs-Kelvin equation for
spherical particles (Eq. 1-3):

$$mkT \ln s = \frac{2\sigma v}{r} \qquad (2\text{-}26)$$

Hence, small particles are in equilibrium with a supersaturation $s_1$,
which is larger than $s_2$ for larger particles.  The system containing
these particles will adjust by the processes of growth and dissolution
to a supersaturation intermediate between $s_1$ and $s_2$; consequently,
the net effect on the smaller particle is that it will dissolve and the
larger particle will grow.  Relative rates of Ostwald ripening may
be established by the following reasoning.

Let us consider two hypothetical crystals of material, A and B,
each of identical size and of approximately the same interfacial energy.
From the Gibbs-Kelvin equation we might conclude that each would
be in equilibrium with a solution of its own ions, the appropriate

supersaturation ratio $s$ being in each case, say, 1.1. Now, if the equilibrium solubility of A for infinite crystals is 1 mole/liter and for B, $10^{-5}$ mole/liter, we conclude that the excess solubility of the two crystals A and B are 0.1 mole/liter and $10^{-6}$ mole/liter, respectively. If the rate of growth is given by the seed crystal-type growth equation, large crystals of A and B will grow in the relative ratio

$$\frac{R_A}{R_B} = \frac{k_1}{k_2}\left(\frac{0.1}{10^{-6}}\right)^x = \frac{k_1}{k_2} \times 10^{5x}$$

In all probability the actual growth rate constants $k_1$ and $k_2$ will not be very different and in consequence the relative rate of growth would be of the order $10^{5x}$ times faster for crystals of A than B. This crude example serves to show that the rate of Ostwald ripening should be much faster for fairly soluble materials than for very sparingly soluble ones. This conclusion is not dependent upon the form of growth law chosen or entirely upon suppositions regarding the interfacial energy, and is borne out by experimental observation. Although there are very few quantitative data available, there have been some recent efforts (70) to follow the kinetics of Ostwald ripening of precipitates within a solid matrix.

The agglomeration mechanism of lowering the interfacial energy is best dealt with within the framework of colloidal phenomena, and is given more attention in Chapter 5. Two important points regarding the agglomeration rate may be stated here. The overall rate is, according to the Smoluchowski theory, a function of the total number of particles and the surface charge. From these theoretical considerations the rate of agglomeration approaches zero when there are less than $10^6$ particles/ml even if these particles are uncharged. For strong surface charge as many as $10^{17}$ or $10^{18}$ particles/ml may be stabilized without any readily detectable agglomeration rate (e.g., colloidal silica).

### 13. Techniques for Following Growth and Precipitation Kinetics

The two main techniques used for following precipitation processes have been conductivity and light scattering. Considerable difficulties are encountered with both methods, though they may be used semiquantitatively. Effective conductivity measurements are limited to simple ionic systems where an appreciable proportion of the initial ionic concentration is eventually removed from solution. Precipitation of sparingly soluble salts may be followed providing that electrode catalysis does not occur. Since there is no direct means of assessing particle numbers, sizes, shapes, or states of aggregation, each of which affect the kinetics of precipitation, the conductivity technique is best adapted to systems where these parameters are controlled, i.e., with seed-crystal growth.

Light absorbance or turbidity measurements are effective (71) when the particles are larger than $\lambda/10$ ($\lambda$ = wavelength of incident light). If the system is monodisperse (i.e., all particles are the same size) and the particles are spherical (some other specific shapes can be handled), the turbidity is given by

$$\tau = N\pi r^2 K \qquad (2\text{-}27)$$

where $K$ is the Mie scattering coefficient which can be obtained from appropriate tables.

Large monodisperse particles also give rise to the higher-order Tyndall spectra, as mentioned previously. Particle sizes may be obtained from these spectra by methods developed by LaMer and Barnes (72,73) and others (74).

Very few inorganic systems meet the above criteria, but for particles of a diameter $<\lambda/10$ average particle sizes may be obtained by use of the Rayleigh equation

$$\tau = A'nv^2 \qquad (2\text{-}28)$$

where $A'$ is a constant related to the refractive index of solute and solvent, $n$ is the total number of precipitate particles, and $v$ is the average particle volume. In general, precipitate particles are too large for application of the above equation, though exceptions may be noted (43).

Probably the most thorough investigation of the applicability of light scattering principles to the determination of inorganic particle size has been presented by Meehan and Beattie (75). They have compared average particle sizes for AgBr sols, deduced from several different light scattering methods, with electron microscopic measurements, and found agreement within 10%. The silver bromide system is probably one of the more suitable systems for this type of analysis since the particles are usually compact and pseudocubic. Readers are however directed to the above work for further details on light scattering methods and application. It is unfortunate that there is no known method of determining particle-size distribution from light-scattering measurements and, in consequence, attention has been turning recently to techniques which are rapid, do not require extensive theoretical interpretation, and supply data upon particle size distributions.

One such method, developed recently, is the use of particle counters which detect particle size distribution. Higuchi and co-workers (76) have reported kinetic studies of the growth and dissolution of cholesterol particles using a Coulter counter. Although the counter is unable to detect particles in the initial stages of growth, a substantial part of the growth curves could be obtained. For this particular system the growth of cholesterol particles was found to have first-order dependence upon the supersaturation and was concluded to be diffusion controlled. Again, the counters are best suited to spherical nonconducting particles. Estimates of the total number of particles in solution are usually fairly accurate, though slightly anomalous size-distribution curves are sometimes obtained. Common difficulties encountered with electronic counters include particles "sticking" in the counting aperture and crystal growth across the aperture, but the technique seems to have definite possibilities.

## 14. Summary

The mechanisms of single-crystal growth are well defined. Kinetic relations for growth from a solution of single crystals are not yet fully substantiated, one major practical difficulty being the presence of very small amounts of adsorbable impurity in solution. However, kinetic relations for the growth of seed crystals from solution are fairly well established; in general, the appropriate equation for the rate of deposition is

$$R = kn(c - c_0)^x$$

where $n$ is the number of seed crystals, $c - c_0$ is the excess solute concentration, and $x$ is the order of reaction. In the cases examined so far, $x$ is identical with the number of ions in the neutral molecule ($AgCl$, $x = 2$; $AgIO_3$, $x = 2$; $(Ba, Sr, Pb)SO_4$, $x = 2$; $Ag_2CrO_4$, $x = 3$, etc.).

A growth equation of the above form is not entirely compatible with the basic crystal-growth equations and it is not yet established whether the number of seed crystals $n$ affects the growth rate through the total surface area as in a surface-reaction phenomenon, or through surface-active sites as with screw dislocations which, though dependent upon $n$, may be independent of the total surface area. In this case one might have, for example, only one dislocation in a crystal face, independent of its total surface area.

Growth of inorganic seed crystals is, then, an interface-controlled process which may be limited by transport across the boundary layer surrounding a crystal, by surface reaction (which is suggested by the order apparently being related to neutral molecule formation), or by an incorporation process. Although each of these mechanisms has been proposed, none has yet been established beyond reasonable doubt. Surface-reaction theories yield the correct form of rate equation and may be related to surface nucleation, but they are generally based upon the concept of equilibrium adsorption. The data do not entirely concur with the other proposed mechanisms, though whether the theory or experiment is at fault is not yet clear.

Precipitation kinetics are believed to follow equations of the same general nature as the seed-crystal kinetics, but the considerable experimental difficulties in such systems have so far prevented a thorough analysis. Particular difficulties are experienced in direct-mixing experiments and although many of these problems might be avoided by using precipitation from homogeneous solution, relatively few data are as yet available.

The factors affecting precipitation kinetics are as follows:

*1.* Numbers of initial impurities present—large numbers of impurities act as nuclei and produce large numbers of growing precipitate particles. The total number, or surface area of the precipitate particles, may affect the kinetic order of the process.

*2.* The basic mechanism is probably a mixture of screw dislocation, surface nucleation, dendritic growth, and agglomeration in many systems and an exact kinetic order cannot be expected to hold.

*3.* Catalysis by active sites in container walls, electrodes, stirrer, etc. often occurs.

*4.* Methods of mixing reactants are very important in controlling the rate of precipitation and precipitate morphology, but may not effect the kinetic dependence on supersaturation.

*5.* Impurities—traces of impurities may hinder both growth and dissolution processes.

*6.* Rate of stirring usually disturbs the boundary layer at the crystal surface and hence the growth rate.

*7.* Temperature—small activation energies are indicative of relatively little direct effect of increased temperature, though increased agglomeration will slow down the precipitation rate.

Most of the reported data show that precipitation is too slow to be diffusion controlled and, with a few exceptions, interface processes have been invoked to account for the kinetics of growth and precipitation. Dissolution and ripening, however, are believed to occur mainly via diffusion-controlled processes.

## References

1. J. A. Palermo and G. F. Bennett, *Ind. Eng. Chem.*, **57** (11), 68 (1965); **56** (10), 38 (1964); D. A. Blackadder, *Chemical Engr. London*, **1964**, 303.
2. W. K. Burton and N. Cabrera, *Discussions Faraday Soc.*, **5**, 33, 40 (1949).
3. F. C. Frank, *Discussions Faraday Soc.*, **5**, 48 (1949).
4. I. M. Dawson, *Proc. Roy. Soc. London*, **A214**, 72 (1952).
5. F. C. Frank, *Advan. Phys.*, **1**, 91 (1952).
6. W. K. Burton, N. Cabrera, and F. C. Frank, *Nature*, **163**, 398 (1949); *Phil. Trans. Roy. Soc. London*, **A243**, 299 (1951).
7. J. W. Gibbs, *Collected Works*, Longmans, London, 1928, p. 325.
8. M. Volmer, *Kinetic der Phasenbildung*, Steinkopf, Dresden, 1939.
9. W. Kossel, *Nachr. Ges. Wiss. Gottingen Math. Physik. Kl.*, 135 (1927).
10. I. Stranski, *Z. Physik. Chem.*, **136**, 259 (1928).
11. R. Becker and W. Döring, *Ann. Physik*, **24**, 719 (1935).
12. J. Frenkel, *J. Phys. USSR*, **9**, 3921 (1945).
13. G. W. Sears, *J. Chem. Phys.*, **31**, 157 (1959).
14. C. W. Bunn and H. Emmett, *Discussions Faraday Soc.*, **5**, 119 (1949).
15. W. J. Dunning and N. Albon, in *Growth and Perfection of Crystals*, R. H. Doremus, B. W. Roberts, and D. Turnbull, Eds., Wiley, New York, 1958.
16. K. B. Keating, *Chem. Eng. Progr.*, **60**, 15 (1964).
17. A. A. Noyes and W. R. Whitney, *Z. Physik. Chem.*, **23**, 689 (1897).
18. W. Nernst, *Z. Physik. Chem.*, **47**, 52 (1904).
19. H. L. Frisch, *Z. Elektrochem.*, **86**, 324 (1952).
20. H. L. Frisch and F. C. Collins, *J. Chem. Phys.*, **20**, 1797 (1952); **21**, 2158 (1953).
21. F. S. Ham, *Phys. Chem. Solids*, **6**, 335 (1958).
22. R. Marc, *Z. Physik. Chem.*, **61**, 385 (1908); **67**, 470 (1909); **68**, 104 (1909); **73**, 685 (1910); **76**, 584 (1911).
23. A. van Hook, *Crystallization*, Reinhold, New York, 1961.
24. C. W. Davies and A. L. Jones, *Trans. Faraday Soc.*, **51**, 812 (1955).

25. J. R. Howard and G. H. Nancollas, *Trans. Faraday Soc.*, **53**, 1449 (1957).
26. G. H. Nancollas and N. Purdie, *Trans. Faraday Soc.*, **59**, 735 (1963).
27. G. H. Nancollas and N. Purdie, *Quart. Rev. London*, **18**, 1 (1964).
28. G. H. Nancollas, *Proc. Intern. Symp. Nucleation Phenomena, Cleveland, 1965*, p. 19.
29. R. H. Doremus, *J. Phys. Chem.*, **62**, 1068 (1958).
30. A. G. Walton, *J. Phys. Chem.*, **67**, 1920 (1964).
31. H. E. Buckley, *Crystal Growth*, Wiley, New York, 1951, pp. 330–385.
32. G. W. Sears, in *Growth and Perfection of Crystals*, R. H. Doremus, B. W. Roberts, and D. Turnbull, Eds., Wiley, New York, 1958.
33. W. I. Higuchi, personal communication.
34. C. W. Davies and G. H. Nancollas, *Trans. Faraday Soc.*, **51**, 823 (1955).
35. G. H. Nancollas and N. Purdie, *Trans. Faraday Soc.*, **57**, 1 (1961).
36. J. R. Howard, G. H. Nancollas, and N. Purdie, *Trans. Faraday Soc.*, **56**, 278 (1960).
37. L. L. Bircumshaw and A. C. Riddiford, *Quart. Rev. London*, **6**, 157 (1952).
38. C. Wert and C. Zener, *J. Appl. Phys.*, **21**, 5 (1950).
39. L. Gordon, M. L. Salutsky, and H. H. Willard, *Precipitation from Homogeneous Solution*, Wiley, New York, 1959.
40. L. Gordon, D. H. Klein, and T. H. Walnut, *Talanta*, **3**, 187 (1959).
41. N. Haberman and L. Gordon, *Talanta*, **11**, 1591 (1964).
42. V. K. LaMer and R. H. Dinegar, *J. Am. Chem. Soc.*, **72**, 4847 (1950).
43. M. J. Jaycock and G. D. Parfitt, *Trans. Faraday Soc.*, **57**, 791 (1961).
44. H. L. Frisch and F. C. Collins, *J. Chem. Phys.*, **20**, 1797 (1952); **21**, 2158 (1953).
45. F. C. Collins and J. P. Leineweber, *J. Phys. Chem.*, **60**, 389 (1956).
46. L. Gordon, D. H. Klein, and T. H. Walnut, *Talanta*, **3**, 177 (1959).
47. A. G. Walton and D. H. Klein, *Kolloid-Z.*, **189**, 141 (1963).
48. G. D. Parfitt and M. J. Insley, personal communication.
49. F. R. Duke and L. M. Brown, *U.S. At. Energy, Comm. Rept. M-3679* (1953).
50. O. E. Hileman and L. Gordon, *Talanta*, **12**, 451 (1965).
51. E. D. Salesin, E. W. Abrahamson, and L. Gordon, *Talanta*, **9**, 699 (1962).
52. L. E. Godycki and R. E. Rundle, *Acta. Cryst.*, **6**, 487 (1953).
53. E. Frasson and C. Panattoni, *Acta Cryst.*, **13**, 893 (1960).
54. P. R. Ellefson, Ph.D. thesis, Case Institute of Technology, 1965.
55. E. D. Salesin, Ph.D. thesis, Case Institute of Technology, 1962.
56. D. Turnbull, Acta Met., **1**, 684 (1954).
57. J. A. Christiansen and A. E. Nielsen, *Acta Chem. Scand.*, **5**, 673, 674 (1957).
58. R. A. Johnson and J. D. O'Rourke, *J. Am. Chem. Soc.*, **76**, 2124 (1954).
59. A. E. Nielsen, *J. Colloid Sci.*, **10**, 576 (1955).
60. R. Weiss, Ph.D. thesis, Columbia University, 1962.
61. A. E. Nielsen, *Acta Chem. Scand.*, **13**, 1680 (1959).
62. K. H. Lieser and A. Fabrikanos, *Z. Physik. Chem. Frankfurt*, **22**, 406 (1959).
63. P. J. Lucchesi, *J. Colloid Sci.*, **11**, 113 (1956).
64. F. R. Duke, R. J. Bever and H. Diehl, *Iowa State J. Sci.*, **23**, 297 (1949).
65. A. G. Walton, *Z. Physik. Chem. Frankfurt*, **35**, 326 (1962).
66. A. G. Walton and T. Hlabse, *Anal. Chim. Acta*, **29**, 249 (1963).

67. B. Lichstein and F. Brescia, *J. Am. Chem. Soc.*, **79**, 1591 (1957).
68. A. E. Nielsen, *Acta Chem. Scand.*, **13**, 784 (1959).
69. H. A. Pohl, *J. Am. Chem. Soc.*, **76**, 2182 (1954).
70. R. A. Oriani, *Acta Met.*, **12**, 1399 (1964).
71. S. H. Maron, P. E. Pierce, and I. N. Ulevitch, *J. Colloid Sci.*, **18**, 470 (1963).
72. V. K. LaMer and M. D. Barnes, *J. Colloid Sci.*, **1**, 71, 79 (1946).
73. V. K. LaMer, *J. Phys. Chem.*, **52**, 65 (1948).
74. P. E. Pierce and S. H. Maron, *J. Colloid Sci.*, 19, 658 (1964).
75. E. J. Meehan and W. H. Beattie, *J. Phys. Chem.*, **64**, 1006 (1960).
76. W. I. Higuchi and H. Y. Saad, *J. Pharm. Sci.*, **54**, 74 (1965).

# CHAPTER 3

# COPRECIPITATION

From a consideration of the modification of growth rates and precipitation kinetics by added impurities, as discussed in the previous chapter, it is apparent that precipitates are capable of carrying down impurities. Such a process is, in some systems, of considerable practical advantage in that trace amounts of rare elements may be concentrated or enriched. Often, however, this coprecipitation is inconvenient in the preparation of pure materials. In nature coprecipitation is a very common phenomenon. Geological deposits virtually always contain foreign ions coprecipitated with the host phase, and the same is true of physiological deposits, kidney, bladder and gall stones, and in bones and teeth, where fluoride ions may replace hydroxide in the hydroxyapatite structure. Also of some concern in recent years has been the possibility of interchange between calcium and radioactive strontium in calcified tissue.

Coprecipitation is important not only as a means of concentrating or separating materials (one is reminded of the chemist's dream of separating gold from seawater), but also as a tool in expanding knowledge of the mechanism of precipitation and the properties of solid solutions.

Conceivably coprecipitation may occur by either adsorption of one material by another, or formation of a solid solution of microcomponent in the host lattice. In its simplest form then, coprecipitation can lead to either adsorption compounds, with the microcomponent adhering to the surface of the host, or mixed crystals with the microcomponent free to diffuse through the interior of solid phase. Most practical situations involve a combination of these features.

Modifications in the form of coprecipitation are brought about by the rate of precipitation, agglomeration, and mutual miscibility of the materials under consideration; the miscibility in turn is determined by a number of basic features related to ion size, polarizability, and charge.

Fundamentally, however, there are four categories into which coprecipitation phenomena may be divided—equilibrium or nonequilibrium reactions with miscible or immiscible components. Of these categories, equilibrium between precipitate and foreign ions leads to mixed crystals and can be treated in terms of the thermodynamics of solid solutions. Equilibrium between immiscible components leads to adsorption compounds which can often be treated in terms of surface-adsorption isotherms. An understanding of nonequilibrium coprecipitation of miscible materials involves a knowledge of the kinetics and mechanism of precipitation, and is consequently very complicated. Nonequilibrium coprecipitation of immiscible components includes the problems of agglomeration and occlusion, but adsorption equilibrium itself is often established fairly rapidly and the nonequilibrium surface condition is not particularly pertinent to the discussion of coprecipitation.

## 1. Equilibrium Systems—Miscible Components

The solubility of one solid in another is a function of the mutual compatibility of ions within the lattice, but in order for thermodynamic equilibrium to be established the minor component B must be free to diffuse throughout the host matrix A. Solid-state diffusion of ions is dependent upon the presence and mobility of imperfections in the host lattice; Schottky and Frenkel defects are the most familiar. Under the conditions of free diffusion and compatibility of impurity with the host lattice, *mixed crystals* are formed.

Experimentally, equilibrium cocrystallization may be achieved by rapid coprecipitation followed by prolonged digestion, or by digesting pure host crystals with a solution containing coprecipitant. The complete reversibility of such systems is shown by the work of Chlopin (1) and co-workers as demonstrated in Fig. 3-1. In this work the distribution of radium in barium bromide was analyzed by (1) introducing powdered barium bromide containing radium to a saturated solution of barium bromide, stirring, and sampling; (2) mixing powdered barium bromide into a solution saturated with barium bromide and containing radium; or (3) by cooling a saturated solution of barium bromide plus radium so that precipitation ensued. As can be seen, the distribution of radium between solid and solution phase is, to the limitation of the experimental accuracy, independent of the method by which equilibrium was attained. (The distribution coefficient D is defined by Eq. 3-4.)

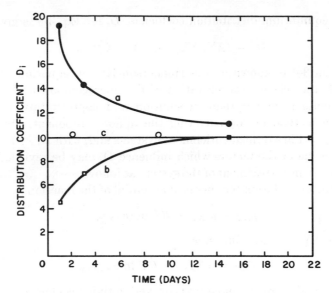

Fig. 3-1. Approach to equilibrium in the radium–barium bromide system as a function of time, at 35°C: curve $a$, activity initially in solid; curve $b$, activity initially in solution; curve $c$, entire system initially in liquid state. (After Chlopin, ref. 1)

Ionic mixed crystals may consist of host, with the coprecipitant having a cation or anion (or neither) in common. For example, the replacement of an anion within the solid may be regarded as a two-step process involving surface adsorption, followed by incorporation into the substrate lattice with free diffusion.

$$X^-(\text{ads}) + Y^-(\text{soln}) \rightleftharpoons Y^-(\text{ads}) + X^-(\text{soln}) \tag{3-1}$$

$$Y^-(\text{ads}) + AX(\text{solid}) \rightleftharpoons AY(\text{solid}) + X^-(\text{ads}) \tag{3-2}$$

The reaction, of course, would be equally general for incorporation of cations.

The overall equilibrium in Eqs. 3-1 and 3-2 is given by

$$AX(\text{solid}) + Y^-(\text{soln}) \rightleftharpoons AY(\text{solid}) + X^-(\text{soln}) \tag{3-3}$$

and it can be seen that this relationship is established independently of the reaction path. Thus, the difficulties encountered in explaining the roles of ion reaction, diffusion, interfacial regions, adsorption, and incorporation into the matrix are avoided in the equilibrium situation, though they are of prime importance in kinetic coprecipitation.

The equilibrium distribution coefficient $D_i$ for Eq. 3-3 is given by

$$D_i = (AY/AX)_{solid}/(Y^-/X^-)_{soln} \qquad (3\text{-}4)$$

Equation 3-4 is known as the Henderson-Kracek equation (2). If $D_i > 1$, the relative concentration of the microcomponent Y in the solid phase is higher than in solution and coprecipitation would afford a method of concentrating the minor component. Systems with $D_i > 1$ are termed enrichment systems and, with $D_i < 1$, depletion. Some of the factors which influence $D_i$ may be revealed by a thermodynamic treatment of the system as follows.

In aqueous solution the chemical potential of the reaction is

$$\mu_{AY} = \mu^0{}_{AY} + RT \ln (a_{AY})_{soln} \qquad (3\text{-}5)$$

and for AY in solid solution is

$$\mu'_{AY} = \mu^{0'}{}_{AY} + RT \ln x_{AY} f_{AY} \qquad (3\text{-}6)$$

where $x$ and $f$ are the mole fraction and activity coefficient, respectively. At equilibrium $\mu_{AY} = \mu'_{AY}$ and

$$\ln [(x_{AY} f_{AY})/(a_{AY})] = -(\mu^{0'}{}_{AY} - \mu^0{}_{AY})/RT \qquad (3\text{-}7)$$

Similarly, for AX

$$\ln [(x_{AX} f_{AX})/(a_A)] = -(\mu^{0'}{}_{AX} - \mu^0{}_{AX})/RT \qquad (3\text{-}8)$$

Thus

$$\ln [(x_{AY} f_{AY})(a_{AX})/(x_{AX} f_{AX})(a_{AY})]$$
$$= [(\mu^0{}_{AY} - \mu^{0'}{}_{AY}) - (\mu^0{}_{AX} - \mu^{0'}{}_{AX})]/RT \qquad (3\text{-}9)$$

For equilibrium between pure AY and its solution

$$\mu_{AY(0)} = \mu^0{}_{AY} + RT \ln (a_{AY})_0 = \mu'_{AY(0)}(\text{solid}) \equiv \mu^{0'}{}_{AY} \qquad (3\text{-}10)$$

Similarly

$$\mu_{AX(0)} = \mu^0{}_{AX} + RT \ln (a_{AX})_0 = \mu'_{AX(0)}(\text{solid}) \equiv \mu^{0'}{}_{AX} \qquad (3\text{-}11)$$

From Eqs. 3-9, 3-10, and 3-11

$$(x_{AY} f_{AY})(a_{AX})/(x_{AX} f_{AX})(a_{AY}) = (a_{AX})_0/(a_{AY})_0 = K_0 \qquad (3\text{-}12)$$

where $K_0$ is the ratio of solubilities as indicated.

For most cases of coprecipitation, the mole fraction of the micro-component (Y or AY) in the solid phase $x_{AY} \ll 1$ and $f_{AY}$ is constant. Equation 3-12 then becomes

$$x_{AY}(a_{AX}/a_{AY})f_{AX} \simeq K_0/f_{AY} \simeq K'_0 \qquad (3\text{-}13)$$

Then from Eq. 3-6, since $x_{AX} \sim 1$,

$$f_{AX} = \exp\,[\mu'_{AX} - \mu^{0'}_{AX}]/RT \qquad (3\text{-}14)$$

Hence, from Eq. 3-13

$$x_{AY}(a_{AX}/a_{AY}) = K'_0 \exp\,[-\overline{\Delta G'}_{AX}/RT] \qquad (3\text{-}15)$$

Now

$$D_i = x_{AY}c_{AX}/c_{AY} = K'_0(\gamma_{AX}/\gamma_{AY})^2 \exp\,[-\overline{\Delta G'}_{AX}/RT] \qquad (3\text{-}16)$$

where $\overline{\Delta G'}_{AX} = \mu^{0'}_{AX} - \mu'_{AX}$, i.e., the modification in the chemical interaction of the solid solvent caused by the presence of the micro-component.

Vaslow and Boyd (3), using a similar formulation, proceed from Eq. 3-12 by putting $f_{AX} \equiv 1$ and putting

$$f_{AY} = \exp\,\{[\mu_{AY} - \mu_{AY}(\text{ideal})]/RT\} \qquad (3\text{-}17)$$

whence

$$D_i \equiv x_{AY}c_{AX}/c_{AY} = K_0(\gamma_{AX}/\gamma_{AY})^2 \exp\,[-\overline{\Delta G'}_{AX}/RT] \qquad (3\text{-}18)$$

In this expression $\overline{\Delta G'}_{AX} = [\mu_{AY} - \mu_{AY}(\text{ideal})]$ represents the change of interaction of the solute relative to its surroundings in the host lattice.

Equations 3-16 and 3-18 point out several important features of equilibrium cocrystallization studies. For the ideal solid solution where there is no modification of the host lattice and where the solution activity coefficient are identical, the homogeneous distribution coefficient $D_i$ should be equal to the liquid-solution solubility ratio $K_0$. Equation 3-16 predicts a dependence of the distribution coefficient $D_i$ upon temperature. Often $\overline{\Delta G'}$ is positive and a decrease of microcomponent in the solid phase is produced by increase in temperature. A typical case, AgBr in AgCl, is shown in Fig. 3-2, and thermodynamic data are given in Table 3-1. It is to be expected that microcomponent ions which do not fit exactly into the host lattice will cause distortion, producing finite values of $\overline{\Delta G'}$.

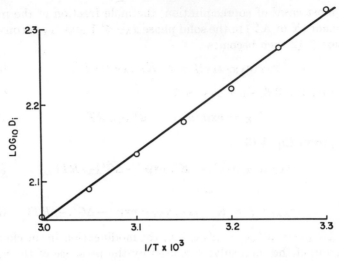

Fig. 3-2. The homogeneous distribution coefficient $D_i$ as a function of $1/T$ for the $Br^-/AgCl$ system. (After Vaslow and Boyd, ref. 3)

TABLE 3-1

The Homogeneous Distribution Coefficient $D_i$ for Different Solid Solutions with the Solubility Ratio $K_0$ and the Excess Free Energy Function $\overline{\Delta G}$ Calculated from Eq. 3-18

| Solid solution | Temp., °C | $D_{obs}$ | $K_0$ | $\overline{\Delta G}$, cal/ mole | Ref. |
|---|---|---|---|---|---|
| AgBr in AgCl | 30 | 211.4 | 315.7 | +287 | 2 |
| AgCl in AgBr | 30 | 0.0036 | 0.0031 | −70 | 2 |
| AgCl in TlCl | 40 | 4.2 | $7.2 \times 10^5$ | +7500 | 2 |
| $Pb(IO_3)_2$ in $Ba(IO_3)_2$ | 25 | 25 | $3.2 \times 10^3$ | +2800 | 4 |
| $Ra(IO_3)_2$ in $Ba(IO_3)_2$ | 25 | 1.42 | 1.32 | −39 | 5 |
| $RaSO_4$ in $BaSO_4$ | 20 | 1.8 | 5.9 | +700 | 6 |
| $SrSO_4$ in $BaSO_4$ | 25 | 3.010 | $1.81 \times 10^{-2}$ | +2480 | 7 |
| $PbSO_4$ in $BaSO_4$ | 25 | $2.55 \times 10^{-2}$ | $9.61 \times 10^{-2}$ | +805 | 8 |

Theoretical calculations of interactions between ions of the micro- and macrocomponent can of course be made on the basis of Madelung theory and some attempts have been made along these lines (9-11). The degree of accuracy has been rather limited thus far. We might expect, however, that $\overline{\Delta G'}$ would be a function of ion size. One limitation regarding ion size is that solid-solution miscibility usually occurs for atoms or ions which misfit (12) by less than 15% (Eq. 3-16 is not valid without modification for salts which do not have a 1:1 anion to cation ratio). These criteria virtually limit the choice of ions suitable for theoretical study to those forming isostructural crystal units. Recently, some coprecipitation data have been published by Ratner and Makavov (13) for alkali halides which enable the ion size effect to be demonstrated (Table 3-2). In Fig. 3-3 $\log_{10} K_0/D_i$ is plotted against the difference in ion radius between microcomponent and host; values of $+\Delta r$ are given by ions larger than the host and those of $-\Delta r$ by ions smaller than the host. It seems fairly clear that, for the alkali halide system at least, there is a good correlation between lattice fit and coprecipitation ability. One notes that if appropriate activity coefficients are taken into account, the ordinate axis in Fig. 3-3 represents $\overline{\Delta G'}/RT$. Although thermodynamic data are not available for this particular system, the experimental results listed in Table 3-1 show that large $K_0/D_i$ ratios, and hence high values of $\overline{\Delta G'}$ are observed in conjunction with a large

TABLE 3-2

Homogeneous Distribution Coefficients for a Series of Alkali Halide Crystals
(after Ratner and Makavov, ref. 13)

| Microcomponent | Host phase | Distribution coefficient, $D_i$ (all at 25°C) |
|----------------|------------|-----------------------------------------------|
| Na$^+$ | KCl | 0.007 |
| Rb$^+$ | KCl | 0.22 |
| Cs$^+$ | KCl | 0.004 |
| Br$^-$ | KCl | 0.263 |
| Rb$^+$ | KBr | 0.42 |
| I$^-$ | KBr | 0.05 |
| Rb$^+$ | KI | 1.02 |
| Br$^-$ | KI | 0.450 |
| K$^+$ | RbCl | 0.86 |
| Cs$^+$ | RbCl | 0.05 |
| K$^+$ | RbI | 0.226 |
| Cs$^+$ | RbI | 0.34 |
| Rb$^+$ | CsCl | 0.160 |
| Rb$^+$ | CsI | 0.048 |

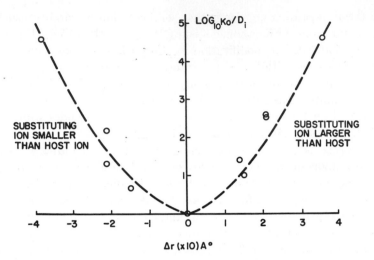

Fig. 3-3. The substitution of either anion or cation in alkali halide crystals causes distortion of the matrix. The greater the distortion, measured by the difference in radius between host and substituting ion ($\Delta r$), the smaller is the relative distribution coefficient $D_i/K_0$. (Data of Ratner and Makavov, ref. 13)

distortion of the host lattice. If the criterion of equilibrium homogeneous distribution is attained with free ion diffusion in the solid matrix, the relation between the distribution coefficient $D_i$ and the solubility ratio $K$ should indicate the degree of compatibility between carrier and microcomponent. Some comparative values of $D_i$ and $K_0$ are given in Table 3-1.

## 2. Structural Principles of Mixed Crystal Formation

The hypothesis that an equilibrium distribution of ions within a solid precipitate occurs via adsorption and incorporation into the lattice and is followed by diffusion of individual ions seems substantiated to a degree by correlation between theory and experiment for a limited class of compounds, i.e., those bearing identical crystal structures for carrier and coprecipitant, provided that a good lattice fit is attained. In extending the principles already evolved to the more general situation, one important feature is the state of the microcomponent within the solid solution. A possibility not previously considered here is that an aggregation of ions forms either neutral molecules or clusters within the matrix.    Quite simple evidence is available which suggests that such features are important in some cases but not in others.    For example, lead, cadmium, and sodium ions are of similar size and lead (or cadmium) is readily coprecipitated with sodium chloride despite differences in the lattice structure and valence of host and trace (14–16).    On the other hand, lead coprecipitates with potassium sulfate but not with sodium sulfate (17); both potassium and lead sulfate have an orthorhombic crystal structure whereas sodium sulfate is monoclinic.    The latter example seems very significant in that it is evidently molecules or groups of molecules which are locked into the host lattice.    The coprecipitation of molecular units rather than individual ions also seems to support some of the mechanistic arguments proposed for the surface-reaction controlled growth theory (see the previous chapter).

Inhomogeneous distribution in equilibrated crystals may also occur by means of "coagulation" of ions within the lattice.    For ions which distort the host lattice, some of the strain may be relieved by forming clusters, which lower the energy of the system in much the same way that agglomeration lowers the energy of a colloidal system.    This grouping or clustering has in fact recently been detected by electron-spin resonance measurements on $Mn^{2+}$ in $CaCO_3$ by Fujiwara (18).    (Alternatively, it might be argued that the distribution of $Mn^{2+}$ in $CaCO_3$ is not determined by equilibrium conditions.)

It can be said, therefore, that only under conditions of substituting ions of approximately equal size and charge with host-lattice ions can a homogeneous mixed crystal be produced, and under these conditions (low excess energy of mixing) the homogeneous distribution coefficient should approach the ratio of the limiting solubility products.

Three-component systems are believed to follow much the same rules as those devised for two-component systems.    For example, radium and lead coprecipitated together in barium nitrate have distribution coefficients as though each were present alone (23).    The same is not true, however, for the cadmium–lead–silver chloride system, where the cadmium and lead apparently compete (24).    This latter situation may be characteristic of anomalous mixed crystals or of the formation of complexes.

The preceding structural principles have evolved mainly from a consideration of the theoretical aspects of coprecipitation.    These developments have been fairly recent, but in fact the rules for effective coprecipitation have been known on a qualitative basis for many years.

As early as 1818, Mitscherlich had proposed that it was only materials of considerable chemical similarity which precipitated together to form mixed crystals. The isomorphous structural relations were pointed out much later by Grimm (1924). Application of the concepts of coprecipitation has, however, received its major impetus from the need to separate and concentrate rare man-made elements and fission products, and, conversely, the use of isotopes has allowed distribution coefficients for trace amounts of material to be established with suitable precision. The coprecipitation of radioactive elements has been surveyed by Kahn (25) and some of these data are reproduced in Table 3-3. Notably the structural principles outlined above have led investigators to devote most effort to the coprecipitation of similar ions. For example, trace elements $^{210}$Pb,

TABLE 3-3a

Homogeneous Distribution Coefficients for Some Radioactive Trace Elements—
Radioactive Lead

(Trace element = $^{212}$Pb except where noted)

| Carrier | Temp., °C | Distribution coefficient, $D_i$ | Carrier | Temp., °C | Distribution coefficient, $D_i$ |
|---|---|---|---|---|---|
| LiF | 20 | 0.02 | KClO$_3$ | — | < 0.04 |
| LiCl | 0 | 19.6 | NaClO$_3$ | — | ~0 |
| LiBr | 20 | ~0 | KBrO$_3$ | — | >1 |
| NaCl | 0 | ~60 | NaBrO$_3$ | — | 0.6 |
| NaCl | 100 | 100 | KNO$_3$ | — | ~0 |
| NaBr·2H$_2$O | 0 | < 0.1 | AgNO$_3$ | — | ~0 |
| NaI | 20 | 13 | Na$_2$SO$_4$ | Hot | ~0 |
| KCl | 0 | 57 | K$_2$SO$_4$ | — | 15–30 |
| KCl | 100 | 10 | Rb$_2$SO$_4$ | — | 15–30 |
| KBr | 0 | −60 | (NH$_4$)$_2$SO$_4$ | — | >1 |
| KI | 20 | 30 | BaCl$_2$·2H$_2$O[a] | 0 | 19.6 |
| NH$_4$Cl | 20 | 0.08 | BaBr$_2$·2H$_2$O | — | 0 |
| NH$_4$Br | 20 | 0.04 | CuSO$_4$·5H$_2$O | — | ~0 |
| NH$_4$I | 20 | 13 | MgSO$_4$·7H$_2$O | — | ~0 |
| TlCl | 20 | 0.002 | Na$_2$SO$_4$·10H$_2$O | — | ~0 |
| | | | Sr(NO$_3$)$_2$·4H$_2$O | 15 | 1.08 |

[a] Trace element = $^{210}$Pb.

TABLE 3-3$b$

Homogeneous Distribution Coefficients $D_i$ for Radioactive Polonium

($^{210}$Po Half-life $=$ 140 days)

| Carrier | Distribution coefficient, $D_i$ | Temp., °C |
|---|---|---|
| $(NH_4)_3IrCl_6 \cdot H_2O$ | 8.8 | Room |
| $(NH_4)_2Cr_2O_7$ | 2.9 | 0 |
| $CuSO_4 \cdot 5H_2O$ | ~0 | — |
| $MgSO_4 \cdot 7H_2O$ | ~0 | — |
| $Na_2SO_4 \cdot 10H_2O$ | ~0 | — |
| $Na_2Te$ | 0.076 | 0 |
| $CaC_2O_4$ | 13–27 | 17 |
| $La_2(C_2O_4)_3$ | 3–13 | 17 |
| $Sc_2(C_2O_4)_3$ | 5.0 | 17 |
| $SrC_2O_4$ | 0.33–0.68 | 17 |

$^{212}$Pb, $^{223}$Ra, $^{224}$Ra, and $^{226}$Ra have commonly been studied in conjunction with barium, strontium, and calcium salts as the host phase. Some surprises emerge: lead apparently does not coprecipitate with $BaBr_2 \cdot 2H_2O$(6) but it does with $BaCl_2 \cdot 2H_2O$ (26). It does not coprecipitate with calcium sulfate (17) with which it is isostructural, but does with rubidium sulfate (6). Accordingly, it is not always possible to predict the degree of coprecipitation between two materials on a structural basis alone. Since theoretical calculations have not been made for such difficult circumstances, it is not yet possible to say what structural implications lie behind these anomalous results.

## 3. Intermediate Miscibility

Although mixed crystals are formed favorably under conditions of isostructural replacement, many examples of coprecipitation involving nonisostructural materials are known. Here again ionic sizes are undoubtedly important, the product of nonisomorphous replacement being known as an anomalous mixed crystal. Often the microcomponent in the anomalous mixed crystal is only of limited solubility in the host phase. Melikhov and co-workers (16) have shown that lead and cadmium chlorides coprecipitate with sodium chloride but are of limited miscibility; their data for cadmium chloride are shown

TABLE 3-3c

Homogeneous Distribution Coefficients $D_i$ for Radioactive Radium

| Carrier | Trace | $D_i$ | Temp., °C | Carrier | Trace | $D_i$ | Temp., °C |
|---|---|---|---|---|---|---|---|
| $KBrO_3$ | $^{224}Ra$ | ~0 | — | $Ba(NO_3)_2$ | $^{224}Ra$ | 1.88 | 0 |
| $NaBrO_3$ | | ~0 | — | $KNO_3$ | | ~0 | Room |
| $NaClO_3$ | | ~0 | — | $AgNO_3$ | | ~0 | — |
| $BaBr_2 \cdot 2H_2O$ | | 11.0 | 0 | $CaSO_4$ | | <0.01 | Hot |
| $BaCl_2 \cdot 2H_2O$ | | 5.3 | 0 | $CaSO_4 \cdot 5H_2O$ | | ~0 | — |
| $Ba(ClO_3)_2 \cdot H_2O$ | | 4.6 | 0 | $MgSO_4 \cdot 7H_2O$ | | ~0 | — |
| $KClO_3$ | | ~0 | — | $K_2SO_4$ | | 15–30 | — |
| $K_2PtCl_6$ | | ~0 | Room | $Rb_2SO_4$ | | 15–30 | — |
| $PbCrO_4$ | | ~0 | 0 | $Ag_2SO_4$ | | ~0 | Room |
| $(NH_4)_2Cr_2O_7$ | | 0.1 | 0 | $Ag_2C_2O_4$ | | ~0 | Room |
| $RbClO_4$ | $^{226}Ra$ | ~0 | 25 | $SrCl_2 \cdot 6H_2O$ | $^{223}Ra$ | 0.016 | 20 |
| $CsClO_4$ | | ~0 | 25 | $Sr(NO_3)_2 \cdot 4H_2O$ | | 0.076 | 15 |
| $Ag_2CrO_4$ | | ~0 | Room | $Sr(NO_3)_2$ | | 9.6 | 33 |
| $Ba(IO_3)_2$ | | 1.85 | 25 | $SrSO_4$ | | 30 | 100 |
| $Pb(NO_3)_2$ | | 2.19 | 25 | $Ba(C_2H_3O_2)_2 \cdot 3H_2O$ | | 0.26 | 0 |
| | | | | $Ba(C_2H_3O_2)_2 \cdot H_2O$ | | 0.4 | 29 |
| | | | | $Ba(C_2H_3O_2)_2$ | | 0.96 | 50 |
| | | | | $d$-Ba tartrate | | 0.84 | 25 |
| | | | | $l$-Ba tartrate | | 0.85 | 25 |
| | | | | $dl$-Ba tartrate | | 1.48 | 24 |

TABLE 3-4[a]

Homogeneous Distribution Coefficients for Nonisostructural Combinations[a]

| Carrier | Micro-component | Temp., °C | Distribution coefficient,[b] $D_i$ | Method |
|---------|-----------------|-----------|------------------------------------|--------|
| Lanthanum oxalate | $Eu^{3+}$ | 0 | 4.8 | |
| | $Am^{3+}$ | | 3.8 | |
| | $Y^{3+}$ | | 3.7 | |
| Ammonium chloride | $Cr^{3+}$ | 0 | 0.0023 | Evaporation |
| | $Fe^{3+}$ | | 0.026 | |
| | $Cu^{2+}$ | | 0.59 | |
| | $Mn^{2+}$ | | 0.75 | |
| | $Ni^{2+}$ | | 0.15 | |
| | $Co^{2+}$ | | 0.15 | |
| Copper sulfate | $Fe^{3+}$ | 18–20 | 0.098 | Direct precipitation; |
| | $Sb^{3+}$ | | 0.005 | prolonged diges- |
| | $Ca^{2+}$ | | 0.005 | tion |
| | $Na^{2+}$ | | 0.001 | |
| | $Co^{2+}$ | | 0.043 | |
| | $Zn^{2+}$ | | 0.042 | |
| | $Ni^{2+}$ | | 0.012 | |

[a] Data from refs. 19–22.

[b] Distribution coefficients are not corrected for ionic charge.

in Fig. 3-4. The precipitate was produced by dissolving all the original material at an elevated temperature and then cooling. It can be seen that the precipitate formed contained increasing amounts of lead as the solution concentration of lead was increased up to the limiting solubility. Changes of the concentration of lead chloride in solution above this level produced no change in the solid content.

Some homogeneous distribution coefficients for materials which are not isostructural with the host are given in Table 3-4.

## 4. Nonequilibrium Conditions

The coprecipitation of ions may be imagined to involve three kinetic processes: transport through solution to the surface, exchange with the surface, and diffusion through the solid. In the previous section all three processes have reached equilibrium and the overall

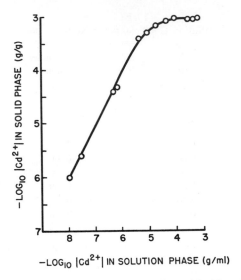

Fig. 3-4. Cadmium ions are soluble in sodium chloride only up to a limiting value. (After Melikhov, Merkulova, and Eval'd, ref. 16)

mechanism has been dealt with accordingly. Under dynamic conditions, such as those applying during precipitation from solution, at least one of these steps will not be at equilibrium. In general, surface exchange and solid-state diffusion are much slower than surface adsorption, so that the adsorption step from solution may be regarded as one of pseudoequilibrium. Under these circumstances the growth of a precipitate particle may be by proceeding via a sequence of deposition of equilibrium layers, each adjusting to the external situation in the bulk solution. If it is further assumed that there is a direct relation between the amount precipitated from solution and the concentration remaining in solution,

$$\frac{dY}{dX} = \lambda \left| \frac{Y}{X} \right| \qquad (3\text{-}17)$$

where $dX$ and $dY$ are the amounts of macro- and microcomponent precipitated, respectively, and $X$ and $Y$ are the corresponding concentrations (mass) in solution; $\lambda$ may be recognized as identical with the homogeneous distribution coefficient $D_i$ for the deposition of any particular layer, but diverging from $D_i$ as the total precipitate forms. Integration of Eq. 3-17 leads to the relation

$$\log (Y_0/Y_f) = \lambda \log (X_0/X_f) \tag{3-18}$$

or

$$\log \left( \frac{\text{original microcomponent in solution}}{\text{microcomponent remaining in solution}} \right)$$

$$= \lambda \log \left( \frac{\text{original macrocomponent in solution}}{\text{remaining macrocomponent in solution}} \right) \tag{3-19}$$

where $\lambda$ is termed the heterogeneous distribution coefficient. The above relation is well known as the Doerner-Hoskins equation (27).

It is noteworthy that the rate of precipitation is likely to affect the formulation of the above distribution equation. At very slow rates of precipitation $\lambda \rightarrow D_i$. For very fast rates the surface equilibrium is not established and the relation becomes controlled by diffusion of the ions from solution:

$$\frac{dY}{dX} = \frac{k_1 |Y|}{k_2 |X|} \tag{3-20}$$

where $k_1$ and $k_2$ are the diffusion rate constants for species A and B. Hence, for this situation $\lambda \rightarrow k_1/k_2$ and since for similar ions $k_1 \sim k_2$, $\lambda \rightarrow 1$ and coprecipitation is unselective, producing neither enrichment nor depletion.

The derivation of Eq. 3-18 is also dependent upon the relation between the amount deposited and the solution "pressure." In the previous chapter it has been noted that the relation between these parameters is linear only for diffusion-controlled growth and that normally some higher power of the solution concentration is involved. No reconcilable explanation between these situations seems to have been proposed.

Despite the rate restrictions noted above, the Doerner-Hoskins equation has been found to apply surprisingly well for many coprecipitation reactions. Some $\lambda$ coefficients are given in Table 3-5. Unfortunately, precipitation rates have not been specified for these reactions and consequently the quoted $\lambda$ values lose some of their significance. However, as a general guide to enrichment or derichment, these values are useful.

TABLE 3-5

Heterogeneous Distribution Coefficients ($\lambda$) for Radioactive Ions

| Carrier | Trace | $\lambda$ | Temp., °C | Carrier | Trace | $\lambda$ | Temp., °C |
|---|---|---|---|---|---|---|---|
| Al(AcAc)$_3$ | $^{210}$Po | 0.5 | Room | Ti$_2$O$_5\cdot x$H$_2$O | $^{231}$Pa | 0.07 | 15 |
| Sc(AcAc)$_2$ | $^{210}$Po | 0.3 | Room | TiO$_2\cdot x$H$_2$O | | 0.015 | — |
| Th(AcAc)$_4$ | $^{210}$Po | 0.7 | Room | ZrO$_2\cdot x$H$_2$O | | 24 | — |
| NaBr | $^{212}$Pb | 25 | 75 | ZrO$_2$ | | 25 | Room |
| LiCl | $^{212}$Pb | 0.4 | 110 | ZrOCl$_2$ | | 20 | Room |
| BaCO$_3$ | $^{226}$Ra | 0.51 | 20 | (NH$_4$)$_2$TaF$_7$ | | 0.3 | 15 |
| CsReO$_4$ | Tc | 2.6 | 14 | K$_2$TaF$_7$ | | 2 | 15 |
| KReO$_4$ | Tc | 0.75 | 14 | (NH$_4$)$_2$TiF$_6$ | | 0.1 | 15 |
| LiO$_2$(NO$_3$)$_2\cdot$6H$_2$O | $^{234}$Th | 20 | — | K$_2$TiF$_6$ | | 0.1 | 15 |
| | | | | (NH$_4$)$_2$ZrF$_6$ | | 0.2 | 15 |
| | | | | K$_2$ZrF$_6$ | | 0.35 | 15 |

The derivation of Eq. 3-19 assumed that both micro- and macro-components changed with time, i.e., $Y_t < Y_0$ and $X_t < X_0$. Experimentally it is possible to keep the concentration of macrocomponent in solution (and sometimes the microcomponent concentration) constant rather than causing it to change during the reaction. This, for example, might be achieved by slow evaporation, which maintains the carrier at saturation concentration throughout the precipitation. Under these conditions the final and initial concentrations of microcomponent in solution ($Y_f$ and $Y_0$) are related by

$$Y_f = Y_0 \exp -(X_0 - X_f)/\lambda' \qquad (3\text{-}21)$$

which is a form of the Walter-Schlundt equation (28). If both components could be kept constant, a form of the homogeneous distribution law should result.

## 5. Experimental Examination of Heterogeneous Distribution

Under conditions of ultraslow precipitation it is to be expected that a near homogeneous situation exists. It has been shown that precipitation from low degrees of supersaturation over a period of days does, in fact, yield homogeneous distribution, even in the absence of agitation of the system (29). When precipitation is more rapid, however, the logarithmic distribution laws take over. Figure 3-5 shows the relationship between the homogeneous and heterogeneous distribution coefficients $D$ and $\lambda$ for various degrees of radium coprecipitation with barium chloride. The results show that $D$ and $\lambda$ values converge for very small amounts precipitated, but even under relatively slow precipitation by evaporation the logarithmic relation is followed.

More recently, slow coprecipitation has been effected by precipitation from chemically-produced homogeneous solution. Salutsky, Stites, and Martin (30) found that barium and radium chromates coprecipitatedby neutralizing acidic solutions (hydrolysis of urea or potassium cyanide), the logarithmic-distribution law being applicable. Subsequently, several materials have been coprecipitated using similar techniques (31); a summary of data is given in Table 3-6. In most systems so far examined, the logarithmic relation is applicable. Those which deviated did not follow the homogeneous relation either, and as a consequence some other form of coprecipitation is probably involved.

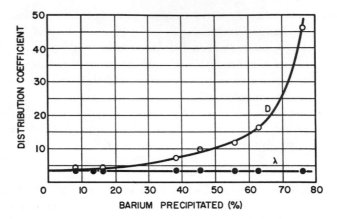

Fig. 3-5. Comparison of homogeneous and heterogeneous coprecipitation coefficients ($D$ and $\lambda$) for the slow evaporation from saturated solutions of radium in barium chloride (20°C) show $\lambda$ to represent the data more effectively (31).

TABLE 3-6

Coprecipitation by Chemical Reaction from Homogeneous Solution

| Micro-component | Substrate | $\lambda$ | Temp., °C | Chemical precipitating reaction | Ref. |
|---|---|---|---|---|---|
| $Ra^{2+}$ | $BaCrO_4$ | 5.5 | 25 | Hydrolysis of urea or cyanide | 28 |
| $Ra^{2+}$ | $BaSO_4$ | 1.21 | 90 | Hydrolysis of sulfamic acid | 28a |
| $Nd^{3+}$ | $Ce_2(C_2O_4)_3$ | 1.75 | — | Dimethyl oxalate hydrolysis | 28b |
| $Yb^{3+}$ | $Ce_2(C_2O_4)_3$ | 1.02 | — | | |
| $Am^{3+}$ | $Ce_2(C_2O_4)_3$ | 5.85 | — | Dimethyl oxalate hydrolysis | 28c |
| $Ra^{2+}$ | $BaCO_3$ | 0.2 | 90 | Hydrolysis of trichloroacetates | 28d |
| $Y^{3+}$ | $Ce_2(C_2O_4)_3$ | 0.64 | — | | |
| $Yb^{3+}$ | $Nd_2(C_2O_4)_3$ | 0.69 | — | | |
| $Sr^{2+}$ | $BaSO_4$ | 0.03 | 83 | Hydrolysis of methyl sulfate | 28e |
| $La^{3+}$ | $Th(IO_4)_4$ | 6.0 | — | Reduction of periodic acid with glycol | 28f |

Rapid direct mixing of reagents in high concentration to form precipitates is the least reproducible method of producing coprecipitation. Local areas of supersaturation, produced on mixing, result in a variety of growth rates and precipitate morphology. Distribution coefficients are often unreliable and irreproducible; in addition, the precipitation rate is so fast that selectivity disappears, giving $\lambda \rightarrow 1$ in concurrence with previous considerations. Direct mixing to produce relatively stable supersaturations at lower concentrations is capable of giving reproducible (at the same rate) heterogeneous distribution coefficients.

Both the homogeneous and heterogeneous coprecipitation equations as derived in this chapter are specifically valid for coprecipitation of ions of equal valence, though they have almost always been used independently of this limitation in the literature. Gordon (32) has rederived equations to take into account replacement of one ion by another of different ionic charge. Thus, for the general reaction

$$y\text{A(solid)} + x\text{B(soln)} = y\text{A(soln)} + x\text{B(solid)}$$

$x$ and $y$ being numerically equal to the valence of ions A and B, then the homogeneous equilibrium is given by

$$(\text{B/A})_{\text{solid}} = D'(\text{B/A}^{y/x})_{\text{soln}} \tag{3-22}$$

and the equation analogous to that of Doerner and Hoskins by

$$\log\,(\text{B}_0/\text{B}_f) = \lambda' v^{y/x-1}/[\text{A}_0{}^{1-y/x} - \text{A}_f{}^{1-y/x}] \tag{3-23}$$

where $v$ is the volume of solution and subscripts 0 and $f$ refer to initial and final concentrations ($y \neq x$).

It is evident, then, that a meaningful interpretation of coprecipitation involving logarithmic distribution coefficients is best attained if the precipitation rate is carefully controlled. It is of interest that $\lambda$ values are quoted for many systems where the precipitation rate varied throughout the reaction, yet there appears to be no appreciable change in $\lambda$. Rate effects will be considered later in more detail.

## 6. Distribution of Microcomponent in the Solid Phase

In the equilibrium stage of coprecipitation it is clear that the microcomponent should be homogeneously distributed throughout the solid phase. Minor deviations, caused by ion clustering, may occur but in general the agreement between theory and experiment for the limited number of cases investigated points to the correctness of this assumption. For logarithmic deposition processes the concepts of Doerner and Hoskins lead to the possible heterogeneous distribution of ions within the matrix, provided that the ions remain localized in their precipitation layers, and for this reason λ is often referred to as the heterogeneous distribution coefficient. The most amenable method of testing this distribution hypothesis experimentally is by sectioning coprecipitate crystals composed of carrier and radioactive tracer as the microcomponent, and taking autoradiographs of the cross section. Jucker and Treadwell (33) have performed such an analysis with radium–barium sulfate precipitated under conditions which conform to the heterogeneous law. They found, in conflict with the Doerner-Hoskins view, that the radium ions were distributed homogeneously within the barium sulfate lattice. Further evidence is needed before definite conclusions are reached, but it would seem that solid-state diffusion might in some cases be sufficiently rapid to render the solid phase relatively homogeneous.

## 7. Rate of Precipitation

Control of the rate of coprecipitation has shown several of the features outlined as rate effects in the preceding section. The most convenient method of controlling precipitation rate is by precipitation from homogeneous solution. Thus, Hermann (34) was able to show that the distribution coefficient for the coprecipitation of americium with lanthanum oxalate decreased from about 6.3 at very slow rates to 1 for fast precipitation rates, oxalate being generated by hydrolysis of ethyl acetate. Hermann's data are reproduced in Fig. 3-6. Block and Gordon (35) have also demonstrated the same effect for the coprecipitation of rare earth and uranium oxalates. Similarly, Klein and Fontal more recently (36) have shown that the heterogeneous distribution coefficient for lead in barium sulfate, when extrapolated back to the zero rate of precipitation, coincides with the theoretical prediction for the homogeneous (equilibrium) distribution coefficient. A schematic diagram of the effect of precipitation rate on distribution coefficients is shown in Fig. 3-7.

In order to obtain a quantitative relation between rate of precipitation and the distribution coefficients, it is necessary to assume a specific particle growth model. We have seen that the surface-reaction theory will give a satisfactory account of heterogeneous

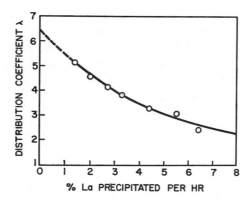

Fig. 3-6. The effect of precipitation velocity on the value of the distribution coefficient λ. (From J. A. Hermann, ref. 34)

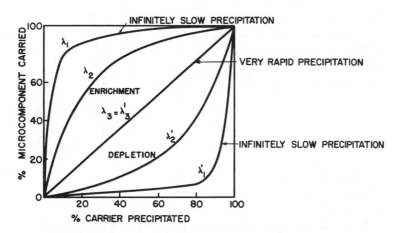

Fig. 3-7. Schematic diagram for the effect of precipitation rate on the distribution coefficient $\lambda$. In enrichment systems $\lambda \to \lambda_1 = D_i$ as the precipitation rate $\to 0$; for fast rates of precipitation $\lambda \to \lambda_3 = 1$. For depletion systems an analogous situation exists with $\lambda \to \lambda_1' = D'$ for close to zero precipitation rates and $\lambda \to \lambda_3' = 1$ for rapid precipitation.

distribution at a specific rate. It is, however, more usual to assume that particle growth occurs by a three-stage process: diffusion to an interfacial layer, a complicated diffusion–reaction process in the interfacial layer, and transport to the growth site. The screw dislocation mechanism might, for example, be limited by the third of the above processes, surface reaction by a modification of the second, and a completely diffusion-controlled precipitation by a combination of the first and second. Diffusion-controlled precipitation is the easiest mechanism to deal with, and well-defined systems are available to test the theoretical implications. Burton, Prim, and Slichter (37) have derived an expression for the distribution coefficient of a diffusion limited precipitation (from melts). The effective distribution coefficient in the steady state is given by

$$k = \frac{1}{1 + [1/k_0 - 1] \exp (-\delta f/D)} \tag{3-24}$$

where $\delta$ is the thickness of the diffusion-dominated interfacial layer, $D$ is the solute diffusion coefficient in solution, and $f$ is the growth rate; $k_0$ is the limiting distribution coefficient.

Bridgers and Kolb (38) have tested this equation by measuring the distribution coefficient of boron in germanium. The effective coefficient was found to decrease rapidly from the equilibrium value of 17.4 to 2.2 at a crystal growth rate of $10^{-2}$ cm/sec. The experimental results are shown in Fig. 3-8a.

Rearrangement of Eq. 3-24 gives

$$[1 - (1/k)] = [1 - (1/k_0)] \exp (-\delta f/D) \tag{3-25}$$

A plot of log 1[ − 1/k] versus the growth rate $f$ (Fig. 3-8b) shows good linearity with an experimentally determined value for the diffusion coefficient of boron in liquid germanium ($D$) of approximately $3 \times 10^{-4}$ cm$^2$/sec, a value in reasonable agreement with expectation.

Naturally, the precipitation of ionic crystals from solution is considerably more complicated. The Russian school has, though, extended the use of the Burton-Prim-Slichter relation to coprecipitation from solution. In their model three layers are postulated: the bulk solution layer, the interfacial layer, and the surface layer which is bound tightly to the surface and may be considered to consist of quasi-crystalline solvent (analogous to the "iceberg" structure) and surface-adsorbed ions. A schematic diagram is shown in Fig. 3-9. Melikhov and co-workers (39,40) have assumed that transportation to the surface layer is governed by the Burton-Prim-Schlicter relation

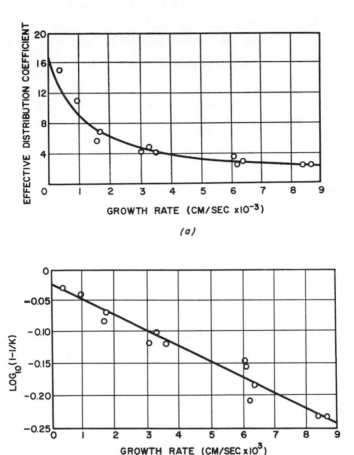

Fig. 3-8. (a) The effective distribution coefficient of boron in germanium as a function of growth rate. (After Bridgers and Kolb, ref. 38) (b) A plot of the logarithm of Eq. 3-25 as a function of growth rate for boron in germanium. (After Bridgers and Kolb, ref. 38)

**LIQUID PHASE**

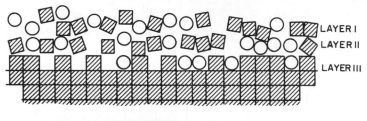

LAYER I

LAYER II

LAYER III

**SOLID PHASE**

Fig. 3-9. A model of the solid–solution interface after Melikhov. The interfacial region may be considered as consisting of the surface layer (III) where solvent molecules and solute ions or molecules are held more or less rigidly. The next layer (interfacial layer II) consists of ions and molecules free to diffuse across the surface and exchange with the surface layer. The solution layer (I) is still under the structural influence of the surface but has no direct contact with the surface.

and that, subsequently, a reaction with the surface ensues involving adsorption, ion exchange with the solid, and surface nucleation. Under these conditions the following general equation was derived

$$\frac{dY}{dX} = \frac{k_0|Y|}{\eta[e^{-\Delta}(1 - k_0) + k_0]} \tag{3-26}$$

where $\Delta = \delta f/D$ and $Y$ is the amount of microcomponent in solution, $X$ is the amount of macrocomponent in solution, and $\eta$ is the mass of solution.

The solution of Eq. 3-26 under specified conditions yields interesting results.

1. Crystallization takes place at constant concentration of macrocomponent ($f$ = constant) but varying concentration of microcomponent. If $\eta$ = a constant, integration of Eq. 3-26 gives

$$Y_f = Y_0 \exp \frac{k_0 (X_f - X_0)}{\eta[e^{-\Delta}(1 - k_0) + k_0]} \tag{3-27}$$

which is analogous to the Walter-Schlundt equation (Eq. 3-21).

2. With isothermal evaporation of solvent the mass of solution $\eta$ changes; in this case integration Eq. 3-26 gives

$$\log \frac{Y_0}{Y_f} = \frac{k_0}{\eta[e^{-\Delta}(1 - k_0) + k_0]} \log \frac{X_0}{X_f} \qquad (3\text{-}28)$$

i.e., the Doerner-Hoskins equation.

The general solution for Eq. 3-26 was not possible under conditions of variation in macro- and microcomponent and with changes also in growth rate and solution mass. However, provided that the supersaturation is low, Melikhov again finds that Eq. 3-26 reduces approximately to the Doerner-Hoskins form.

One important point brought out by the Russian work is that the Doerner-Hoskins logarithmic distribution law is only a limiting form of the general case and should not be regarded as fitting all dynamic situations.

## 8. Adsorption Compounds

The formation of mixed crystals and the laws pertaining thereto are, to a certain extent, rather idealized in that the lattice structure is assumed to be coherent enough to block the diffusion of ions other than those which are essentially the same size as the ions of the host lattice. Under the conditions of isothermal evaporation or precipitation from homogeneous solution, it is quite common to produce precipitates consisting of fairly large well-defined crystals which might well be expected to conform to the above requirements. In other words, the precipitates are of low surface area at all stages of the precipitation, and agglomeration and recrystallization are minimal. However, the situation is not the same with precipitates formed by direct mixing and subsequently aged. In this case the original supersaturation of the macrocomponent may well have been large enough to cause homogeneous nucleation, which would probably lead to a sequence of growth–agglomeration–recrystallization phenomena. Under these circumstances at some stage in the precipitation the surface area of the product is large, and surface adsorption, independent of any growth mechanism, can be an important means of inducing coprecipitation. Thus, in the final product the microcomponent would be located mainly at the "inner" surface of each precipitate particle.

The amount of material coprecipitated by surface adsorption may be represented by a relation analogous to the homogeneous distribution law, i.e.,

$$\frac{Y(\text{surface})}{Y(\text{solution})} = b\,\frac{X(\text{surface})}{X(\text{solution})} \qquad (3\text{-}29)$$

Paneth (41) has assumed that $b$ is the ratio of solubilities of substrate and coprecipitant in parallel with the homogeneous distribution coefficient $D_i$. An example of the use of the above relation is where $Y$ is $Pb^{2+}$ and $X$ is $Ba^{2+}$ for the barium-lead sulfate system. In this case, $b$ is the ratio of solubility of barium sulfate to lead sulfate. Kolthoff and MacNevin (42) find $b$ experimentally to be 0.12 at 25°C, compared with the calculated value of 0.08. Presumably an expression for $b$, which is similar to that for $D_i$ in Eq. 3-16, may be derived, in which the activation energy for the surface process is related to the modified surface interaction of one adsorbate caused by the presence of the other; $b$ would then be identical with the solubility ratio only if the two ions were of equal charge, size, and polarizability.

In terms of the overall mechanism of coprecipitate formation, the trace ion adsorbs on the surface of the precipitate and then either exchanges directly with an ion in the substrate or reacts with an ion of opposite charge before incorporation into the substrate lattice. With true adsorption compounds it may be assumed that the microcomponent is insoluble in the macrophase and that ion exchange (or molecular exchange) with the substrate is zero. However, since exchange with the substrate is relatively slow, rapid coprecipitation can be effected purely through surface adsorption. Such a view rationalizes the old concept that adsorption is the fundamental mechanism of all modes of coprecipitation. It is, though, apparent that ions which are adsorbed most strongly on the substrate are not necessarily those that fit exactly into the lattice and, consequently, adsorption is possibly not as fundamental a process to coprecipitation as was originally supposed. True adsorption "compounds" consist, then, of a microcomponent whose ions or molecules are strongly adsorbed on the substrate, but these ions or molecules are of such a size that they are incompatible with the host lattice. The best method of attempting to delineate adsorption compounds from other types seems to be the use of preformed precipitate substrate with a solution of coprecipitant. Adsorption is usually rapid (seconds or minutes rather than hours or days for the formation of solid solutions) and can be characterized in terms of the prevailing surface conditions. The three main features controlling the amount of microcomponent precipitated by the adsorption mechanism are the extent of substrate surface, surface charge, and complexing ability of the microcomponent with the ion of opposite charge on the surface. The first of these parameters, as previously mentioned, is determined to a large extent by the method of preparation of the substrate; a large surface area is produced by direct mixing of the precipitating species at high concentration. Surface charge is determined both by the ions and their concentration in solution and the nature and size of ions in the solid phase. Reference in this context is usually made to the silver halide systems, which have been studied rather extensively (43). The principles outlined more fully in Chapter 4 and 5 are as follows. Crystals in neutral solutions possess a surface charge due to the slight displacement of either anions or cations at the solid surface resulting from a relaxation of interionic forces. For silver halides the anions are displaced toward the solid surface. Consequently, if silver halide precipitates are dispersed in aqueous solution at pH 7, the particles assume a negative charge. This surface charge is probably accentuated by the fact that of the silver and halide ions passing into solution to maintain the equilibrium solubility product, some halide ions are adsorbed in excess on the surface because their large ionic radius results in a lower degree of solvation than that for the silver ion. The solid surface may be represented schematically, as in Fig. 3-10. Addition of other ions to the system affects the surface in various ways; for example, addition of soluble silver salts will cause adsorption of silver ions which first neutralize the net negative surface charge, then render it positively charged. Other halide ions in the system can be adsorbed or, if their size is suitable, can exchange with anions in the solid phase. Ions which behave in this manner are referred to as potential-determining ions. Addition of "neutral" ions causes compression of the electrical double layer in the vicinity of the surface and these ions may not be directly involved in surface adsorption. These are known as counterions.

It has been found that cationic microcomponents which will coprecipitate effectively in the presence of excess negative surface charge will not precipitate to any extent when the substrate charge is positive (44) (Table 3-7). The criterion that a strong surface complex is

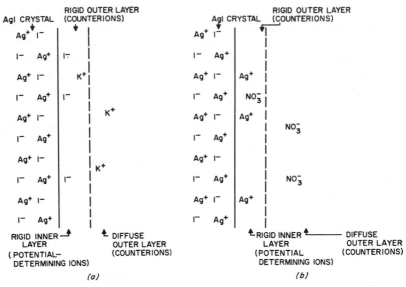

Fig. 3-10. Schematic diagrams of the electrical double layer on charged silver iodide particles (ref. 25, p. 125)

TABLE 3-7

Coprecipitation of Europium Adsorbed on Silver Iodide
Showing the Effect of Net Surface Charge

| $p$Ag | $p$I | | Amount of europium coprecipitated, mg-equiv/mole AgI |
|:---:|:---:|---|:---:|
| 5 | 11 ⎫ | Surface charge + ve | ~0 |
| 6 | 10 ⎬ | (with no Eu³⁺) | ~0 |
| 7 | 9 ⎭ | | ~0 |
| | | isoelectric point | |
| 8 | 8 ⎫ | Surface charge − ve | 1.1 |
| 9 | 7 ⎬ | (with no Eu³⁺) | 1.75 |
| 10 | 6 ⎭ | | 2.1 |

formed is requiring, in effect, that the adsorption energy be greater than the solvation energy of the free ion. In other words, the adsorption product is insoluble or sparingly soluble.

## 9. Coprecipitation of Liquids

There is no *a priori* reason why liquids should not coprecipitate with solids except, perhaps, that an unfavorable excess free energy of mixing will ensue because the interactions between solvent molecules and the host lattice will, in general, be weaker than those of foreign ions. It cannot be expected then that large concentrations of solvent molecules will coprecipitate in true solid solutions. There are, however, circumstances in which solvent molecules are found in close association with a host lattice. These may be put into four categories: (*1*) crystals forming with solvent molecules as part of the solvation structure in the normal crystal lattice; (*2*) solvent molecules as part of the crystal structure; (*3*) solvent molecules incorporated in conjunction with the coprecipitation of foreign ions; (*4*) occlusion and entrapment at macroscopic sites.

*1.* In the first of these areas many crystals are known to form with water molecules located at specific lattice sites. No common hydrated inorganic material is insoluble or slightly soluble in water so that, strictly speaking, phenomena associated with water of crystallization cannot be justified in terms of precipitation processes. It is of interest, though, to realize that the presence or absence of solvating molecules in the lattice sometimes plays an important part in maintaining an ordered lattice. Three cases can be distinguished: the crystal lattice of the residue after dehydration is practically identical with that of the inorganic constituents of the original hydrate, as with zeolites; a phase showing little or no evidence of crystalline structure is produced upon dehydration (most hydrates are in this category); and the dehydrated residue crystallizes to give a new solid phase. Two types of localization of solvent molecules usually occur in the hydrates—water of crystallization being held in coordination complexes around the metallic ions of the lattice and "structural" water. The coordination water is more loosely held in simple hydrates and may be removed with a desiccant *in vacuo*. Structural water is often not so easily removed. Thus, for copper sulfate pentahydrate, four molecules of water are easily removed at room temperature *in vacuo*, but the last can only be removed at high temperatures, the latter process being accompanied by hydrolysis of the sulfate.   Both types of solvent molecules are exchangeable with solution, indicating that mechanisms exists for the solid-state diffusion of solvent molecules.

*2*. The structural water in the copper sulfate case seems to be associated with one copper sulfate "molecule." Thus, it is possible that solvent molecules allow a crystal lattice to achieve a lower-energy configuration than the ions alone can maintain.   This form of coprecipitation is a special case, but the dispersion of solvent molecules in the solid matrix is not limited by such rigid requirements. Since there are always Frenkel defects present in crystals at normal temperatures, it is reasonable to suppose that the crystal lattice of precipitates contains migratory lattice holes which could hold solvent molecules.   Walton and Walden (45), for example have, shown that water coprecipitates with barium sulfate and exists as a solid solution, as demonstrated by x-ray unit-cell distortions.   Indications were that a group of three water molecules replaced a barium sulfate unit in the lattice.   These water molecules were probably not structure aiding in the same sense as those in copper sulfate because removal from the lattice left a stable defect lattice.

*3*. Coprecipitation of ions with a host phase might be expected to concurrently coprecipitate solvation molecules if the combined guest and solvate ion is of an appropriate size.   One example of such a process is demonstrated by the coprecipitation of lithium ions in barium sulfate (46).   Each lithium ion carries with it one water of solution in the product.

*4*. Occlusion and entrapment is usually a result of the growth process, including agglomeration and dendritic intergrowth (the latter is demonstrated in Chapter 5).   Although quantitative characterization is not possible, the existence of microscopic pools of occluded solution is of some interest since it sometimes enables geologists to trace back the nature of the seas, lakes, pools, ponds, etc. from which rocks were originally generated.

## 10.  Coprecipitation in Geochemistry and Physiology

The application of coprecipitation theory to extraction and concentration of radioactive isotopes is clear, as is the important role which the use of radioactive tracers has played in the elucidation of coprecipitation phenomena. The rules are much the same, only applied in reverse to the preparation of pure precipitates in analytical chemistry.

In geochemical and physiological coprecipitation we are not generally faced with separation or purification by precipitation, but more with the "fait accompli" of the finished product. The questions which might be asked here are concerned with the structural modifications which the microcomponent superimposes upon the host.

The geochemical formation of ores and their subsequent aging and recrystallization fulfill the requirements for homogeneous distribution of ions most adequately. Normally, there will be several microcomponents deposited within the lattice of the carrier, but as yet the few model studies which have been performed have concentrated on the formation of two solid-component systems. In addition to the structural information obtainable from model systems, some reconstruction of the formative processes in rock and ore formation are possible. An interesting study by Holland and co-workers (47) has directed attention to the cocrystallization of strontium with the calcium carbonates, calcite and aragonite, and of calcium with strontianite. Aragonite and strontianite were produced by precipitation from homogeneous solution using the hydrolysis of trichloroacetate ion to generate carbonate ions in solution. Calcite was produced by direct application of $CO_2$ gas to an ammoniacal calcium solution under hydrothermal conditions. Under these conditions the precipitation followed a Doerner-Hoskins-type relation; the results are shown in Table 3-8.

TABLE 3-8

Coprecipitation of Some Compounds of Geological Significance

| Carrier | Microcomponent | $\lambda$ | Temp., °C |
|---|---|---|---|
| Aragonite | $Sr^{2+}$ | 0.59 | |
| Calcite | $Sr^{2+}$ | 0.076 | |
| Strontianite | $Ca^{2+}$ | (0.3–0.5) | |
| Calcite | $Mn^{2+}$ | 10.0 | 175 |
| Calcite | $Zn^{2+}$ | 55 | 167 |

Although, ideally, $\lambda$ obtained at zero rate of precipitation (i.e., $D_i$) should be compared with the naturally occurring mineral, Holland and co-workers were able to define fairly closely the components of the original solutions which led to geological carbonate sedimentation and recrystallization many centuries ago, hence, performing an interesting piece of historical detective work.

Some of the structural implications in the above work are also of considerable interest. As strontium replaced calcium in the orthorhombic aragonite structure, x-ray diffraction patterns showed a linear increase of unit-cell dimensions with strontium content. This would seem to indicate that the microcomponent ions are distributed homogeneously within the host lattice. The variation of the $a_0$ dimension of the unit cell with strontium content is shown in Fig. 3-11.

There seem to have been no investigations on model coprecipitation systems directed toward physiological problems as yet, and conse-

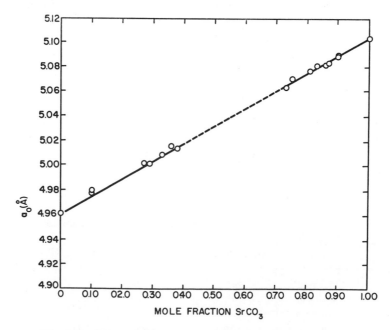

Fig. 3-11. The variation of the $a_0$ dimension of the unit cell of $(Ca,Sr)CO_3$ as a function of the mole fraction of $SrCO_3$.

quently many important features are unresolved. However, some structural investigations of the replacement of various ions in the bone mineral structure have been undertaken. One interesting study by Posner and co-workers (48) has involved the replacement of $OH^-$ ions by $F^-$ ions in the bone mineral $[Ca_5(OH)(PO_4)_3]_2$. Normally, bone mineral (hydroxyapatite) crystals are very small and are consequently subject to rapid exchange processes with the bathing serum. In some diseased conditions (i.e., Paget's disease) rapid growth and resorption occur simultaneously. Posner's group has shown that introduction of fluoride ions into the hydroxyapatite lattice has the effect of increasing the unit-cell size crystallinity and the size of individual crystallites and reducing the solubility. Posner has suggested that such modifications are useful in the treatment of Paget's disease, and, of course, their beneficial effect on tooth preservation (the mineral component in teeth is also hydroxyapatite) is well known.

## References

1. V. Chlopin, *Chem. Ber.*, **64**, 2655 (1931).
2. L. Henderson and F. Kracek, *J. Am. Chem. Soc.*, **49**, 738 (1927).
3. F. Vaslow and G. E. Boyd, *J. Am. Chem. Soc.*, **74**, 4691 (1952).
4. A. Polessitsky, *Acta Physicochim. USSR*, **8**, 864 (1938).
5. A. Polessitsky and A. Karataewa, *Acta Physicochim. USSR*, **8**, 259 (1938).
6. O. Hahn, *Applied Radiochemistry*, Cornell Univ. Press, Ithaca, N.Y., 1933.
7. C. Chang, Ph.D. thesis, University of Minnesota, 1958.
8. I. M. Kolthoff and G. E. Noponen, *J. Am. Chem. Soc.*, **60**, 197 (1938).
9. A. W. Tobolsky, *J. Chem. Phys.*, **10**, 187 (1942).
10. W. E. Wallace, *J. Chem. Phys.*, **17**, 1095 (1949).
11. G. S. Durham and J. A. Hawkins, *J. Chem. Phys.*, **19**, 149 (1957).
12. W. Hume-Rothery, G. W. Mabbott, and K. M. Channel-Evans, *Phil. Trans. Roy. Soc. London*, **233**, 1 (1934).
13. A. P. Ratner and L. L. Makavov, *Radiokhimiya*, **4**, 13 (1962).
14. H. Kading, *Z. Physik. Chem.*, **A162**, 174 (1932).
15. M. S. Murkulova, *Zh. Neorgan. Khim.*, **3**, 25 (1958).
16. I. V. Melikhov, M. S. Merkulova, and G. Eval'd, *Radiokhimiya*, **1**, 3 (1959).
17. O. Hahn, *Naturwissenschaften*, **14**, 1196 (1926).
18. S. Fujiwara, *Anal. Chem.*, **36**, 2259 (1964).
19. V. I. Grebeinshchikova and R. V. Bryzgalova, *Radiokhimiya*, **2**, 152 (1963).
20. V. I. Grebeinshchikova and R. V. Bryzgalova, *Radiokhimiya*, **2**, 159 (1960).
21. B. C. Purkayastha and S. N. Bhattacharryya, *J. Inorg. Nucl. Chem.*, **10**, 103 (1959).

22. G. I. Gorshtein and I. A. Kafavova, *Zh. Prikl. Khim.*, **35**, 1934 (1962).
23. V. Chlopin and A. Polessitsky, *Z. Physik. Chem.*, **A145**, 67 (1929).
24. C. Wagner, *J. Chem. Phys.*, **18**, 62 (1950).
25. M. Kahn, *Radioactivity Applied to Chemistry*, A. C. Wahl and N. A. Bonner, Eds., Wiley, New York, 1951, p. 393.
26. A. Polessitsky, *Z. Physik. Chem.*, **A161**, 325 (1932).
27. H. A. Doerner and W. M. Hoskins, *J. Am. Chem. Soc.*, **47**, 662 (1925).
28. Z. Walter and H. Schlundt, *J. Am. Chem. Soc.*, **50**, 3266 (1928).
28a. L. Gordon and K. Rowley, *Anal. Chem.*, **29**, 34 (1957).
28b. A. M. Feibush, K. Rowley, and L. Gordon, *Anal. Chem.*, **30**, 1605 (1958).
28c. J. A. Hermann, Ph.D. thesis, University of New Mexico, 1955.
28d. M. L. Salutsky and J. G. Stites, *U.S. At. Energy Comm. Rept MLM 723* (1957).
28e. L. Gordon, C. C. Reimer, and B. P. Burtt, *Anal. Chem.*, **26**, 842 (1954).
28f. K. J. Shaver, *Anal. Chem.*, **28**, 2015 (1956).
29. R. Mumbrauer, *Z. Physik. Chem.*, **A156**, 133 (1931).
30. M. L. Salutsky, J. G. Stites, and A. W. Martin, *Anal. Chem.*, **25**, 1677 (1953).
31. L. Gordon, M. L. Salutsky, and H. H. Willard, *Precipitation from Homogeneous Solution*, Wiley, New York, 1959, Chap. 8.   Review.
32. L. Gordon, *Record. Chem. Prog. Kresge-Hooker Sci. Lib.*, **17**, 125 (1956).
33. H. Jucker and W. D. Treadwell, *Helv. Chim. Acta*, **37**, 2002 (1954).
34. J. A. Hermann, Ph.D. thesis, University of New Mexico, 1953; J. A. Hermann and J. F. Suttle, in *Treatise on Analytical Chemistry, Part 1*, Vol. 3, I. M. Kolthoff and P. J. Elving, Eds., Interscience, New York, 1961, Chap. 32.   Review.
35. J. Block and L. Gordon, *Talanta*, **10**, 351 (1963).
36. D. H. Klein and B. Fontal, *Talanta*, **12**, 35 (1965).
37. J. A. Burton, R. C. Prim, and W. P. Slichter, *J. Chem. Phys.*, **21**, 1987 (1953).
38. H. E. Bridgers and E. D. Kolb, *J. Chem. Phys.*, **25**, 648 (1956).
39. I. V. Melikhov and M. S. Merkulova, *Radiokhimiya*, **1**, 626 (1959).
40. I. V. Melikhov, *Radiokhimiya*, **2**, 509 (1960).
41. F. Paneth, *Radioelements as Indicators*, McGraw-Hill, New York, 1928.
42. I. M. Kolthoff and W. MacNevin, *J. Am. Chem. Soc.*, **58**, 725 (1936).
43. See review by M. Kahn, ref. 25, pp. 124–126.
44. D. Tesla-Tokmanovski, M. J. Herak, V. Pravdić, and M. Mirnik, *Croat. Chem. Acta*, **37**, 79 (1965).
45. G. Walton and G. H. Walden, *J. Am. Chem. Soc.*, **68**, 1750 (1946).
46. G. Walton and G. H. Walden, *J. Am. Chem. Soc.*, **68**, 1742 (1946).
47. H. D. Holland, M. Borosik, J. Munoz, and U. M. Oxburgh, *Geochim. Cosmochim. Acta*, **28**, 1287 (1963); *At. Energy Comm. Res. Develop. Rept. Princeton University* 2 and 3 (1962–3).
48. A. S. Posner, E. D. Eanes, R. A. Harper, and I. Zipkin, *Arch. Oral Biol.*, **3**, 549 (1963); E. D. Eanes, I. Zipkin, R. A. Harper, and A. S. Posner, *Arch. Oral Biol.*, **10**, 161 (1956).

# CHAPTER 4

# SURFACE PROPERTIES

## 1. Energetics of Interfaces

In Chapter 1 the interfacial energy of the crystal–solution boundary was seen to be an important parameter in the classical description of precipitate nucleation. It turns out that the crystal surface or interfacial energies are fundamental to any discussion of the shape or surface properties of crystals precipitated from solution. On a simple basis, adsorption of impurities or surface-active agents onto the precipitate surface will occur if the interfacial energy, and hence the energy of the system, is lowered in the process. The driving force to such a change is therefore the change in interfacial energy and in general, high surface-energy materials adsorb surfactants more strongly than do low surface-energy substrates.

These parameters are related formally by the Gibbs adsorption equation

$$- d\sigma = RT\Gamma d \ln c \qquad (4\text{-}1)$$

where $d\sigma$ is the change of surface energy brought about by adsorbing $\Gamma$ moles/cm$^2$ of surfactant from an external concentration $c$.

A simple picture of the relationship between interfacial forces may be obtained by considering the thermodynamics of the systems shown in Figs. 4-1$a$ and $b$. In Fig. 4-1$a$, a solid and liquid, each of surface area $A_r$, are in equilibrium with vapor from the liquid. In placing the solid in the liquid a change in energy of the system

$$\Delta E = A_r(\sigma_{\mathrm{SL}} - \sigma_{\mathrm{LV}} - \sigma_{\mathrm{SV}}) + U_{12} \qquad (4\text{-}2)$$

is achieved where $\sigma_{\mathrm{SL}}$, $\sigma_{\mathrm{LV}}$, and $\sigma_{\mathrm{SV}}$ are the interfacial and surface energies of the solid–liquid interface, liquid surface, and solid surface, respectively; $U_{12}$ is the total interaction between solid and liquid which might, for example, include hydrogen bonding or polar interactions. (In practice additional energetic terms arise from distortion of molecular arrangement at the interface. For most of the following discussion this effect will be omitted.)

113

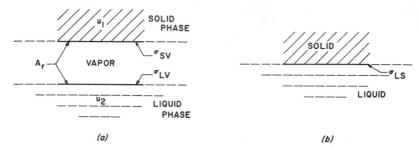

Fig. 4-1. Schematic diagrams of the formation of a liquid–solid interface.

For a reversible system in which the solid is in equilibrium with the surroundings, $\Delta E = 0$. Hence

$$\sigma_{SL} = \sigma_{LV} + \sigma_{SV} - U_{12}/A_r \tag{4-3}$$

It can be seen from this relationship that strong interfacial forces of the type described above tend to lower the interfacial energy. If we wished to evaluate interfacial energies, it seems feasible that they could be calculated if the liquid and solid surface energies were known and if the nature and extent of the interaction between the two phases could be estimated. The first of these parameters, the surface energy of the liquid phase (equal to the surface tension), is generally known. The second and third parameters are not so easily obtained, but recent advances have partially resolved the problem.

## 2. The Surface Energy of Solids

The surface energy, or energy required to form unit surface area, of a solid is a parameter which is not easily obtained by either experimental or theoretical methods. Experiments measuring the energy required to cleave, drill, or crush solids were generally unsuccessful until the last decade when elaborate experimental methods finally made the accurate evaluation of crystalline surface energies possible by measurement of the force required to extend cracks in crystals (1,2). The data, which apply to the formation of crystal surfaces *in vacuo* (or, strictly speaking, to the formation of surfaces in the presence of the vapor from the crystal), are still very sparse and, consequently, some effort has been directed toward the theoretical evaluation of surface energies.

If in Figs. 4-1a and 4-1b two identical pieces of crystal had been used instead of a solid and liquid, the crystal surface energy (energy required to form unit surface area) might have been represented by

$$\sigma_\mathrm{S} = U_{12}/A_r \qquad (4\text{-}4)$$

Thus, as a first approximation it is possible to calculate surface energies if the internal interactions in the solid can be estimated. Stranski, who first used and extended the above type of approach (3), has pointed out that for real crystals with discrete surfaces, edges and corners are formed which modify the energetic requirements. These features, however, are important only for very small crystals or crystals with large numbers of surface faults, cracks, steps, etc. By confining our attention, then, to relatively large, well-formed crystals, it is possible, knowing the molecular or ionic distribution, to calculate surface energies by the summation of molecular or ionic interactions. In practice, these calculations are not particularly accurate because of the fact that interaction potentials are not known with sufficient accuracy. In addition, the theoretical exposition applies (or has done so far) to the rather artificial condition of producing surfaces in a complete vacuum.

## A. IONIC SURFACES

When ionic lattice energies are calculated theoretically, an estimate to within about 10% of the experimental value may be achieved by summing the electrostatic forces alone. Further refinement including Born repulsive forces brings the agreement to within about 2% and inclusion of dipolar, quadrupolar, and zero point energies usually brings the theoretical result into close alignment with experiment. In ionic surfaces the same interacting forces are at play, but the relative importance is much changed (see Table 4-1). In some cases the Born repulsive forces outweigh the electrostatic interactions and it is the other components which control the magnitude of the surface energy. Since an accurate evaluation of the latter parameters is not attainable at present, only approximate results can be obtained. An example of the foregoing difficulties has been the attempted calculation of the surface energy of magnesium oxide; values from $-298$ to $+1362$ ergs/cm² were reported (4). Fortunately, not all materials have such an unfavorable balance of interacting forces.

Benson and co-workers (5), in fact, have performed a number of elegant calculations for the surface energy of alkali halides; the results are demonstrated in Table 4-2. It is usual in this type of calculation to assume the crystal to be at 0°K, thus minimizing the anisotropic surface vibrational energy.

In real crystals at normal temperatures there is an equilibrium established with the vapor from that crystal so that the condition of cleaving a crystal in a total vacuum could not be achieved. Also, if a crystal is split to form new surfaces, as required by the theoretical model, several changes occur which are not accounted for by the simple approach. Since the ions, atoms, or molecules in the new surface are no longer surrounded by the lattice distribution of neighboring entities, the bulk lattice parameters are no longer maintained. A relaxation process usually occurs which tends to lower the surface energy. Other processes which tend to lower the surface energy also will occur spontaneously, several of them giving rise to fundamental effects routinely observed in surface chemistry. Some of these effects are particularly pertinent to a discussion of precipitate surfaces.

In ionic surfaces there are two important ways that the ions can rearrange which lead to a decrease in surface energy. These are polarization effects, caused by electronic rearrangements, and anion or cation displacement. Both processes lead to a charged surface and are consequently of importance in colloid chemistry. Figure 4-2 shows the sequence of rearrangements leading to lower surface

TABLE 4-1

Calculated Relative Contributions of Ionic Interactions to the Crystal Lattice and Surface (100) Energies[a]

|  | $E_s$, % | Repulsive, % | Dipole–dipole, % | Dipole–quadrupole, % | Zero point, % |
|---|---|---|---|---|---|
| NaCl (lattice $E$) | 110.8 | −12.7 | +2.8 | 0.05 | −0.9 |
| (surface $E$) | 183.8 | −130.5 | +42.3 | 4.4 | — |
| KCl  (lattice $E$) | 109.4 | −12.8 | +4.2 | 0.05 | −0.9 |
| (surface $E$) | 153.6 | −100.8 | +42.8 | 4.4 | — |

[a] The second-order lattice interactions play a major part in determining the surface energy.

TABLE 4-2

Calculated Contributions of the Different Forces to the Surface Energy
(0°K) of a (100) Face for Nearest Neighbor Spacing $a_{min}$
(all energies in ergs/cm$^2$) (5)

| | $a_{min}$, Å | Electro-static | Dipole–dipole | Dipole–quadrupole | Repulsive | $\sigma$ |
|---|---|---|---|---|---|---|
| LiF | 1.981 | 954.8 | 131.4 | 16.1 | −933.7 | 169 |
| LiCl | 2.532 | 457.3 | 124.2 | 15.4 | −387.9 | 209 |
| LiBr | 2.718 | 369.7 | 115.5 | 14.1 | −302.0 | 197 |
| LiI | 2.986 | 278.8 | 109.2 | 13.5 | −221.0 | 181 |
| NaF | 2.290 | 618.1 | 82.7 | 8.8 | −500.3 | 209 |
| NaCl | 2.780 | 345.5 | 79.5 | 8.6 | −245.3 | 188 |
| NaBr | 2.948 | 289.7 | 77.8 | 8.3 | −199.4 | 177 |
| NaI | 3.194 | 227.8 | 76.2 | 8.4 | −151.9 | 161 |
| KF | 2.655 | 396.6 | 84.1 | 8.3 | −294.2 | 195 |
| KCl | 3.095 | 250.4 | 69.8 | 7.2 | −164.3 | 163 |
| KBr | 3.252 | 215.8 | 65.0 | 6.6 | −136.2 | 151 |
| KI | 3.482 | 175.8 | 60.6 | 6.3 | −106.3 | 135 |
| RbF | 2.818 | 331.7 | 87.5 | 9.1 | −241.9 | 186 |
| RbCl | 3.237 | 218.8 | 72.1 | 7.6 | −143.2 | 155 |
| RbBr | 3.390 | 190.5 | 66.2 | 6.8 | −119.9 | 144 |
| RbI | 3.615 | 157.1 | 60.8 | 6.3 | −94.5 | 130 |
| CsF | 2.964 | 285.1 | 109.8 | 12.0 | −216.5 | 190 |

energy and the charged surface. At one time it was thought that the accumulation of charge could be great enough to make the net surface energy zero. Such a premise led Knapp (6) to formulate a stability theory of colloidal particles which implied that minute crystallites could be completely stabilized by diminution of interfacial energy by electrical charge. Unfortunately, although this theory is not correct, it is still used occasionally to explain the limiting size of some very small crystals produced in aqueous systems. As yet, the rearrangement of ions in surfaces has not been thoroughly explored theoretically, but it seems reasonable that with the advent of high-speed computers progress will be made in this area. The best estimates so far for the reduction in surface energy by ionic rearrangement are of the order of 20% (7). Changes due to polarization apparently vary considerably, being fairly small for most alkali halide crystals and much larger for polarizable materials such as $TiO_2$.

In order to calculate surface energies it is necessary, then, to have fairly detailed knowledge of the interaction potential between ions within the bulk crystal and also to know something of the special conditions which arise at surfaces because of the deficiency of nearest-neighbor ions.

Most calculated values available in the literature pertain to NaCl-type structures, but Benson and co-workers (8) have extended such calculations to some fluorite structures; the results are given in Table 4-3. Recently, a method developed by Walton and co-workers (9,10) has enabled approximate surface energies to be calculated for noncubic crystals. This method involves a comparison of the summed interaction potentials between ions in a small crystal with the interaction potentials of the same crystal buried in an infinite three-dimensional array. Some results for orthorhombic sulfates are given in Table 4-4.

TABLE 4-3

Surface Energies ($0°K$) of Some Fluorite Type Crystals[a] (ergs/cm²) (8)

|  |  | Electrostatic | Repulsive | Other | Total |
|---|---|---|---|---|---|
| $CaF_2$ | (110) | 1737.3 | −884.1 | 228.3 | 1081.5 |
|  | (111) | 1097.5 | −760.4 | 205.5 | 542.7 |
| $SrF_2$ | (110) | 1455.4 | −785.3 | 207.9 | 878.0 |
|  | (111) | 919.7 | −667.1 | 184.5 | 437.0 |
| $BaF_2$ | (110) | 1190.2 | −632.6 | 195.4 | 753.0 |
|  | (111) | 752.3 | −530.4 | 171.3 | 393.2 |

[a]Surface energies were not corrected for surface relaxation.

TABLE 4-4

Calculated Surface Energies for Some Orthorhombic Sulfates[a] (ergs/cm²)

|  | Electrostatic | Repulsive | Other | Total |
|---|---|---|---|---|
| $BaSO_4$ | 1162 | −420 | 252 | 994 |
| $SrSO_4$ | 1286 | −442 | 266 | 1110 |
| $PbSO_4$ | 1338 | −582 | 226 | 1062 |
| $CaSO_4$ | 734 | −356 | 196 | 574 |

[a] Surface energies at 25°C may be estimated semiempirically by allowing for a 20% reduction in surface energy due to surface relaxation and a further 20% for the temperature difference. Thus, *ab initio* calculations for the surface free energy of these four materials at 25°C give (approximately) $BaSO_4$, 640 ergs/cm²; $SrSO_4$, 710 ergs/cm²; $PbSO_4$, 680 ergs/cm²; and $CaSO_4$, 370 ergs/cm².

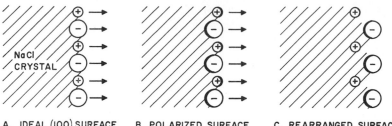

A. IDEAL (100) SURFACE     B. POLARIZED SURFACE     C. REARRANGED SURFACE

Fig. 4-2. Schematic representation of surface relaxation leading to a polarized surface. The creation of the electrical double layer at the surface lowers the surface energy. (From W. A. Weyl, *Structure and Properties of Solid Surfaces*, R. Gomer and C. S. Smith, Eds., University of Chicago Press, Chicago, 1953, p. 153)

The methods of calculation involved in the preceding work are fundamental to an understanding of surface properties but are not particularly convenient to apply since they involve computer programming. Furthermore, in view of the complexities involved, the final result cannot be expected to be particularly accurate. It is, however, possible to assess the approximate surface energy of ionic crystals by semiempirical methods, which are rapid and, in many cases, at least as accurate as the more elegant mathematical approaches. First, the surface energy of a liquid is related to its surface tension $\gamma$ by

$$\gamma = \sigma - T\Delta S \qquad (4\text{-}5)$$

where $\gamma$ may be regarded as the Helmholtz free energy or work function for the system and $\Delta S$ as the entropy change in creating the surface. It is common to regard $\Delta S$ as small or zero in a liquid surface since the molecules can adjust their positions freely to relieve stresses. Thus, the surface energy and surface tension of a liquid may be taken as equal. Surface energies of solids, by analogy, are often estimated from extrapolated surface tensions of the molten salt. Comparison between some calculated surface energies for alkali halide crystals and the surface tension extrapolated to 0°K, for example, show fair agreement (Table 4-5). (The use of $\sigma$ as surface free energy in Chapter 1 implies no volume or surface entropy change in forming a new surface.)

To give some idea of the dependence of $\sigma_{SV}$, $\sigma_{SL}$, and $\sigma_{LV}$ on the actual properties of the ions, it may be stated that, in general, small

TABLE 4-5
Surface Energies at 0°K (ergs/cm²)

| Salt | NaF | NaCl | NaBr | NaI | KF | KCl | KBr | KI |
|---|---|---|---|---|---|---|---|---|
| 100 Plane (theory)[a] | 171 | 155 | 145 | 132 | 160 | 134 | 124 | 111 |
| From extrapolated surface tension | 335 | 190 | 178 | 138 | 242 | 173 | 159 | 139 |

[a] Shuttleworth's values, ref. 7.

highly charged ions interact strongly, giving rise to a large vaporization energy in the liquid state and also a high surface tension. In the solid state such ions will give rise to a large sublimation energy and a high surface energy; correspondingly, there will be a high fusion energy and melt–solid interfacial energy. In view of these relations, it is not surprising that the surface tension of molten salts has been found to be a function of the lattice energy and the molecular volume of those salts. This relation is shown in Figs. 4-3 and 4-4.

It should now be evident that the surface energy of a crystal face is a function of the packing and arrangement of ions in that surface.

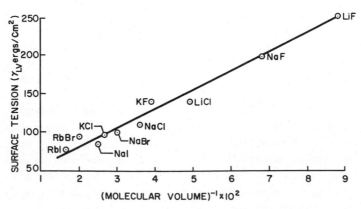

Fig. 4-3. The surface tension of molten alkali halides at the melting point is shown as an inverse function of the molecular volume.

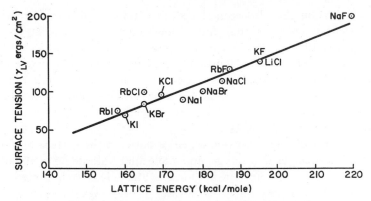

Fig. 4-4. The surface tension of molten alkali halides at the melting point as a function of crystal lattice energy.

For example, the (110) and (111) planes of fluorite-type crystals are of considerably different surface energies (Table 4-3), as are those of (100) and (110) planes of alkali halide crystals (Table 4-6). Such a result leads us to an important practical consideration in the morphological properties of precipitates. Under conditions of precipitate growth close to thermodynamic equilibrium, small precipitate particles take on a compact shape of minimum surface energy, i.e., the low-energy planes are predominant. Hence, the precipitation of sodium chloride at low degrees of supersaturation produces cubic crystals, the low-energy (100) planes being exposed. In many cases the low-energy planes correspond to the atomic arrangement of the faces of the unit cell and, consequently, the shape of the grown crystal often reflects the unit-cell structure.

The relationship between the average overall surface energy $\bar{\sigma}_\infty$ of an orthorhombic crystal and that of the individual faces is given by

$$\sigma_a = \frac{1}{3}\bar{\sigma}_\infty[1 + (a/b) + (a/c)]$$

$$\sigma_b = \frac{1}{3}\bar{\sigma}_\infty[1 + (b/a) + (b/c)]$$

(4-6)

$$\sigma_c = \frac{1}{3}\bar{\sigma}_\infty[1 + (c/a) + (c/b)]$$

where $a$, $b$, and $c$ are the unit-cell dimensions.

A comparison then between the surface tension of a molten salt and the surface energy of that salt assumes a definite relation between the configuration of the ions in the solid and molten state. It is usually assumed that the molten-salt surface tension corresponds most closely to the surface energy of the low-energy planes and, in the case of the alkali halide, this relation seems to be supported to some degree by the fair agreement between calculation and experiment, as demonstrated in Table 4-5.

The empirically deduced relationships between the surface tension of a melt and the lattice energy and molecular volume have already been demonstrated. Since in the model (Fig. 4-1), which is used for the description of interfacial or surface energy, the production of crystal surface requires the breaking of interatomic "bonds," the strength of which is related to the lattice energy, the surface energy might also be expressed in terms of the lattice energy. Indeed, such a relation has been proposed recently (11):

$$\bar{\sigma}_{hkl} = \frac{U_T}{6F_{hkl}mN_0\bar{x}^2} \tag{4-7}$$

where $U_T$ is the lattice energy at temperature $T$, $\bar{x}$ is the mean ionic radius, $F_{hkl}$ is a structur factor, and $mN_0$ is the number of ions in one mole of solid. The numerical value of $F_{hkl}$ depends upon the crystal face and atomic arrangement under consideration, but for alkali halide crystals $F_{100}$ is approximately 9 at 25°C and $F_{111} = 3$. Equation 4-7 is, of course, an approximation which does not hold for

TABLE 4-6

Comparison of the Calculated Surface Energies for (100) and
(110) Surfaces of Alkali Halide Crystals (ergs/cm²) (5)

| Salt | (100) | (110) | Salt | (100) | (110) |
|------|-------|-------|------|-------|-------|
| LiF  | 169   | 832   | LiCl | 209   | 558   |
| NaF  | 209   | 640   | NaCl | 188   | 445   |
| KF   | 195   | 483   | KCl  | 163   | 352   |
| RbF  | 186   | 433   | RbCl | 155   | 323   |
| CsF  | 190   | 406   | CsCl | —     | 244   |
| LiBr | 197   | 486   | LiI  | 181   | 405   |
| NaBr | 177   | 396   | NaI  | 161   | 338   |
| KBr  | 151   | 317   | KI   | 136   | 274   |
| RbBr | 144   | 291   | RbI  | 130   | 254   |
| CsBr | —     | 225   | CsI  | —     | 202   |

crystals where there is a considerable covalent content or a large degree of surface polarization. However, the simplicity of such a relation is an obvious advantage when a rapid estimate of surface energy is required. Table 4-7 contains surface energy data assessed from Eq. 4-7 and from extrapolation of the surface tension of the melt. In most cases the values are comparable and, conceding the difficulty of exact calculations, quite acceptable.

TABLE 4-7
Approximate Values for the Surface Energy of Ionic Crystals

| Material | Lattice energy, kcal/mole | Approximate surface energy, (ergs/cm²)[a] | Surface tension extrapolated to 25°C |
|---|---|---|---|
| NaCl | 183 | 169 | 169 |
| KCl | 164 | 108 | 142 |
| LiCl | 198 | 193 | 178 |
| LiF | 240 | 336 | 345 |
| AgCl | 206 | 172 | 170 |
| AgBr | 202 | 156 | 161 |
| AgI | 199 | 121 | — |
| MgO | 939 | 1357 | — |
| Mg(OH)$_2$ | 680 | 513 | — |
| Ca(OH)$_2$ | 617 | 393 | — |
| Sr(OH)$_2$ | 577 | 229 | — |
| TlI | 159 | 117 | — |
| CaF$_2$ | 617 | 463 | — |
| CuCl | 216 | 170 | — |
| CaCO$_3$ | 714 | 469 | — |
| MgCO$_3$ | 760 | 605 | — |
| ZnS | 852 | 750 | — |

[a] Calculated from Eq. 4-6 with $F_{hkl} = 9.0$. The use of such a factor has not been verified for nonalkali halide crystals, but seems to give reasonable values in many cases. The quoted surface energy will be that of the lowest energy surface.

It is apparent, then, that the surface energy of a crystal may be regarded as being composed of various interaction components which, for ionic crystals, arise from electrostatic ($^i\sigma_{SV}$) and dispersive ($^d\sigma_{SV}$) forces. Thus

$$\sigma_{SV} = {}^i\sigma_{SV} + {}^d\sigma_{SV} \qquad (4\text{-}8)$$

This separation of interaction terms becomes particularly important when the solid–liquid interface is considered in more detail.

## B. Organic Crystals

The principles involved in calculating the surface energy of organic crystals are much the same as those involved with ionic crystals, except that the interaction forces are predominantly short range. In consequence, it is often quite simple to obtain approximate surface energy values by evaluating nearest-neighbor interactions. Although lattice energies are generally not established for organic materials, the sublimation energy is a convenient parameter which establishes the strength of molecular interactions. A very simple example of the foregoing is the calculation of the surface energy for a material of simple cubic structure, as demonstrated in Fig. 4-5. If the crystal is cleaved to form two surfaces, one molecular "bond" is cleaved for each surface molecule. The surface energy is hence $\epsilon_B/2$ (two new surfaces are formed) per molecule or $\epsilon_B/2a^2$ per unit area where $a$ is the effective molecular diameter.

The sublimation energy per mole of solid $\epsilon_S$ may be considered, for nearest-neighbor interactions, to be composed of $6N_0/2$ bonds (6 neighbors, $N_0$ = Avogadro's number, each bond counted twice); i.e., $\epsilon_S \sim (6N_0\epsilon_B/2)$. Hence

$$\sigma_{SV} = \frac{\epsilon_B}{2a^2} = \frac{\epsilon_S}{6N_0a^2} \tag{4-9}$$

Several more refined approaches (7,12) have been published and the results are generally close to the values predicted from the surface tension of the molten material.

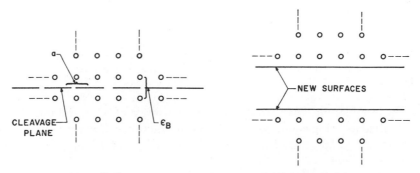

Fig. 4-5. Schematic diagram of crystal cleavage in terms of intermolecular forces. In the fresh surfaces each atom or molecule has fewer nearest neighbors and the change in molecular environment is invested as surface energy.

The result of the calculations is that the $\sigma_{SV}$ term in Eq. 4-3 can, in many cases, be estimated, provided the presence of foreign vapor does not modify the surface energetics.

## 3. Liquid–Solid Interactions

The remaining term in Eq. 4-3, i.e., $U_{12}$, the solid–liquid interaction, is now the missing link in the evaluation of solid–liquid interfacial energies.

When a solid is immersed in liquid, the liquid molecules are adsorbed at the interface and often attain a definite orientation with respect to the solid. The overall energy change is given by

$$\Delta E = \sigma_{SV} - \sigma_{SL} \sim -\Delta H_{imm} \qquad (4\text{-}10)$$

(volume changes in the system are negligible), where $\Delta H_{imm}$ is the heat of immersion. The measured heat evolved in the process of immersing solids in liquids is related to the free energy of immersion via the entropy change, $\Delta S$, of surface adsorbed molecules by

$$\Delta G_{imm} = \Delta H_{imm} - T\Delta S \qquad (4\text{-}11)$$

For noninteracting liquid molecules $\Delta S \rightarrow 0$ and some estimate of the interfacial energy and free energy may be made from the heat or enthalpy of immersion and solid-surface energies where available. (Surface energy and free energy are equal at $T = 0°K$.) Some heats of immersion are listed in Table 4-8. However, this method of arriving at interfacial energies is not particularly useful since it involves a difference between two quantities ($\sigma_{SV}$ and $\Delta H_{imm}$), neither of which is known with any precision.

A different line of approach, proposed recently by Fowkes (13–16), has proven somewhat more profitable for certain types of solid–liquid interactions. He has proposed that, of the individual components leading to the surface energy of the solid and surface tension of a liquid, some interact and some do not. An example would be the interface between a metal and water. The surface energy of the metal $\sigma_{SV}$ has components due to electronic interactions forming metal "bonds" and the normal dispersive forces; thus

$$\sigma_{SV} = {}^{m}\sigma_{SV} + {}^{d}\sigma_{SV} \qquad (4\text{-}12)$$

Similarly, water may be considered to have two components to its

TABLE 4-8

Heats of Immersion (ergs/cm$^2$) for Inorganic Solids in Various Liquids[a,b]

| Liquid | Solid | | | | | | | |
|---|---|---|---|---|---|---|---|---|
| | BaSO$_4$ | SrSO$_4$ | PbSO$_4$ | TiO$_2$ | SiO$_2$ | ZrO$_2$ | SnO$_2$ | CaCO$_3$ |
| Water | 490 | 315 (45) | 490 (45) | 520 | 600 | 600 | 680 | 762 (46) |
| Methanol | 338 (44) | 200 (45) | 320 (45) | 500 | | | | |
| Ethanol | 335 (44) | | | | 520 | | | |
| Propanol | 335 (44) | | | | | | | |
| n-Butanol | 330 (44) | | | 350 | 420 | | | |
| Hexanol | 340 (44) | | | | | | 500 | |
| Octanol | 330 (44) | 215 (45) | 310 (45) | | | | | |
| Ethyl acetate | 370 | | | 360 | 460 | | | |
| Nitrobenzene | 399 (24) | | | 280 | | 310 | 530 | |
| Chlorobenzene | 347 (24) | | | | | | | |
| Phenol | 364 (24) | | | | | | | CaSO$_4$ |
| Carbon tetrachloride | 220 | | | 240 | | | 320 | 156 (50) |
| n-Pentane | 110–120 (47) | | | 135 (49) | | | | |
| n-Hexane | | | | | | | | |
| Benzene | 139 (24) | | | 150 | 150 | | 220 | |
| Isooctane | | | | 100 | | | 120 | |

[a] Reference numbers in parentheses.
[b] All other data from ref. 48.

surface energy due to dispersive forces and hydrogen bonding; thus

$$\sigma_{LV} = {}^h\sigma_{LV} + {}^d\sigma_{LV} \qquad (4\text{-}13)$$

Of these forces, it is very unlikely that the metallic bonds interact with water molecules or that the water molecules form hydrogen bonds with the metal. Consequently, only dispersive forces interact. Fowkes proposes that the interfacial energy between the metal and water is given, therefore, by

$$\sigma_{SL} = \sigma_{SV} + \sigma_{LV} - 2({}^d\sigma_{SV}{}^d\sigma_{LV})^{1/2} \qquad (4\text{-}14)$$

This equation is analogous to Eq. 4-3; solid–liquid interaction is represented by the last term on the right of both equations.

Equation 4-14 may readily be tested for the interfacial energy between two immiscible liquids (1) and (2) by modification to

$$\sigma_{12} = \sigma_1 + \sigma_2 - 2({}^d\sigma_1{}^d\sigma_2)^{1/2} \qquad (4\text{-}15)$$

In many cases the total surface energy of a liquid is composed only of dispersive forces, i.e., $\sigma_{LV} = {}^d\sigma_{LV}$ (e.g., hydrocarbons) and, since the interfacial energy or tension between two liquids is measurable, Eq. 4-15 may be validated. Hence, by a stepwise process of choosing one liquid in which only dispersive forces are acting and another in which other (e.g., hydrogen bonding) forces are operative, a table of molecular interaction components may be constructed. For example, the contributions to the surface energy of water (72.8 ergs/cm² at 20°C) are found to be 51.0 ergs/cm² due to hydrogen bonding ($^h\sigma_{LV}$) and 21.8 ± 0.7 ergs/cm² due to dispersive forces. The approach may be extended to the mercury–water interface (Fig. 4-6), which is also amenable to direct experimental investigation; the interfacial energy by calculation is 424.8 ergs/cm² compared with experimental values of 426.2 and 427 ergs/cm². In view of this agreement it is valuable to attempt an extension of the same type of consideration to the more general case applying to the precipitate–solution interface. In this case the polar surface energy of an ionic crystal is represented by Eq. 4-8, i.e.,

$$\sigma_{SV} = {}^i\sigma_{SV} + {}^d\sigma_{SV} \qquad (4\text{-}8)$$

For nonionic crystals $^i\sigma_{SV} = 0$, but a hydrogen bonding component may be present.

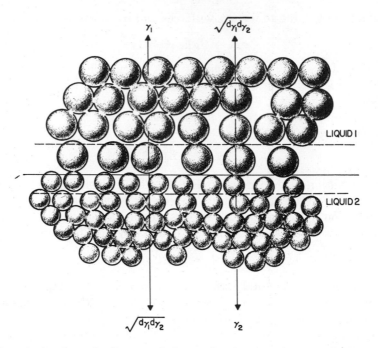

Fig. 4-6. A schematic diagram of the tension forces acting at a liquid–liquid interface. The surface tension component in one liquid is balanced by the dispersive interactions between the two liquids. (After Fowkes, ref. 13)

For the interface between an ionic precipitate and water, the interaction will involve dispersive forces and a polar interaction which is enhanced by an induced dipole in the water molecules. Hydrogen bonding is also possible if the precipitate contains suitable atoms. In the absence of hydrogen bonding the crystal–solution interfacial energy is given by

$$\sigma_{\text{SL}} = \sigma_{\text{SV}} + \sigma_{\text{LV}} - 2[(^d\sigma_{\text{SV}}{}^d\sigma_{\text{LV}})^{1/2} + U^p] \qquad (4\text{-}16)$$

where $U^p$ is the polar interaction term.

Equation 4-16 would then give the interfacial energy of a precipitate–liquid interface if all the components could be evaluated.

## 4. Evaluation of Interfacial Energies

Although Eq. 4-16 represents a modification of Eq. 4-3, which is particularly useful for assessing the interfacial energy of the interface between molecular crystals and solution ($U^p = 0$), it still suffers from the disadvantage of including the $\sigma_{SV}$ term which, as we have seen, is not amenable to accurate calculation. Fowkes has devised an ingenious method for circumnavigating this difficulty, which follows.

If another equation can be found relating the energetics of the various interfaces—liquid/solid, liquid/vapor, and solid/vapor—the solid/vapor term $\sigma_{SV}$ might be eliminated from Eqs. 4-14 and 4-16. One such equation, generally referred to as Young's equation, relates the contact angle $\theta$ of a drop resting on a plane surface to the surface tension of the liquid in that drop, $\gamma_{LV}$, the surface tension of the solid, $\gamma_{SV}$, and the interfacial tension, $\gamma_{SL}$, by

$$\gamma_{LV} \cos \theta = \gamma_{SV} - \pi_e - \gamma_{LS} \qquad (4\text{--}17)$$

where $\pi_e$ is the "equilibrium" film pressure.

This equation, derived on the basis of force balance as shown in Fig. 4-7, has been the subject of a great deal of controversy because of the unbalanced forces in the vertical direction. However, Zisman and co-workers (17–20) have shown that the contact angle does apparently represent a fundamental property of the solid surface, at least for low-energy organic or polymeric surfaces.

As previously stated, the surface tension and energy of a liquid may be taken to be equal whereas the anisotropic tensions in a solid surface render an inequality between the two parameters. Benson and co-workers (21), in fact, have shown that the surface tension of ionic crystals is a factor of two or so higher than the surface energy. It is not uncommon though to find solid-surface tension and surface energy used interchangeably in the literature. For present purposes, however, we shall assume a thermodynamic analog to Eq. 4-17, allowing that the contact angle is an equilibrium property (22). For rigid insoluble surfaces this assumption may have some validity. In real systems the surface can attain equilibrium by one of two methods. The surface may be sufficiently pliable to undergo distortion to achieve the equilibrium situation, as shown in the sequence of

Fig. 4-8.   For ionic crystals the same crater effect is sometimes attainable by dissolution at the center of the drop with deposition at the edge.   Such effects, for example, are observable for $PbI_2$ and TlI surfaces with water drops (Fig. 4-9 shows craters on a TlI surface).

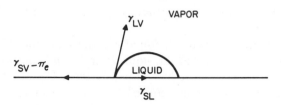

Fig. 4-7. Schematic diagram of the force balance between solid/liquid, liquid/vapor, and solid/vapor tensions achieved with a rigid substrate.

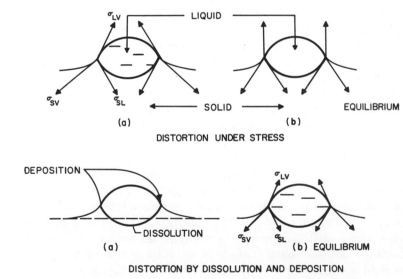

Fig. 4-8. Schematic diagrams of distortion caused under surface stress.   In the upper diagrams the substrate is deformable and assumes the equilibrium situation under the influence of surface stresses.   The lower diagrams show the result of equilibrium being attained with a rigid but sparingly soluble substrate.

Fig. 4-9. This micrograph shows the effect of dissolution and redeposition of material on a thallium iodide surface under the influence of small water drops held at equilibrium vapor pressure and then removed. The surface remodels itself to minimize the interfacial forces.

With the above reservations we will wish to use the relation

$$\sigma_{LV} \cos \theta = \sigma_{SV} - \pi_e{}' - \sigma_{LS} \qquad (4\text{-}18)$$

in conjunction with Eq. 4-14. For contact angles $\theta > 0$, $\pi_e{}'$ is usually taken to be zero, whereby a combination of Eqs. 4-14 and 4-18 gives

$$\cos \theta = -1 + 2\frac{\left(^d\sigma_{SV}\,{}^d\sigma_{LV}\right)^{1/2}}{\sigma_{LV}} \qquad (4\text{-}19)$$

If the molecules of the liquid phase are interacting with dispersive forces only (e.g., hydrocarbons), $^d\sigma_{LV} = \sigma_{LV}$ and the contact angle of such a liquid on the surface under investigation establishes $^d\sigma_{SV}$. If the liquid molecules interact with additional forces (e.g., hydrogen bonding with water or ethanol), $^d\sigma_{LV} \neq \sigma_{LV}$ and $^d\sigma_{LV}$ may be established either from tables compiled for this parameter or by measurements of the interfacial energy between the liquid and a hydrocarbon.

By this means Fowkes has established $^d\sigma_{SV}$ values for some low-energy surfaces from the data of Zisman et al. Table 4-9 contains these data. Since dispersive forces are predominant as molecular interactions in many of the materials mentioned in Table 4-9, the $^d\sigma_{SV}$ term will be close to, or identical with, the surface energy of the material. Furthermore, not only is the interfacial energy $\sigma_{SL}$ calculable for such cases from Eq. 4-14 but the free energy of immersion, which is extremely difficult to obtain by other means, also may be estimated from Eq. 4-10 via Eq. 4-14.

TABLE 4-9
The Dispersive Component of the Surface Energy for some
Organic (Polymeric) Compounds

| Solid | $^d\sigma_s$, ergs/cm$^2$ |
|---|---|
| Polyhexafluoropropylene | 18 |
| Polytetrafluoroethylene | 19.5 |
| Paraffin wax | 25.5 |
| Polymonochlorotrifluoroethylene | 30.8 |
| Polyethylene | 35 |
| Polystyrene | 44 |

In consequence, the interfacial energy of organic precipitates can be completely evaluated in terms of the above approach. As yet, there is no data available for comparison between nucleation data and values based on contact angles. Undoubtedly such a comparison will eventually be forthcoming.

## 5. Thermodynamic Determination of Dispersive Forces

For higher-energy substrates it is to be expected that a liquid will be more strongly adsorbed. Practically, the immersion of finely divided materials of this type leads to measurable heats of immersion. If the polarization forces are inactive at the interface and once again dispersive forces alone contribute to the interfacial energy, the contribution of the solid may be assessed from Eq. 4-10:

$$\Delta H_{imm} = \sigma_{SL} - \sigma_{SV} = \sigma_{LV} - 2(^d\sigma_{SV}{}^d\sigma_{LV})^{1/2} \quad (4\text{-}20)$$

Fowkes uses a more complicated expression in conjunction with surface tensions, as follows. Since

$$\Delta H_{imm} = \Delta G + T\Delta S \qquad (4\text{-}21)$$

($\Delta V$ is small or zero), then

$$\Delta H_{imm} \sim (\gamma_{SL} - \gamma_{SV}) - T\left(\frac{\partial G}{\partial T}\right) \qquad (4\text{-}22)$$

Using a modification of this equation, Fowkes has estimated dispersive contributions to solid surface tensions from heats of immersion; some values are given in Table 4-10.

TABLE 4-10

The Dispersive Component of the Surface Tension for
Some Inorganic Compounds

| Solid | $^d\gamma_s$, ergs/cm$^2$ |
| --- | --- |
| Anatase | 91 |
| Ferric oxide | 107 |
| Stannic oxide | 118 |
| Barium sulfate | 118 |
| Silica | 123 |
| Rutile | 143 |

## 6. Polar Interfacial Forces

The evaluation of the interaction between polar solvent molecules, e.g., water, and an ionic surface, e.g., barium sulfate, is of paramount importance since most of the precipitate–liquid interfaces of interest to the analytical chemist are of this type. Unfortunately, a solution to this problem is an order of magnitude more complicated than those considered previously and has not yet been resolved. A semiempirical approach may be considered by returning to Eq. 4-16. The term $U^p$ in this equation consists of two parts, the interaction due to the permanent dipole in the liquid ($\mu$), and the induced dipole forces.

Il'in (23) has found, from heats of adsorption, that the interaction between many polar liquids and ionic surfaces is given by

$$U_{LS} = \frac{\mu e^2}{r_0^2 s}$$
(4-23)

where $e$ is the charge on the ion, $r$ is the distance between dipole and surface ion, and $s$ is the area occupied by the adsorbed molecule. On substitution into Eq. 4-16 and thence into Eq. 4-21, it can be seen that the polar heat of immersion ($\Delta H_{imm}$) contains an extra term, i.e.,

$$\Delta H^p_{imm} = \Delta H_{imm} - \frac{2\mu e^2}{r_0^2 s}$$
(4-24)

Hence, the polar contribution increases the heat of immersion (becomes more negative) and polar solvents, as expected, will interact more strongly with ionic solid surfaces. The heat of immersion for a series of polar molecules of about the same size should show a linear relation with the dipole moment. Such a relation has been described by several workers, two examples being (24,25) the series PhOH, PhCl, PhNO$_2$, and C$_6$H$_6$ on barium sulfate, and a series of organic materials on rutile, as shown in Fig. 4-10.

Thus, it is possible to estimate the contribution of permanent dipolar forces to both the interfacial energy and the heat of immersion. Induced polarization effects seem to be minimal for such cases, but for the solid–water interface the heat of immersion is often much higher than can be accounted for by a dipolar interaction. Although induced polarization is a possible source for this added interfacial "bonding," it seems more likely that interphase bonding in the form of hydrogen bonds is a major source of interaction. Each individual surface will be different in its atomic arrangement and it seems virtually impossible to arrive at a general formulation. The best that can be said at present is that it is likely that, of the heat given off when materials of the barium sulfate type are immersed in water, about 20% is due to dispersive forces, 50% to polar interactions, and 30% to hydrogen bonding.

Despite the current impasse in the direct calculation of the interfacial energy for most of the precipitates which are of general interest, several important features have emerged. Since the dispersive force contribution from many different liquids is similar, the more

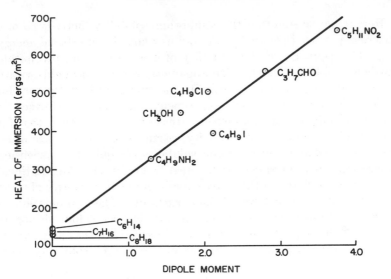

Fig. 4-10. The heat of immersion of rutile in some organic solvents is shown as a function of the (vapor phase) dipole moment. (After Chessick, Zettlemoyer, Healy, and Young, ref. 25)

polar in general will be absorbed more strongly and will have a lower interfacial energy against any specific ionic solid. Furthermore, for a series of similar solids (for example, Ba, Pb, Sr, Ca, and Mg sulfates) as the ions decrease in size, the dipolar interaction increases, as do the surface energy of the solid and the heat of immersion. In summary, the interaction between planar low-energy solid surfaces and nonpolar liquids may be adequately investigated by contact angle measurements (with reservations) and from singular immersion heats. High-energy planar polar interfaces require, for an accurate assessment, reliable immersion free-energy data, few of which are currently available in the literature.

## 7. Curved Surfaces

In Chapter 1 it was shown that the Gibbs-Kelvin equation as applied to the solubility of small crystals was a necessary assumption in the development of classical nucleation theory. Modifying Eq. 1-3 for a spherical particle

$$m \ln a/a_0 = \frac{2\sigma_{LS}v}{kTr} \qquad (4\text{-}25)$$

Here it can be seen that the equilibrium solubility (activity) $a$ of a spherical particle is related to the radius $r$ and the interfacial energy $\sigma_{LS}$.   Consequently, if the solubility of a series of small precipitate particles could be investigated, it apparently would be straightforward to calculate $\sigma_{LS}$.   Such a possibility has intrigued investigators for at least 50 years and many experiments have been performed in attempts to discern such an effect.   It is obvious, however, that for a reasonable increment in solubility, particles of a 100 Å size order should be used and, since a unique solubility is required, a suspension of particles, all of the same radius, must be produced.   An additional criterion for performing the above experiment is the necessity of using particles with compact well-defined surfaces.   The combination of these requirements has unfortunately not yet been achieved, nor, in fact, were the requirements recognized in several of the early experiments.   Recently, with the advent of radiotracer solubility tech-

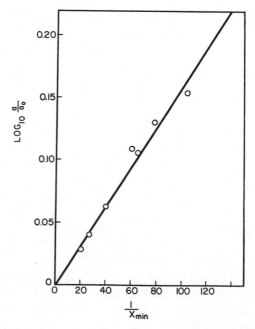

Fig. 4-11. The logarithmic supersaturation ratio is shown as a function of the inverse (minimum) particle size for strontium sulfate particles in water. [After B. V. Enüstün and J. Turkevich, *J Am. Chem. Soc.*, **82**, 4507 (1960)]

niques and electron microscopy for investigating particle morphology, it has proven possible to control several of the undesirable features present in the older work. Slight variations from monodisperse particle sizes have been treated in terms of distribution functions, and on this basis strontium sulfate particles do indeed show increased solubility with decrease in size as shown in Fig. 4-11. From this data, the $\sigma_{LS}$ for the strontium sulfate–water interface was found to be $84 \pm 8$ ergs/cm$^2$ as calculated from Eq. 4-25. This value is of the same order as the same parameter calculated from nucleation data, seemingly lending credibility to both sets of experiments.

### 8. Surface Enthalpy

Another experimental method of exploring surface energetics has been the calorimetric approach, developed by Brunauer and co-workers (26,27). They have shown that the heat of solution of silicates in a mixture of nitric and hydrofluoric acids is a function of the surface area of the particles prior to dissolution (Fig. 4-12). Since the particles completely dissolve in solution, it is evident that the excess heat given off over and above the true heat of solution is due

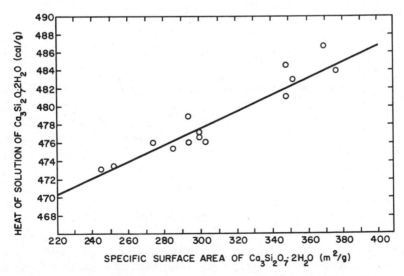

Fig. 4-12. Variation of the heat of solution of $Ca_3Si_2O_7 \cdot 2H_2O$ with specific surface area. (After Brunauer, Kantro, and Weise, ref. 27)

to the total surface enthalpy $\Delta H_s$. The values obtained for $\Delta H_s$ from experiments on a number of materials are given in Table 4-11. The total surface enthalpy may be equated with the surface energy of the crystalline material, provided the volume change accompanying dissolution is negligible. The calculated surface energy values which are available for calcium oxide and silica seem to support this assertion.

TABLE 4-11
Surface Enthalpies Calculated from Heat of Dissolution Data

| Material | Surface enthalpy, ergs/cm$^2$ | Surface energy |
|---|---|---|
| CaO | $1310 \pm 200$ | 1100–1350 |
| Ca(OH)$_2$ | $1180 \pm 100$ | 400? |
| SiO$_2$ | $259 \pm 3$ | $275 \pm 25$ |
| Si(OH)$_2$ | $129 \pm 8$ | |
| Ca$_3$Si$_2$O$_7 \cdot 2H_2O$ | $386 \pm 20$ | |

Again, lack of extensive data is apparent in this area. Extension of such an approach could provide a very useful assessment of the energetics of interfaces.

## 9. Adsorption from Solution

The principles of adsorption from solution can be concluded from the preceding discussion. Compounds which will be most strongly adsorbed from solution will undergo chemical bonding with the substrate (e.g., hydrogen bonding) and will yield a strongly diminished interfacial energy. This chemical adsorption probably occurs whenever the absorbate contains hydroxyl groups and the adsorbent electron donors, or vice versa. An interesting example of this type is the adsorption of the amino acid glycine onto hydroxylated silica.

It is believed that this step underlies the disease silicosis in the human body, since it replaces one of the biosynthetic protein-generating processes. Physical adsorption may involve either polar attraction between substrates and adsorbate or dispersive forces in the adsorbed phase. Typical of the former process is the adsorption of cyanine dyes with their resonating dipole on silver halide surfaces, an important photochemical reaction. Very few adsorption processes important in analytical chemistry seem to proceed by means of dispersive forces alone.

It has been customary to describe adsorption processes in terms of adsorption isotherms but most materials studied, e.g., carbon black, rutile, alumina, and silica, although important in industrial practice, are not particularly pertinent to a discussion of precipitate properties. Furthermore, experiments relating to adsorption from solution by such adsorbents are by now available as student exercises. One notes, however, that one of three fundamental adsorption isotherms is usually used to represent adsorption at the precipitate surface from solution.

When the heat of adsorption $\Delta H$ is independent of coverage $\theta'$, the Langmuir isotherm

$$\theta' = \frac{Ac}{1 + Ac} \tag{4-26}$$

where $c$ is the solution concentration and $A$ is a constant, should hold.

Usually the heat of adsorption is not independent of surface coverage and the most active surface sites are filled first. Under these conditions the heat of adsorption may change linearly with $\theta'$, so that

$$-\Delta H = -\Delta H_0(1 - \alpha\theta') \tag{4-27}$$

where $\Delta H_0$ is the limiting heat of adsorption.

This leads to the Temkin isotherm (28), which may be written in approximate form

$$\theta' = -\frac{RT}{\alpha\Delta H_0} \ln Bc \tag{4-28}$$

If the heat of adsorption varies exponentially with the surface coverage, then

$$\theta' = Ke^{-RT\Delta H_m} \tag{4-29}$$

where $K$ and $\Delta H_m$ are constants.

Equation 4–29 is of the same form as the Freundlich isotherm

$$x = bc^{1/n'} \tag{4-30}$$

where $b$ and $n'$ are constants.

## A. Adsorption of Ions

Many measurements of adsorption isotherms for ions on precipitate surfaces have been made. Most of the older work showed a logarithmic relationship between the concentration of potential-determining ion in solution and that adsorbed on the surface, i.e.,

$$\Gamma_{A^+} = k_1 \ln [A^+] + \text{const}_1 \tag{4-31}$$

$$\Gamma_{B^+} = k_2 \ln [B^-] + \text{const}_2 \tag{4-32}$$

Such relationships have been found to fit the data for silver ions on silver halides, lead ions on lead sulfate, lead chromate and lead halides, and, except in the presence of chloride ions, barium on barium sulfate (29,30). The anions present seem to have a strong effect upon the amount of cation adsorbed; for example, fewer silver ions are adsorbed as the anions change in the series $C_6H_5COO^-$, $NO_2^-$, $BrO_3^-$, $CH_3COO^-$, and $ClO_4^-$.

It is to be noted that equations with the forms of 4-31 and 4-32 are the Temkin isotherm type. More precise recent measurements have shown that the adsorption isotherms for ions show some deviations from Eqs. 4-31 and 4-32. Anderson and Parsons (31) have investigated the adsorption of iodide ions at a mercury–water interface by electrochemical means. The adsorption again follows the Temkin isotherm in the 10–20% coverage range, the heat of adsorption when extrapolated to zero coverage being of the order 11.5 kcal/mole. The adsorption of ions at the precipitate–solution interface is likely, therefore, to lower the interfacial energy significantly.

Although the preceding results tend to indicate that a logarithmic relation between adsorbed and free ions holds for the solid–liquid interface, the situation is by no means as simple as this. According to Lange and Berger (29) the adsorption of ions from solutions of lithium, sodium, potassium, nickel, or copper chlorides onto barium sulfate surfaces gives a direct relation between adsorbed and free ion concentrations. The logarithmic law is also refuted by some radioactive tracer studies (p. 146) which point to a linear relationship in certain concentration ranges. Therefore, there does not seem to be any unified theory applicable to ion adsorption on precipitates, though perhaps more credence should be given to isotopic investigations which relate directly to adsorbed concentrations rather than to the indirect electrochemical measurements. The derivation of the Doerner-Hoskins coprecipitation equation (Chap. 3) is based upon the assumption of a Langmuir-type ion adsorption; some approaches to precipitation kinetics have also involved a similar assumption.

It is interesting to note that, if the ion adsorption is of the Temkin form, then $k_1$ and $k_2$ in Eqs. 4-31 and 4-32 are inversely proportional to the limiting heat of adsorption. In turn, the limiting heat of adsorption should be a function of the size of the adsorbed ion; consequently, the degree of adsorption for any particular concentration should decrease with increase of ion radius for similar ions. As an example of this effect, decreasing adsorption is known to occur with increase in ion size for the sequence of transition metal ions $Co^{2+}$, $Zn^{2+}$, $Fe^{2+}$, $Mn^{2+}$, and $Cd^{2+}$ on $CaCO_3$.

## B. ADSORPTION OF MOLECULES

The principles involved in the adsorption of molecules (e.g., dyes and surfactants) at the precipitate surface are essentially the same as those for the solvent–solid interaction. Physical adsorption will be strongest for the most polar materials adsorbed on the highest energy surface. Specific effects are particularly important in controlling the morphology of precipitates; for example, crystals of sodium chloride structure possess a checkered symmetrical configuration of ions on the (100) faces but contain ions of only one sign in the (111) faces. Hence, ionic surfactants will frequently adsorb strongly on (111) alkali halide crystal faces, minimizing growth normal to these faces and completely changing the crystal habit. One notes that crystal growth always occurs in the presence of a few stray impurity molecules and that inhibition of growth generally occurs because of adsorption of such molecules. In most cases crystal growth is not completely inhibited by molecular adsorption, and the crystal continues to grow by a combination of tunneling and incorporation of the surfactant into the crystal lattice. In addition, it is rare that the molecular configuration of the surfactant is such that it can uniformly cover a surface. Consequently, there are usually active sites which continue to grow and modify the crystal. Since physical adsorption can be regarded as a dynamic situation, ions and surfactants are continually competing for surface sites and growth can generally proceed.

Nonpolar molecules might be expected to be less specific in the manner in which they adsorb. Although there is relatively little evidence on this point, the manner in which the epitaxial growth of polymer molecules ensues on ionic substrates (Chap. 2) suggests strongly that induced dipoles do occur even in the normally non-polar long-chain hydrocarbons. It would not be surprising, there-fore, if gelatin molecules adsorbed with a specific orientation on silver halide surfaces, a process generally assumed to be random. The influence of molecular adsorption on the growth habit is considered in more detail in Chapter 5.

## 10. Real Surfaces

Thus far, surfaces have been considered as planar, faultless, and discrete: that is, solution, vapor, or vacuum is on one side of the phase boundary and crystal is on the other. Whereas the formation of steps and defects in the crystal have been noted in terms of crystal growth, their presence also modifies the adsorption process. For organic crystals where nearest-neighbor interactions are the dominant forces, the adsorbed molecule is clearly held most strongly at the position where it will have most crystal molecules adjacent to it. The same can also be said of adsorbed ions. Hence, the energetics of adsorption in real systems should take into account the heterogeneity of substrates. Usually the effect is to be expected at low degrees of coverage where these surface-active sites are only partially covered.

Up to this point, the nature of the surface of a discontinuity has been ignored. The classical work of Gibbs on diffuse interfaces is well known, but the challenge of the diffuse interface in solid–liquid systems has been met in different ways. Essentially, the Gibbs concept is that the density of the system does not change abruptly across the interface but decreases more gradually through a diffuse region of thickness $\delta$. If an interface is discrete and not diffuse, it is a straightforward matter to define the "surface of tension." If the surface is allowed to deform into a diffuse interface, the thickness of the diffuse region $\delta$, according to Tolman (32), is

$$\delta = \frac{\Gamma_A}{\rho_I - \rho_{II}} \tag{4-33}$$

where $\rho_I$ and $\rho_{II}$ are the densities in the interior of phases I and II and

$\Gamma_A$ is the density referred to the "surface of tension." Some recent work by Mutaftschiev (33) has shown that the discontinuity can be regarded as being confined to a region extending one molecule to either side of the interface providing that the radius of surface curvature is large.

## 11. Rates of Adsorption and Surface Exchange

In the various models proposed for the role of precipitate surfaces in growth kinetics, coprecipitation, and adsorption, some importance has been attached to the existence of a pseudoequilibrium between ions in the surface layer and those in solution. If equilibrium at the surface is attained rapidly, then there would seem to be some justification in relating growth kinetics to such an adsorbed layer.

One convenient method of exploring surface adsorption is by use of radioactive tracer ions. Since it is convenient to deal with small concentrations of radiotracer in solution, a precipitate of moderate surface area may be expected to adsorb a significant fraction of the total trace concentration. Figure 4-13 shows the uptake of $^{212}Pb$ ions on lead chromate and lead sulfate as a function of time. It can be seen that, with lead chromate in particular, the major portion ($\sim 95\%$) of the tracer is taken up within the period before the first measurement ($<1$ min). In a very short time, then, rapid adsorption occurs on the surface or in the surface layer (provided the precipitate is fresh). Over a longer period (hours) two competing phenomena affect the uptake of radioactive tracer. First, if the absorbed ion is compatible with the substrate lattice, it will exchange with the solid, thus decreasing the activity in solution and on the surface. However, as the precipitate ages, the surface area decreases by recrystallization and the activity in solution tends to increase, as does the concentration of tracer per unit area of free surface. Some agglomeration and internal entrapment may also occur. The net rate of uptake consequently will be dependent on the total surface area of precipitate. Mirnik (34) has suggested that the uptake of radioactive ions by precipitate surfaces is entirely a function of surface remodeling. For example, TlI precipitates will not exchange to any extent with $Tl^+$ ions after extensive aging ($\sim 200$ min). Figure 4-14 shows the results of Mirnik and co-workers for the uptake of $Tl^+$ by TlI. If the precipitate surface area is initially very large,

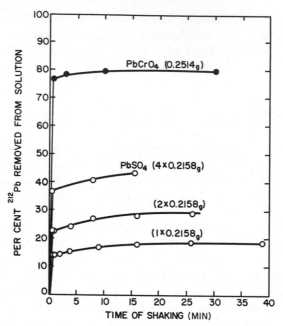

Fig. 4-13.   Deposition of $^{212}$Pb on powdered PbCrO$_4$ and PbSO$_4$ from saturated solutions of these salts.   (From F. Paneth, ref. 52)

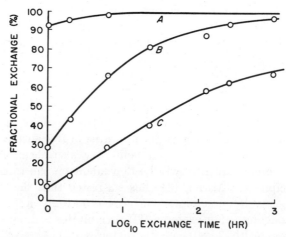

Fig. 4-14. The uptake of radioactive Tl$^+$ on TlI is shown as a function of precipitate aging time ($A$ is for 1-min aging, $B$ for 10 min, and $C$ for 1000 min).   The implication is that the rate of uptake is governed by surface recrystallization. (After Mirnik, ref. 34)

then a net loss of trace ion from the precipitate may take place as recrystallization and agglomeration occur.   One notes that some solid phases incorporate trace ions internally (by solid diffusion) much more rapidly than others.   Examples of rapid internal incorporation are silver and the halides in silver halide precipitates (35–38).   The conclusions from this type of work, then, are that a substantial part of the uptake of trace ions by ionic surfaces is achieved rapidly and, hence, under dynamic conditions the surface layer is probably close to equilibrium except for very fast crystal growth.   Treatment for several days usually yields uptake of further radioactive ions by recrystallization and solid diffusion.

## 12. Aging of Precipitates

The surface remodeling of TlI with aging is by no means unique. Extensive studies in this area have been performed by Kolthoff and co-workers (39) and have been reviewed by Laitenen (40).   Aging may be regarded as a process which changes the effective precipitate surface area with time.   The actual processes involved are probably agglomeration, recrystallization, and surface modifications caused by the attainment of surface equilibrium.   Factors affecting agglomeration are examined in Chapter 5 and recrystallization processes probably involve a combination of Ostwald ripening and cementing of agglomerated particles.   The ripening process described in Chapter 2 for spherical particles of radius $r$ may be extended to a consideration of the irregularly shaped particles usually precipitated from solution under normal conditions.   It has already been shown that the larger particles are normally dendritic in nature and the dendrite tips, having a small radius of curvature, can only be in equilibrium with a supersaturated solution.   Thus, in a solution close to saturation the dendrite arms will dissolve and the bulk particle will grow, thus reducing the effective precipitate surface area.   Cementing of agglomerated crystals also has the same effect of reducing the effective surface area.

Perhaps the most interesting of the surface aging effects relates to specific effects of excess ions.   It might be expected that the presence of materials which increase solubility would also increase the recrystallization and aging rate.   Often this is true; for example, the rate of aging (i.e., decrease in available surface area) for barium sulfate (41) and lead chromate (42) is increased by acid and decreased by ethanol. However, the effect of excess lattice ions, which is not directly related to solubility, is often quite marked. Barium sulfate ages faster in excess sulfate than in excess barium ions. Silver chloride and bromide also age faster in the presence of excess anion. It has been postulated that the latter effects are due to the formation of complex ions in the surface layer (43). The rate of aging is often reduced to practically zero by the presence of an adsorbed layer of dye. Thus, specific surface areas may be estimated by radioisotope exchange without the added complexity of surface aging if an adsorbed dye layer is present.

### 13. Estimation of Precipitate Surface Areas

The rapid uptake of radioactive tracers leads to one convenient method of determining a precipitate surface area *in situ*. It is usually assumed that the number of adsorbed tracer atoms $n_t(\text{ads})$ is related to the solution concentration of trace ions $n_t(\text{soln})$ by the simple expression

$$n_t(\text{ads}) = \frac{n_s(\text{ads})}{n_s(\text{soln})} x[n_t(\text{soln})] \qquad (4\text{-}34)$$

Here $n_s(\text{soln or ads})$ refers to the total number of ions of the same species as the tracer in solution or adsorbed. It is further assumed that there is a direct relation between adsorbed and solution concentration, an interpretation which is not entirely in accord with other methods (p. 140). However, with the above assumptions, and the further assumption that the surface area $S$ is given by

$$S = n_s l^2 \qquad (4\text{-}35)$$

where $l$ is the average distance between ions of the same species as the radioactive tracer in the substrate lattice; $l$ may be obtained from

$$l = \left( \frac{\text{MW}}{aN_0\rho} \right)^{1/3} \qquad (4\text{-}36)$$

MW is the molecular weight of the solid material, $a$ is the number of gram atoms of the tagged species per mole of solid, $N_0$ is Avogadro's number, and $\rho$ is the density.

The surface areas calculated from this type of approach generally are in good agreement with those obtained by other methods (Table 4-12) and it is interesting therefore to explore some of the implications of the radioactive tracer method further.    First, if the tracer is a cation, it presumably occupies surface sites adjacent to anions in the substrate; the reverse is true for anions.    Hence, if the lattice arrangement is to be satisfied, the adsorbed ions must be essentially desolvated.    In other words, it would seem that it is the solid surface itself which exchanges with trace ions.    This situation is rather unsatisfactory because true surface exchange would seem to be a process involving considerable activation energy and inertia.    On the other hand, rapid exchange with ions in the solvation layer associated with the surface is much more feasible, though the accuracy of surface area determination argues against the latter possibility.    Actually, determination of surface areas by tagged anions and cations does not give the same result.    Stow and Spinks (37), for example found that the surface area of a strontium sulfate preparation appeared to be a factor of two smaller when tagged sulfate ions were used instead of tagged strontium.    (Such an effect, of course, might be related to the displacement of surface ions as shown in Fig. 4-2.)

TABLE 4-12
Comparison of Surface Area Determinations[a]

| | Surface area, $cm^2/g$ | | | |
| Precipitate | Microscopic | Isotopic exchange | Adsorption | Reference |
| --- | --- | --- | --- | --- |
| $BaSO_4$ | | 220 | 430 (nitrogen) | |
| | — | | 268 (butane) | 51 |
| | | | 173 (salicylic acid) | |
| $PbCl_2$ | 2800 | 3000 | | 52 |
| $PbCrO_4$ | 570 | 380 | | 52 |
| $PbSO_4(1)$ | 130 | 134 | | 52 |
| $PbSO_4(2)$ | | 5300 | 1700 (ponceau 2R) | 52 |
| $PbS(1)$ | 80 | 47 | | 52 |
| $PbS(2)$ | | 7000 | 37,000 (methylene blue) | 52 |

[a] Taken from J. H. Wang, *Radioactivity Applied to Chemistry*, A. C. Wahl and N. A. Bonner, Eds., Wiley, New York, 1951, Chap. 10.

Other methods of measuring precipitate surface areas, such as the adsorption of dyes, appear then to have some advantages over the radio-active tracer method in that specific ion adsorption problems are avoided.    In turn, the adsorption methods have the advantage that precipitates can be examined *in situ* in contrast with the BET method which requires the separation and drying of precipitate before surface area assessing by gas adsorption.

It seems unlikely that surface areas can be determined to better than 10% by any of the preceding methods, though experimental reproducibility alone with the tracer method might lead to an *apparent* surface area which is more accurate.

## 14. Summary

The precipitate surface is the key to the unlocking and resolving of most of the problems of crystal growth, coprecipitation, and crystal morphology.    Because of the complex nature of the interface and its sensitive reaction to impurities, the atomistic properties are not easily determined.    The heterogeneous surface structure leads to unresolved problems in each of the aforementioned areas and also in adsorption properties and surface area determinations.    The surface structure also causes difficulties in relating measured thermodynamic properties, e.g., heat of immersion and adsorption, to plane surface models.    It is, however, in this latter area that significant progress has been made in the past few years.    The derivation of interfacial energies from such thermodynamic data seems to lead to consistent and reasonably reproducible results.    Whereas nonpolar precipitate interfaces can be characterized in terms of the model thermodynamic approach, the interfacial energy of ionic crystal/solution interfaces as yet cannot be fully evaluated theoretically.    There still remains much scope for the experimental determination of heats of immersion and adsorption, and for surface enthalpies and interfacial energies. The same is true for the theoretical development of interfacial forces at polar interfaces.

## References

1.  J. J. Gilman, *J. Appl. Phys.*, **31**, 2208 (1960).
2.  A. R. C. Westwood and T. T. Hitch, *J. Appl. Phys.*, **34**, 3085 (1963).
3.  I. N. Stranski, *Monatsh. Chem.*, **69**, 234 (1936).
4.  G. C. Benson and R. McIntosh, *Can. J. Chem.*, **33**, 1677 (1955).

5. F. Van Zeggeren and G. C. Benson, *J. Chem. Phys.*, **26**, 1077 (1957).
6. L. F. Knapp, *Trans. Faraday Soc.*, **17**, 457 (1921).
7. R. Shuttleworth, *Proc. Phys. Soc. London*, **A62**, 167 (1949).
8. G. C. Benson and T. A. Claxton, *Can. J. Phys.*, **41**, 1287 (1963).
9. A. G. Walton, *J. Chem. Phys.*, **39**, 3162 (1963).
10. A. G. Walton and D. R. Whitman, *J. Chem. Phys.*, **40**, 2722 (1964).
11. A. G. Walton, *J. Am. Ceram. Soc.*, **48**, 151 (1965).
12. P. W. M. Jacobs and F. C. Tompkins, in *Chemistry of the Solid State*, W. E. Garner, Ed., Butterworths, London, 1955, Chap. 4.
13. F. M. Fowkes, *J. Phys. Chem.*, **67**, 2538 (1963).
14. F. M. Fowkes, *Advan. Chem. Ser.*, **43**, 99 (1964).
15. F. M. Fowkes, *Ind. Eng. Chem.*, **56**, 40 (1964).
16. F. M. Fowkes, in "Adhesion," *ASTM Special Tech. Publ. No. 360* (1964).
17. E. G. Shafrin and W. A. Zisman, *J. Colloid Sci.*, **7**, 166 (1952).
18. F. Schulman and W. A. Zisman, *J. Colloid Sci.*, **7**, 465 (1952).
19. H. W. Fox and W. A. Zisman, *J. Colloid Sci.*, **5**, 514 (1950); **7**, 428 (1952).
20. M. K. Bernett and W. A. Zisman, *J. Phys. Chem.*, **65**, 2266 (1961).
21. G. C. Benson and K. S. Yun, *J. Chem. Phys.*, **42**, 3085 (1965).
22. J. L. Moilliet and B. Collie, *Surface Activity*, Van Nostrand, Princeton, 1951.
23. B. V. Il'in, *Proc. Symp. Chemistry Cement*, P. P. Budnikov et al., Eds., Sci. Technol. Soc. of Ind. of Bldg. Materials, Moscow, 1956.
24. B. V. Il'in, V. F. Kiselev, and G. I. Aleksandrova, *Dokl. Akad. Nauk SSSR*, **102**, 1155 (1955); *Chem. Abstr.*, **50**, 3870h (1956).
25. J. J. Chessick, A. C. Zettlemoyer, F. H. Healy, and G. J. Young, *Can. J. Chem.*, **33**, 251 (1955).
26. S. Brunauer et al., *Can. J. Chem.*, **34**, 729, 1483 (1956).
27. S. Brunauer, D. L. Kantro, and C. H. Weise, *Can. J. Chem.*, **37**, 714 (1959).
28. S. Brunauer, K. S. Love, and R. G. Keenan, *J. Am. Chem. Soc.*, **64**, 751 (1942).
29. V. E. Lange and R. Berger, *Z. Elektrochem.*, **36A**, 171 (1930).
30. V. A. Kellermand and V. E. Lange, *Kolloid-Z.*, **81**, 88 (1937).
31. W. Anderson and R. Parsons, *Proc. Intern. 2nd Congr. Surface Activity, London*, **III**, 45 (1957).
32. R. C. Tolman, *J. Chem. Phys.*, **17**, 333 (1949).
33. M. B. Mutaftschiev, *Compt. Rend.*, **259**, 572 (1964).
34. M. Mirnik, *Kolloid-Z.*, **163**, 25 (1959).
35. K. Zimiens, *Arkiv Kemi*, **A21**, 17 (1946).
36. A. Langer, *J. Chem. Phys.*, **10**, 321 (1942); **11**, 11 (1943).
37. I. M. Kolthoff and A. O'Brien, *J. Am. Chem. Soc.*, **61**, 3409 (1939).
38. R. Stow and J. Spinks, *J. Chem. Phys.*, **17**, 744 (1949).
39. I. M. Kolthoff and C. Rosenblum, *J. Am. Chem. Soc.*, **55**, 2656, 2664 (1933); **56**, 1264, 1658 (1934); **57**, 597, 607, 2573, 2577 (1935); **58**, 116, 121 (1936); I. M. Kolthoff and W. von Fischer, *ibid.*, **61**, 191 (1939); I. M. Kolthoff and F. T. Eggertsen, *ibid.*, **63**, 1412 (1941); I. M. Kolthoff and R. C. Bowers, *ibid.*, **76**, 1523 (1953).
40. H. A. Laitenen, *Chemical Analysis*, McGraw-Hill, New York, 1960.
41. I. M. Kolthoff and R. A. Halversen, *J. Phys. Chem.*, **43**, 605 (1939).

42. I. M. Kolthoff and G. E. Noponen, *J. Am. Chem. Soc.*, **60**, 499, 505 (1938).
43. I. M. Kolthoff and H. C. Yutzy, *J. Am. Chem. Soc.*, **59**, 1215 (1937).
44. B. V. Il'in, A. V. Kiselev, V. F. Kiselev, O. A. Likhacheva, and K. D. Shcherbakova, *Dokl. Akad. Nauk SSSR*, **75**, 827 (1950).
45. B. V. Il'in and V. F. Kiselev, *Dokl. Akad. Nauk SSSR*, **82**, 85 (1952).
46. W. H. Wade and N. Hackerman, *J. Phys. Chem.*, **63**, 1639 (1959).
47. N. N. Avgut, G. I. Berezin, A. V. Kiselev, and I. A. Lygina, *Izv. Akad. Nauk SSSR, Otd. Khim. Nauk*, **1960**, 1948; through *Chem. Abstr.*, **57**, 89f (1962).
48. W. D. Harkins and G. E. Boyd, *J. Am. Chem. Soc.*, **64**, 1195 (1942).
49. W. D. Harkins and R. Dahlstrom, *Ind. Eng. Chem.*, **22**, 897 (1930).
50. E. G. J. Willing, Ph.D. thesis, London University, 1950.
51. P. Emmet and T. DeWitt, *Ind. Eng. Chem. Anal. Ed.*, **13**, 28 (1941).
52. F. Paneth, *Radioelements as Indicators*, McGraw-Hill, New York, 1928.

# CHAPTER 5

# MORPHOLOGY

The morphology or physical appearance of precipitates is determined by nucleation and growth rates, colloidal stability, recrystallization and aging processes, and various habit modifications brought about either by ions or molecules present in solution or by the solvent itself. Thus, by controlling these parameters precipitates can be produced with either the properties of well-formed, relatively large ($>1$ $\mu$) crystallites or, at the other extreme, amorphous or even gel-like products.

## 1. Solubility

The first and most obvious feature affecting the grain size of a precipitate is its solubility. The sparingly soluble materials, e.g., barium sulfate, many carbonates, and silver halides, almost invariably precipitate as very small particles, whereas the fairly soluble alkali halide crystals are readily grown to a large ($>1$ mm) size. Many such relationships have been pointed out (1,2) with the result that attempts to grow large crystals of sparingly soluble materials have generally been related to the process of increasing their solubility. Some examples are the growth of quartz crystals from alkaline solutions at high temperatures, growth of silver chloride from ammonia, and lead sulfate from concentrated solutions of alkali salts. The effects of solubility may be recognized as twofold: first, the final particle size will depend upon the number of nucleation sites and the amount of material precipitated, i.e., the solubility effect is related to supersaturation and nucleation. Second, with relatively little material in solution the growth rate will be slow at controllable levels of supersaturation. Therefore, coarse crystalline precipitates of sparingly soluble salts could be prepared without changing the solubility if (1) the number of nucleation sites is kept to a minimum, and (2) a method of delivering new material to the growing crystallites can be found.

The first of these two criteria requires that homogeneous nucleation be avoided, that is, the supersaturation must be kept low. It will be seen later that the degree of supersaturation also strongly affects the degree of crystal perfection. In consequence, one satisfactory method of preparing coarse-grained precipitates is precipitation from homogeneous solution. The possibilities in this area are well known by now and are summarized in Gordon, Salutsky, and Willard's book (3). Thus, by controlled precipitation a large number of precipitates have been produced in coarse form. Some of these are shown in Table 5-1.

TABLE 5-1

Formation of Coarse Crystalline Precipitates by Precipitation from Homogeneous Solution

| Precipitate | Method | Reagent |
|---|---|---|
| Sulfates (Ba, Pb, Sr, Ca, etc.) | Generation of anion | Dimethyl sulfate hydrolysis, sulfamic acid hydrolysis, thiosulfate–persulfate reaction |
| Sulfides (Sb, Bi, Mg, Cu, As, Cd, Pb, Sn, Hg) | Generation of anion | Thioacetamide hydrolysis |
| Phosphates (Zr, Hf) | Generation of anion | Hydrolysis of triethyl phosphate, tetraethyl pyrophosphate, metaphosphoric acid |
| Chlorides (Ag, Tl) | Generation of anion | Hydrolysis of allyl chloride |
| Phosphates (Ca) | Change of pH | Hydrolysis of urea or cyanate |
| Oxalates (Mg, Ca, Zn, La) | Generation of anion | Hydrolysis of dimethyl or diethyl oxalate |
| Oxalates (Mg, Ca, Zn) | Change of pH | Urea + bioxalate |
| Calcium salts (fluoride, sulfate) | Generation of cation | Hydrolysis of ethylene chlorohydrin in presence of Ca–EDTA complex |
| Carbonates (rare earths, Ca, etc.) | Generation of $CO_2$ | Hydrolysis of trichloroacetates, cyanate, etc. |
| Chromates (Pb, Ag) | Change of pH | Hydrolysis of urea or cyanate |

With slow controlled growth of sparingly soluble salts it is often feasible to produce monodisperse precipitates, i.e., precipitates containing particles of equal size. This feature is very desirable from an investigatory standpoint since the particle size, shape, and surface area each may be determined with much better precision than is the case with the heterodisperse precipitates, which usually result from precipitation by direct mixing.   Consequently, particle growth rates and precipitation kinetics might, in theory, be estimated and used to test the rate laws.   Much of the early work in this area was performed by LaMer and co-workers (4,5) upon sulfur sols by the ingenious use of the higher-order Tyndall spectra (HOTS).   This phenomenon manifests itself, for particles in the micron size range, by exhibiting individual spectral colors at various angles to the incident white light beam.   Usually red and green are the predominant colors, although suspended latex particles show a range of colors, possibly caused by secondary refraction in some cases.   The use of this light scattering technique [readers are best referred to the publications of LaMer et al. (4,5) and Pierce and Maron (6)] has unfortunately found only limited use in the investigation of inorganic precipitates since the crystallites are not spherical as is required by the basic theory. Thus, theoretical developments are awaited before major progress can ensue.   One very interesting system has been reported which apparently breaks all the basic rules of precipitate morphology (7). If a solution of potassium iodate ($0.001–0.003M$) is slowly added to an equivalent volume and concentration of lead nitrate solution, a monodisperse precipitate of lead iodate is produced which shows strong HOTS after about 15 min.   Here then is a system which is monodisperse, but is produced by rather uncontrolled conditions. The explanation probably lies in the formation of intermediate complexes which slowly decompose to yield the product.   Even more unusual is the fact that the precipitate crystals are *spherical*.   Lanthanum iodate crystals may also be prepared in a similar manner ($0.003M$ lanthanum nitrate, $0.029M$ iodic acid) and are monodisperse and spherical (Figs. 5-1 and 5-2).   The crystals produced in these investigations were in the range 625–780 m$\mu$ in radius for lanthanum iodate and 770–970 m$\mu$ for lead iodate, depending upon the exact concentrations used.   This unexpected crystal shape is not readily explained, although decomposition of an unspecifically adsorbed surface complex seems to be one possibility.   The effect of adsorbed complexes on the morphology of precipitates is examined in more detail later, but a comparable situation to the production of spherical lead and lanthanum iodate crystals seems to be that of spherical barium sulfate crystals, which may be produced by adding sodium citrate to the reactant mixture (8).

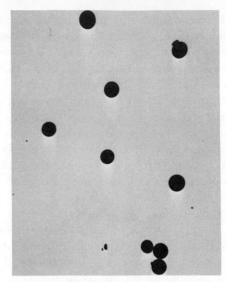

Fig. 5-1. Lead iodate crystals produced by direct precipitation from potassium iodate solution (7) (magnification ca. 5000×).

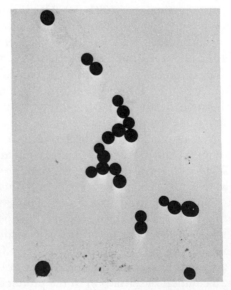

Fig. 5-2. Lanthanum iodate crystals produced by direct precipitation (7) (magnification ca. 3500×).

At the other end of the scale, von Weimarn (9) and others have shown that precipitates of sparingly soluble materials such as barium sulfate, when formed by direct mixing of high concentrations of appropriate reagents, consist of such small particles that long-range crystalline order is lost and the product is amorphous. The latter is, of course, a result of the tremendous homogeneous nucleation rate experienced at high degrees of supersaturation. Some of the aspects of nucleation at high degrees of supersaturation throw further light on the amorphous nature of precipitates under such conditions.

At concentrations close to those of homogeneous crystal nucleation, the critical nucleus is typically the size of a few unit cells; however, at higher concentrations the critical nucleus is much smaller and loses its identity with the new phase. In other words, the solid phase starts to grow without "knowing" what its final structure will be. For simple compounds the ions or molecules will rapidly reorganize to satisfy the minimum energy requirement of the regular lattice; however, there are many complicated structures known where it is not easy for the ions or molecules to rearrange in the appropriate configuration. Some examples are the apatites and many silicates, cholesterol, and most polymers and enzymes. It may be stated that for these materials and many others there is a large entropy change upon crystallization. Thus, even for slow growth of complicated silicates from solution there is often an intermediate amorphous gel structure from which the molecules eventually sort out a suitable configuration. Hydroxyapatite, with 18 ions per unit cell, also probably undergoes a transition state before attaining its normal structure. Polymers and enzymes form amorphous material when deposited rapidly from solution and cholesterol, which has 32 molecules per unit cell, also crystallizes via a metastable precursor.

Although solubility usually plays an important part in determining the overall size of crystals produced by methods other than precipitation from homogeneous solution, there are known cases where *decreased* solubility leads to larger crystals. Lewin and Vance (10), for example, have produced larger strontium sulfate crystals from sulfuric acid solutions than from pure aqueous solutions, despite the lower solubility in the acid. They suggest that hydrogen ions play a vital part in this unusual effect.

## 2. Rate of Growth

In view of the entropy factors influencing the growth of well-defined crystals, it is not surprising that crystal morphology undergoes a profound change with the total rate of deposition of solid material. For slow growth rates, precipitate particles often take on a compact, well-defined shape which is related to the crystal structure.   By using direct mixing and subsequent aging, Suito and Takiyama (11) have produced rhombic barium sulfate crystals and Black, Insley, and Parfitt (12) have shown that monodisperse cubic silver chloride particles are produced by hydrolysis of allyl chloride in silver nitrate solution (Fig. 5-3).   However, in the latter study it was found that individual cubes were achieved only if either chloride or silver ions were in excess in solution.   In the region of the isoelectric point a high proportion of "twinned" crystals was produced.   Twinned crystals are well defined crystallographically but contain two or more crystals included at a definite mutual orientation.   Thus, it is clear that ions in solution or, more precisely, in the vicinity of the interface play an important part in habit modification.

At faster rates of growth, changes in crystal habit are observed and at higher supersaturations dendritic growth usually sets in. The snowflake is, of course, the often-quoted epitome of dendritic

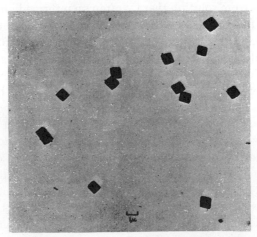

Fig. 5-3. Micrograph showing the morphology of silver chloride produced by precipitation from homogeneous solution (12).

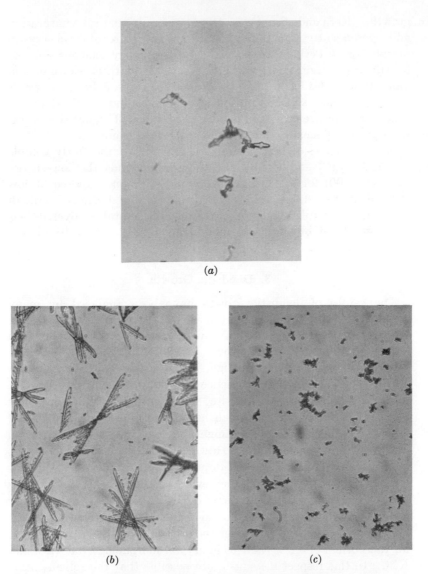

Fig. 5-4. The morphology of most precipitates is dependent upon the super-saturation from which they are produced.   Typical of supersaturation effects are those shown for lead sulfate precipitates.   At low concentrations the crystals are small and compact (a), at higher concentrations, larger dendrites are formed (b), and at high concentrations very small crystals are produced (c).

growth.    Kern and co-workers (13,14) maintain that supersaturation and, consequently, growth rate are the major features affecting crystal morphology.    Perhaps typical of the morphology changes induced by supersaturation and growth rates are the data of Kolthoff and van't Riet for lead sulfate precipitation (15) (Figs. 5-4a–c).    Crystals produced at low supersaturation are compact and small, at higher concentrations are large and dendritic, and at still higher concentrations are much smaller, but compact, and agglomerated.

Kern (13) has observed similar changes with the fairly soluble materials NaCl and CsCl.    For these compounds the low-energy surfaces [(100) for NaCl and (110) for CsCl] were exposed at low concentrations.    Increase in supersaturation caused dendritic growth on both, and at still higher concentrations the crystals recovered their compact shape but exposed high-energy (111) and (100) planes, respectively.

### 3. Dendritic Growth

The causes of dendritic growth have been analyzed by many workers but three predominant mechanisms have been suggested. When crystallization occurs from a melt, the rate-limiting step is often imposed by the mechanism of heat transfer.    If the growing crystal cannot dissipate heat fast enough, it can adjust its surface area to optimize heat dissipation and hence takes on the dendritic form.    A model three-dimensional dendrite, shown in Fig. 5-5, demonstrates the large surface area which can be attained for a relatively small mass.    A similar mechanism might be ascribed to crystallization from concentrated solutions.    However, Sover and Kriwobok (16) maintain that in the absence of impurities supercooled metals do not form dendrites.    This and other evidence suggests that impurities play an important part in causing dendritic growth.    On the other hand, Kern and Tillman (14) found that many impurities producing habit modifications do not lower the critical level of supersaturation for the normal onset of changes in crystal morphology for NaCl and KCl.    In this respect it seems quite possible that the solvent plays some role in the onset of dendritic formation.

Nielsen (17) claims that there are normally three growth mechanisms by which precipitates develop—screw dislocation at low supersaturation, surface nucleation, and eventually diffusion-controlled growth from higher supersaturation.    The third of these mechanisms

Fig. 5-5. A schematic model of a dendritic crystal. (After Saratovkin)

is said to correspond to the ill-formed or dendritic crystallite produced in these systems.

The most plausible explanation for the mechanism of dendrite formation has been put forward by Saratovkin (18). Crystal growth of ionic crystals may be considered as a process in which the ions diffuse to the surface and the solvating molecules diffuse away from the ions at the surface. Consequently, there is two-way "traffic" at the surface and, under fast growth conditions, a "traffic jam" occurs. If solvent molecules cannot diffuse away from the surface quickly enough, they block the growth of normally fast-growing surfaces. However, corners which have been pushed into less severely blocked areas continue to grow. This sequence is depicted in Figs. 5-6a and 5-6b and shows the development of high-energy planes. If the layers grow rapidly, a similar situation can arise in the formation of side branches which, provided the system were homogeneous, would be symmetrical (Figs. 5-7a, b).

Dendrite growth provides a means of entrapping surface adsorbed impurities in reentrant angle traps (Figs. 5-8a, b). This mechanism is, of course, quite important in coprecipitation processes.

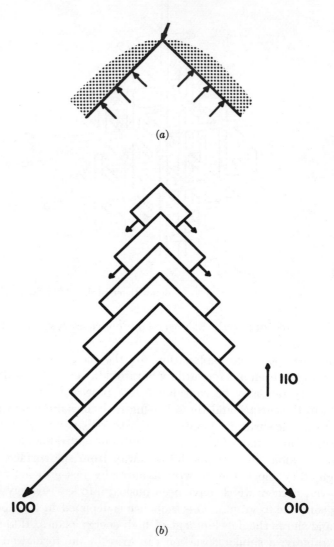

Fig. 5-6. Schematic representation of the development of a crystal dendrite. In (a) the dotted area represents an excess of solvent molecules. The corner projects into an area of solution which is not depleted of solute and develops in the form (b).

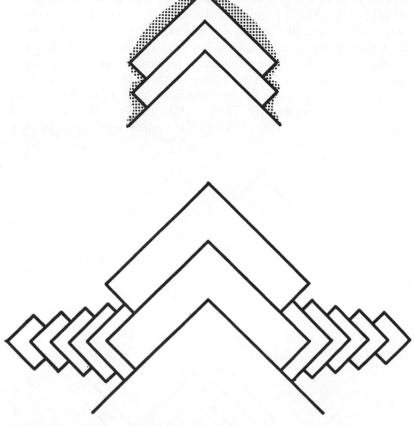

Fig. 5-7. The development of side branches occurs in much the same manner as that of the main branch (Fig. 5-6). Again the shaded area represents solute depleted areas of solution. The side dendrites project into the more concentrated areas of solution.

## 4. Instability of the Interface

From the preceding considerations of growth-related morphology, it is evident that changes in the structure of the interface between crystal and solution must result from changed growth rates. Until recently the criteria relating interface stability to crystal morphology had not been recognized. One of the most interesting theoretical advances in this area has come about as a result of the approach developed by Mullins and Sekerka (19,20). This theory seeks to examine perturbations to the discrete crystal shape. If the crystal is perturbed from its compact, low surface-energy form by some random fluctuation, the protuberance pushes into an area of greater solute concentration, thus promoting further growth. Opposing this tendency is the interfacial energy which, in terms of the small radius of curvature, promotes dissolution. Although it is not pertinent to reproduce here the mathematics of this approach or its extension, as

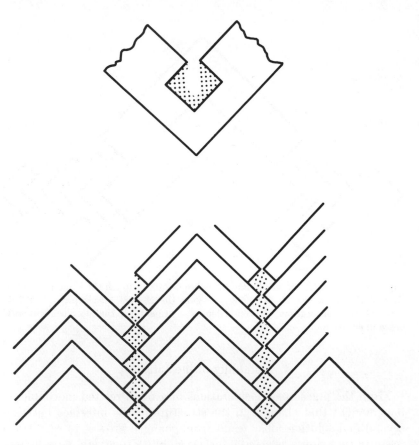

Fig. 5-8. Development of dendrites leads to entrapment of foreign materials, solvent, etc. at reentrant angle traps.

devised by Cahn et al. (21), the limiting features which evolve are as follows: stable growth faces are promoted by (1) small particle size, (2) high interfacial energy, and (3) slow growth rates.

The collapse of the stable interface at high growth rates corresponds to the change from interface to diffusion-controlled growth kinetics. This deduction is then in accord with the observations of Nielsen.

Perhaps the most important feature of this approach is that it predicts that the onset of dendritic growth occurs at a "critical" degree of supersaturation which is, in turn, directly related to the interfacial energy. Such deductions should lead to further studies relating precipitate morphology to environmental parameters.

## 5. Fragmentation of Dendrites

Recent discoveries relating to the mode of melt solidification suggest that dendrites may play a much greater part in crystallization than is indicated merely by the morphology. Jackson and co-workers (22,23) have found that, under conditions of rapid crystal growth, ammonium chloride dendrites undergo fragmentation in such a manner that the side branches fall off as indicated in Figs. 5-9a and 5-9b. Thus, in melt solidification, separated segments of crystalline material are probably carried into the bulk melt by convection, where they act as nuclei for further crystallization. Hence, the initial growth spurt is followed at some later stage by a further formation burst or secondary particle growth (ancillary nucleation). A similar process is also sometimes observed when precipitates form from solution. The mechanism is obscure but it seems possible that the slight increase in crystal temperature on crystallization would promote greater solubility, particularly in the solution-depleted areas close to the branching positions, and hence cause fragmentation. This type of phenomenon seems to be related to several observations relating to precipitate morphology, as follows:

(1) Precipitation of crystals from solution by direct mixing sometimes results in the formation of a primary crop of badly formed crystals (including dendrites) and, at a later stage (after a period of several minutes), a secondary crop of very small crystals (24). Since the secondary generation could not be homogeneous nucleation at such low concentrations, crystal fragmentation seems the only possibility.

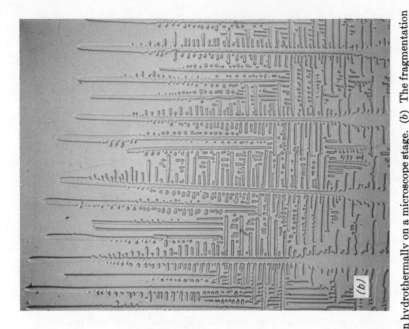

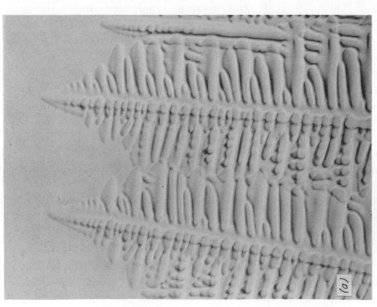

Fig. 5-9. (a) Formation of ammonium chloride dendrites grown hydrothermally on a microscope stage. (b) The fragmentation of dendrites occurs by the separation of side branches (this is *not* a dissolution process in the usual sense). The side branches may then act as ancillary nuclei. (Micrographs by K. A. Jackson and J. D. Hunt)

(*2*) As explained in Chapter 1, the morphology of crystalline precipitates at concentrations in the range where homogeneous nucleation is believed to occur is almost always dendritic, and therefore fragmentation must be considered as an alternative to the homogeneous nucleation theory in some cases, although such a possibility has apparently not yet been explored.

(*3*) Melia and co-workers (25,26) have shown that in stirred solutions inorganic seed crystals generate many secondary nuclei, the numbers produced being dependent upon the rate of stirring and the degree of supersaturation. This process, called secondary or ancillary nucleation, is of course not so much a matter of nucleation as of fragmentation and crystal growth. In all probability, the laboratory seeding of supersaturated solutions proceeds via the fragmentation process.

As stated previously, the extent to which fragmentation causes particle generation in unstirred systems is unknown, but it seems probable that, by a combination of thermal agitation, particle collision, and sedimentation, and the further possibility of selective resolution, some secondary generation is inevitable in systems where dendritic growth is occurring.

## 6. Whisker Formation

Although the formation of crystal whiskers from the vapor phase is quite common, it is relatively rare for solution-grown crystals, particularly inorganic ones. Whiskers are generally believed to grow via the dislocation mechanism, the growth of the tip being in accord with the dendritic growth mechanism, i.e., controlled by the convection of solvent molecules (27). A similar effect may be induced by the adsorption of impurities preventing three-dimensional growth. Whisker formation emanating from a screw dislocation is shown in Figs. 5-10*a* and *b*. Whiskers formed from organic crystals and polymeric materials are sometimes hollow and grow along a very fine "leader" whisker—the mechanism of this form of growth is not understood, although some suggestions for enzyme fibers have been made (28,29).

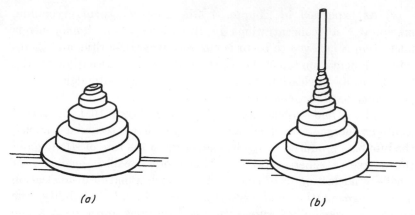

Fig. 5-10. Development of a whisker from a screw dislocation.

## 7. Crystal Habit

Crystals formed from controlled, low supersaturation are generally compact and well formed; the detailed shape depends upon crystal structure and the environment from which the crystals were grown. The environment factors, in turn, may be divided into the influences of solvent and those due to ions or molecules of species other than those in the pure crystal. Under ideal equilibrium conditions the shape of a crystal will be such that its total surface energy is a minimum, i.e.,

$$\sum \sigma_i A_i = \text{minimum at constant volume} \qquad (5\text{-}1)$$

Thus, for alkali halides growing from vapor, the low surface-energy (100) planes should predominate and the equilibrium form is cubic An alternative way of reaching the same conclusion is via the two-dimensional crystal growth equation (Eq. 2-4), which predicts a rapid growth rate on the high-energy surface. Figure 5-11 shows schematically the disappearance of a high-energy face. Stranski and co-workers (30,31) have examined both the theoretical and practical aspects of equilibrium crystal shape and conclude that (theoretically) the equilibrium forms are cubic for the NaCl-type structure (32,33), rhombic dodecahedral for CsCl (34), octahedral for $CaF_2$ (35) and rhombohedral for $CaCO_3$ and $NaNO_3$. Similar conclusions were reached by Hartman (36) who found that the equilibrium crystal form should favor the following surface planes: NaCl (100), CsCl (110), CaF$_2$ (111), CaCO$_3$ (calcite) (100), and anatase (011), (001), and (112). In many cases the low-energy planes are those which correspond to the unit-cell surfaces so that a relation between crystallographic structure and precipitate morphology is to be expected.

In practice, however, the shape of crystalline particles is controlled less by considerations of minimum surface energy than by the method of crystal growth. The reason for this is that one part of a crystal surface does not "know" what another part is doing except in terms of messages in the form of growth steps, dislocations, etc. which pass in its vicinity. Growth by the dislocation mechanism does involve surface energetics in its formulation and, hence, growth morphology generally depends in a rather secondary manner upon the surface energetic requirement. Table 5-2 gives the x-ray crystal structure and theoretical and observed crystallite shapes for some common precipitates. With few exceptions, the shape of the precipitate particles is adequately predictable in terms of crystal structure and the appropriate low-energy surface planes. However, the crystal habit of some of the more soluble materials cannot be said to be simply related to their unit cell structure. For example, K$_2$SO$_4$, K$_2$CrO$_4$, and (NH$_4$)$_2$SO$_4$ crystals are all of the rhombic K$_2$SO$_4$ structure but crystallize with completely different habits, as shown in Fig. 5-12. It is noteworthy that many of the crystals which grow with unusual habits contain oxygen atoms and therefore it seems possible that solvent interactions may play a specific part in modifying growth habit in some instances. Although the habit of most inorganic

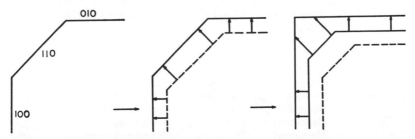

Fig. 5-11. Schematic diagram of the elimination of a high-energy (110) crystal face. Growth occurs most rapidly on high-energy faces in such a manner that eventually they become eliminated or diminished in area as compared with the low-energy faces.

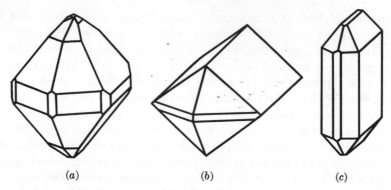

$(a)$                    $(b)$                    $(c)$

Fig. 5-12. Habit, from pure solution of $(a)$ $K_2SO_4$, $(b)$ $K_2CrO_4$, and $(c)$ $(NH_4)_2SO_4$ crystals.

TABLE 5-2

Comparison of Theoretical (Equilibrium) and Experimental Precipitate Morphology

| Precipitate | X-ray crystal form | Theoretical shape | Observed |
|---|---|---|---|
| AgCl | Cubic (NaCl) | Cubic | Cubic PFHS |
| AgBr | Cubic | Cubic | Cubic—direct precipitation |
| AgI | Cubic ZnS hexagonal ZnO | — | Cubic and hexagonal PFHS |
| BaSO$_4$ | Rhombic | Rhombic | Rhombic PFHS with rounded corners (other forms under different conditions) |
| CaCO$_3$ (calcite) | Rhombohedral NaNO$_3$ | Rhombohedral | Rhombohedral PFHS |
| CaCO$_3$ (aragonite) | Rhombic | — | Acicular crystals PFHS |
| CaF$_2$ | Cubic | Octahedral | Octahedral—slow evaporation |
| CdI$_2$ | Hexagonal | — | Hexagonal—slow evaporation |
| CdS ($\alpha$) | Hexagonal | — | Hexagonal—direct precipitation |
| PbCrO$_4$ | Monoclinic | — | Acicular—PFHS |
| PbCl$_2$ | Hexagonal | — | Hexagonal—direct precipitation |
| PbI$_2$ | Hexagonal | — | Hexagonal—direct precipitation |
| PbSO$_4$ | Rhombic | Rhombic | Hexagonal—direct precipitation |
| PbS | Cubic (NaCl) | Cubic | Cubic—direct precipitation |
| SrSO$_4$ | Rhombic | Rhombic | Same as BaSO$_4$ |

crystals is known only in the case where water has been the solvent, there is good reason to believe that solvents that interact strongly with ions or molecules in a particular plane will stabilize that face by lowering the interfacial energy.

## 8. Habit Modification by Solvent

Wells (37–39) has been instrumental in pointing out the solvent effect in modifying the habit of several organic crystalline precipitates. Many organic crystals are prismatic or bipyramidal in habit (Fig. 5-13); however, iodoform, which forms bipyramidal crystals when grown from aniline, forms prismatic crystals when grown from cyclohexane. Similarly, anthranilic acid crystals are essentially bipyramidal when grown from ethanol and prismatic with pyramidal faces when grown from glacial acetic acid. If anthranilic acid crystals formed in ethanol are transferred to glacial acetic acid and grown further, they take on the habit characteristic of the new solution. The same is true if the crystals were formed in acetic acid and transferred to ethanol. This change in habit is indicated in Fig. 5-14.

Investigations of the preceding type give direct indications of the surface orientation of substrate and solvent molecules. Often the relationships are very complicated and only rather general conclusions may be reached. For example, in compounds which contain —OH

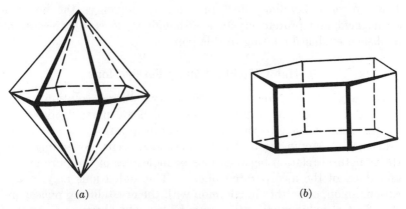

(a)                                  (b)

Fig. 5-13. Variation of the crystal habit of iodoform when grown from (a) aniline and (b) cyclohexane. (After Wells, ref. 38)

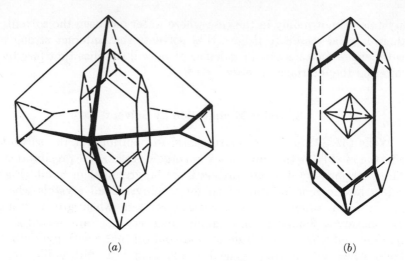

(a)    (b)

Fig. 5-14. Variation of the crystal habit of anthranilic acid grown from
(a) ethanol and (b) glacial acetic acid.    (After Wells, ref. 38)

or —NH$_2$ groups, the faces which contain high concentrations of
these groups will be stabilized by solvents capable of hydrogen bonding.   The compound pentaerythritol, $C(CH_2OH)_4$, has a tetragonal
structure with the —CH$_2$ groups lying predominantly in the (100)
planes and the —OH groups in the (110) planes.   In aqueous solution
the (100) surface is absent and a (110) bipyramid is dominant (39).
This hydrogen bonding effect presumably influences the habit of
amino acid and protein crystals, although there is, at present, no
published evidence relating to this point.

### 9. Habit Modification by Foreign Ions

The addition of foreign ions to a crystallizing solution causes
changes in the crystallization process which are partially described
by the changes in growth rate and coprecipitation, as elaborated
previously.   Modification of habit may also occur, depending upon
the structural relation between ions or molecules of the pure crystal
and those of the incorporated phase.   The added ions may have a
cation, anion, or neither in common with the crystallizing phase, and
the effect of habit modification may be brought about as a result of
changes in the lattice dimension by incorporated ions or surface

blocking. In other words, habit modifications may be observed with mixed crystals or with adsorption compounds. In the first of these two categories, mixed crystal formation, it has been demonstrated that isostructural combinations usually coprecipitate (Chap. 3) and, in consequence, the habit modification is usually one of degree rather than of complete change. For example, potassium chromate and sulfate are completely miscible in the solid phase. When each is grown from its own pure solution, a characteristic habit is produced (as shown in Fig. 5-12). Mixed crystals of potassium sulfate and chromate are generally of a morphology intermediate between these structures, depending upon the relative concentration of each component. Other rhombic salts which show similar relations are permanganates with sulfates and permanganates with perchlorates.

The equilibrium shape of many crystals is too complicated to be handled by direct calculation of the surface energy for each individual plane and then minimizing for a particular volume, as is required by Eq. 5-1. The approximate role of surface energetics may be arrived at by the following reasoning. At equilibrium each facet is in equilibrium with the same solution concentration $s$. The difference between the chemical potential of the finite crystal bounded by these facets and that of an infinite crystal is, for a symmetrical crystal, given by

$$v\Delta\mu = \frac{2\sigma(\hat{n})}{\lambda(\hat{n})} \tag{5-2}$$

where $\sigma(\hat{n})$ is the interfacial energy of the facet which lies at unit normal distance $\lambda(\hat{n})$ from the center of symmetry. In other words, the facet lying farthest from the center of symmetry (in a unit normal direction from that facet) is of highest interfacial energy. Small changes in lattice position of the constituent ions are known to cause fairly large changes in surface energy, which consequently modify the habit considerably. Lowering of the interfacial energy, by crystal–solvent interaction or by ion adsorption, can also be recognized as a habit-modifying influence in terms of Eq. 5-2.

Of the combinations known to form anomalous mixed crystals, lead ions cause potassium chloride crystals to grow in the octahedral habit. A few of the possible habit modifications of the cubic system are shown in Fig. 5-15. This series is induced by lead ions on potassium chloride; low concentrations cause the disappearance of the

(100) faces and appearance of the octahedral (111) planes.  Higher concentrations ($>1\%$) cause higher-index planes to appear, giving a faceted sphere.  One notes, however, that Mehmel and Nespital (40) have concluded that a separate phase $KPbCl_3$ is formed from KCl and $PbCl_2$, which may account for both the habit modification and the coprecipitation of these two materials.

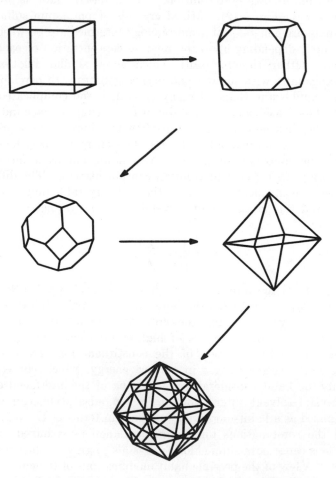

Fig. 5-15. Some possible modifications of a cubic system showing first the formation of the octahedral faces, then higher-index faces.

Lead chloride also shows some peculiarities when precipitated alone. Lewin (41) reports that lead chloride crystals precipitated from hydrochloric acid show the expected hexagonal form, but in an excess of lead ions, rodlike crystals are produced (with dendrites at higher concentrations).

Raynaud and Pouradier (42) have found that if silver nitrate is added to a solution of potassium bromide and iodide, the first crystals to be produced are hexagonal and characteristic of silver iodide and, at a later stage, are cubic and characteristic of silver bromide. The effect may be characterized by the percentage of bromide in the solid phase: 0–4% Br⁻ crystals are hexagonal; 58–100% Br⁻ crystals are cubic in habit.

Because of the relative ease with which observations may be made upon the habit of fairly soluble crystals, much effort has been directed to this problem. Kuznetsov (43) has investigated the habit modification of ammonium chloride by a large number of ions and finds that $Fe^{2+}$, $Ni^{2+}$, $Co^{2+}$, $Cu^{2+}$, $Cd^{2+}$, and $Cr^{2+}$ all changed the ammonium chloride mode of crystallization. These ions are said to interact (presumably cocrystallize) with $NH_4Cl$. Other ions, which had no effect, were $Na^+$, $K^+$, $Li^+$, $Ba^{2+}$, and $Ca^{2+}$. Alum crystals have also been investigated extensively (44,45), habit modifications being noted for $Na^+$, $Ba^{2+}$, $Pb^{2+}$, $Li^+$ nitrates, $NaBrO_3$, KCl, KBr, $K_2SO_4$, $Na_2SO_4$, and $Cu^{2+}$. It would appear from the preceding data that the formation of anomalous mixed crystals and habit modification are closely linked and ions which are only adsorbed onto the crystal surface, in general, do not cause major changes in crystalline morphology.

## 10. Modification by Organic Materials and Dyes

One of the most widely quoted examples of habit modification by an organic material is the effect of urea upon sodium chloride. This change is brought about by the strong adsorption of urea upon the (111) crystal faces, causing a change of habit from cubic to octahedral. Many similar cases are known for the conversion to exposed (111) planes for cubic, rhombic, and tetragonal crystals (46). There are perhaps three general explanations for this phenomenon—viz., the (111) planes are of high surface energy and are likely to cause strong adsorption; the (111) planes are uncharged and present a strongly polar interface; the atomic arrangement within the (111) planes coincides with the configuration of the adsorbing phase. The first two of these possibilities are closely related and the residual charge theory has been postulated by several authors (47–49). This theory seems to account for the modification of alums by ions, and since urea, citric, and tartaric acids, and many dyes also modify the crystal habit by promoting (111) planes, the theory seemed acceptable. However, Frondel (50) has shown that predictions made on this basis are not always accurate. In many cases dyes adsorb on the (100) and not the (111) faces of sodium and lithium fluoride and the same is true of silver bromide and chloride.

Recent theories have laid emphasis on the configuration of the polar groups belonging to the adsorbed species. For example, Whetstone and co-workers (51–53) have shown that for a large number of organic dyes habit modification is achieved only when the polar groups of the dye molecules match the ion arrangement of the substrate. Substrates investigated by these workers were $NH_4NO_3$, $KNO_3$, $NaNO_3$, and $(NH_4)SO_4$.

Buckley (54) and others have studied the habit-modifying effects of several hundred dyes on crystals, mainly of the rhombohedral type. A characteristic of these dyes is that only small amounts are required (often 1 part in 10,000) to bring about the modification. In a typical case ($KClO_4$), the dye converts the predominantly (001)–(110) habit to (011). At larger dye concentrations, however, the (011) converts to predominantly (102).

Habit modification of cubic systems to needle forms is not unusual. Nyvlt (55), for example, reports this modification for sodium chloride crystals in the presence of small amounts of polyvinyl alcohol.

## 11. Liquid Crystals

Whereas most crystals dissolve in suitable solvents to form a homogeneous solution phase, some do not. These crystals may exist in a form which has long-range order as with the solid phase, but which is liquid in nature: hence the terminology liquid crystal or mesophase. The mesophase has been characterized mainly for the pure solid component which enters into liquid-crystal form above its melting point. Such solids do in fact show anomalous melting, the lowest transition point being the conversion of solid to mesophase and subsequent transitions at higher temperatures correspond to interconversion between different structures of mesophase and finally to the homogeneous liquid melt. The formation of the so-called smectic, nematic, and cholestoric phases from solids are not particularly relevant to a discussion of precipitates. However, solutions of certain materials form liquid crystals which may be of considerable importance in biological systems (56,57). For example, lipids exhibit liquid crystalline behavior and the formation of lipid–cholesterol complexes may form a mesophase precursor to the arterial deposition processes leading to atherosclerosis. Usually solutions of liquid crystals are identified by the production of birefringence under examination with polarized light. The solution under examination appears fairly clear with normal illumination but shows a number of birefringent areas when viewed under polarized light. Little is known of the nucleation or precipitation mechanism for conversion of liquid crystal to solid phase, except that in biological systems it is usually irreversible. For this reason, details of the molecular structure and properties of liquid crystals will not be expounded here. The reader is referred to a recent book upon this subject (58).

## 12. Agglomeration

One of the most vexing problems in attempting to relate precipitate morphology to external (solution) conditions and to the mode of nucleation and growth is the formation of agglomerates. The principles involved in agglomerate formation may be recognized in the theory of von Smoluchowski (59,60). In this theory each collision between particles leads to permanent contact and the rate of this process is diffusion controlled (61). Using Fick's diffusion equation as a basis, the number of particles $n_t$ at time $t$ is given in terms of the $n_0$ original monodisperse particles at $t = 0$ by

$$n_t = \frac{n_0}{1 + 4\pi D_1 R n_0 t} \tag{5-3}$$

where $D_1$ is the particle diffusion coefficient and $R$ is the primary particle radius. An alternative form of Eq. 5-3 is often used, viz.,

$$n_t = \frac{n_0}{1 + t/T} \tag{5-4}$$

where $T$, the "coagulation time," is the time taken to just halve the original number of particles.   These equations are applicable only to the binary collision process in which all collisions are effective and where there is no energy barrier to the agglomeration process.   Under these conditions for a water-dispersed phase, $T \sim 2 \times 10^{11}/n_0$.   If we define arbitrarily that systems that are agglomerated have more than 10% of their particles agglomerated in less than 1000 sec, then we may say that aqueous systems containing $10^7$ particles/ml or less are essentially "nonagglomerating."   The agreement between experiment and theory is quite good for a number of systems (62); one such system is shown for the agglomeration of kaolinite in Fig. 5-16.

However, most precipitates cannot be dealt with in terms of a nonactivated process because of charge stabilization.   The nature of the interfacial layer is a matter of some conjecture, but it is clear that, particularly for "lyophobic" materials, charge stabilization greatly affects the agglomeration rate.   Colloidal silica can, in fact, be rendered "stable" with as many as $10^{17}$ particles/ml.

It can be seen then that, provided the nuclei suitable for catalyzing the formation of the solid phase number fewer than $10^7$ particles/ml, there is unlikely to be considerable aggregation during the precipitation and growth process.   Homogeneous nucleation, on the other

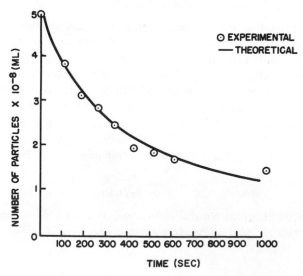

Fig. 5-16. Comparison of the theoretical (von Smoluchowski) and experimental rates of agglomeration for a kaolin suspension (59).

hand, generally leads to a sufficiently large number of particles that agglomeration will occur, even if there is some charge stabilization. Von Smoluchowski considered the hindered agglomeration process as one in which only a fraction $\alpha$ of the colliding particles adhered to each other. Then the coagulation time $T$ becomes

$$T = \frac{1}{8\pi D_1 R n_0 \alpha} \tag{5-5}$$

Later and more sophisticated approaches (63,64) have treated coagulation in terms of the potential barrier between particles carrying a like charge. The rate of coagulation is said to be reduced by a factor $W$, where

$$W \sim \frac{1}{2xR} \exp (V_{max}/kT) \tag{5-6}$$

$x$ is the electrolyte concentration, and $V_{max}$ the maximum potential of interaction as two particles approach each other.

The magnitude of the surface charge or potential arising from excess ionic adsorption at the interface is not readily assessable because, although the charge gives rise to particle mobility in an electric field, the potential which is measurable from this electrophoretic mobility relates to the charge at the surface of shear between the boundary layer and solution, and not to that at the particle–solution interface. Since the surface potential and measured (zeta) potential coincide only at the isoelectric point, most studies have been directed toward elucidating the conditions under which the surface charge may be rendered to zero.

## 13. Ionic Effect on Stability

Ionic effects on agglomeration and precipitation may be divided into two categories: those caused by ions involved in building the precipitate crystal lattice (potential determining) and those not directly involved in precipitation. There is considerable experimental evidence (65) that the nature of the charge of the particles suspended in solute originates mainly from adsorbed potential-determining ions. Constituent ions, which form the crystal lattice of the precipitate, are adsorbed in preference to other ions that might be present in solution. The charge on the colloidal particles thus depends on whether the positive or negative "lattice" ions are in excess during precipitation.

Early investigations showed that ions other than those involved in the lattice, which have a charge opposite to the charge of the suspended particles, may cause agglomeration. The effectiveness of these nonconstituent ions in causing agglomeration increases with an increase in their valency. These relations are given qualitatively by the the rule of Schulze and Hardy which states that the coagulating influence of counterions is an inverse power of the ion valency. A statistical expression derived by Whetham (66) gives these coagulation values (critical coagulation concentration) in the form

$$C_1:C_2:C_3:C_4 \ = \ 1:\frac{1}{x}:\frac{1}{x^2}:\frac{1}{x^3} \tag{5-7}$$

The influence of the radius of the coagulating ion was first pointed out by Ostwald (67). Summarizing the available experimental evidence, he derived an empirical relationship between the radius and the coagulation value of an ion:

$$(1 - f_k) \, (r + a) \ = \ b \tag{5-8}$$

where $f_k$ is the activity coefficient for the coagulating ion, $r$ is the ionic radius in angstroms, and $a$ and $b$ are constants characteristic of the system. Many more factors, such as the concentration of the sol, the manner of the addition of the electrolyte, the mixing rate, etc., are known to influence the coagulating ability of ions.

The subject is rather complicated, and the lack of a systematic approach, as well as different criteria for the definition of coagulation values, led to inconsistent results in earlier experimental work.

In later work, experiments designed to investigate the colloidal properties of solids in liquids have evolved along two different paths. The Dutch colloid school (62,64) has favored work with dialyzed sols and development of theories relating to model systems, whereas the Yugoslav school has placed more emphasis on the properties of precipitates *in statu nascendi*. For present purposes the Yugoslav approach, as represented by the extensive work of Težak and co-workers (68–73), seems more appropriate to a consideration of precipitation processes.

The criteria for the determination of coagulation values, by now, have been thoroughly investigated by the Yugoslav school. These criteria have been based on the analysis of the kinetics of coagulation of sols *in statu nascendi*. The coagulation kinetics were followed by measuring the changes in the turbidity of a system from "birth to death" (from mixing to precipitation).

Under carefully defined conditions, Težak and his collaborators examined the influences of various factors on the coagulation values of electrolytes. Typically, silver halide sols have been used as model systems. The results may be summarized as follows:

(*1*) The logarithm of the coagulation values (log *c*) of various coagulating ions decreases linearly with increasing valences. These results are in general agreement with the Schulze-Hardy rule and with Whetham's formulation of the rule.

(*2*) The logarithm of the coagulation values of various counterions of the same valence decreases linearly with increasing (crystallographic) radius.

(3) Regardless of the valence and size of the counterions, their coagulation values decrease with increasing concentration of the sol.

(*4*) The coagulation values of the counterions are practically constant over a wide range of concentrations of the stabilizing ions (lattice ions).

The general effect of coagulating ions with increasing valence on the stability of a sol (69) is depicted in Fig. 5-17. Relationships (70)

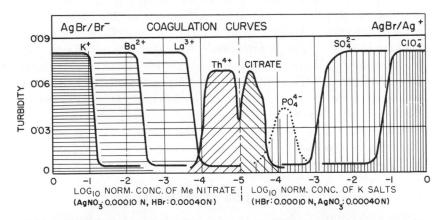

Fig. 5-17. Schematic presentation of precipitation and coagulation curves for silver bromide *in statu nascendi* showing the effect of coagulating ions (the curves represent precipitation, 10 min after mixing).

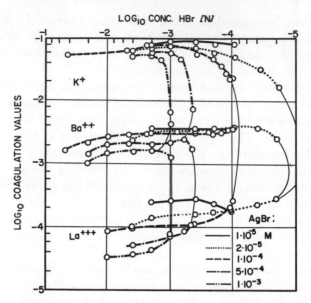

Fig. 5-18. Influence of the concentration of sols and stabilizing ions on the coagulation values of potassium, barium, and lanthanum nitrates (70).

between the coagulation values of mono-, di-, and trivalent ions ($K^+$, $Ba^{2+}$, $La^{3+}$), the concentration of stabilizing (lattice) ions ($Br^-$), and the sol (AgBr) concentration are shown in Fig. 5-18. The coagulation values change sharply for low concentrations of stabilizing ions but are relatively impervious to higher concentrations. It is also evident from the plot that the coagulation values decrease with sol concentration. The curves obtained for mono-, di-, and trivalent ions of the same sol concentration are equidistant, which is in agreement with Whetham's formulation of the Schulze-Hardy rule.

The correlation of the ionic size of the coagulating ions and the logarithm of their coagulation values (71) (2) is given in Fig. 5-19. It can be seen that a linear relationship was observed in all cases.

## 14. Solvent Effect on Stability

The effect of the solvent on the stability of colloid suspensions may be regarded as very complex. A clear differentiation should be made between the influence of relatively large amounts of organic solvents, where the dielectric constant is changed considerably, and the addition of small quantities of nonelectrolytes, which may influence the surface properties of the solid phase while not greatly affecting the overall dielectric constant (72).

Since lyophobic suspensions are stabilized by electrical repulsion, the dielectric constant of the surrounding medium plays an important part in stability theories. Thus, an effort has been made, both experimentally and theoretically, to define the relationship between coagulation concentrations of counterions and the dielectric constant of the solvent. The Verwey-Overbeek (62,64) picture of flocculation caused by compression of the electrical double layer leads to a

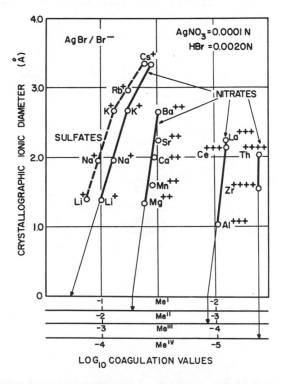

Fig. 5-19. The relationship between the crystallographic radii of coagulating cations and their coagulation values for negative silver bromide sols *in statu nascendi* (71).

theoretical relation between critical coagulation concentration and solvent dielectric constant of the form

$$C_{coag} \propto (\text{dielectric constant})^3$$

This relation is in fair agreement with some results (Table 5-3) but can only be said to be a rough approximation. The results of systematic experimental studies on silver halide sols (69,72,73) have shown that the logarithm of the coagulation values of mono-, di-, and trivalent electrolytes increases linearly with the increasing dielectric constant of the medium. These results are in qualitative agreement with earlier observations, which have been reviewed by Ostwald, Kokkoros, and Hoffmann (74). However, it has been found that sols prepared in different mixtures of solvents having the same dielectric constants do not necessarily have the same stability, thus indicating that specific solid–liquid interactions occur.

TABLE 5-3

The Effect of the Dielectric Constant of the Solvent upon the Stability of Suspended Precipitates

| Suspension | Flocculating electrolyte | Solvent | Flocculation concentration, mmole/liter | Dielectric constant |
|---|---|---|---|---|
| AgI | NaClO$_4$ | Water | 142[b] | 78.5 |
| | | Acetone | 1.4[b] | 20.7 |
| HgS | NaCl | Water | 13[c] | — |
| | LiCl | Methanol | 4.7[a] | 32.6 |
| | LiCl | Propanol | 3.3[a] | 20.1 |
| | SrCl$_2$ | Water | 0.88[c] | |
| | CaCl$_2$ | Methanol | 0.095[a] | |
| | CaCl$_2$ | Propanol | 0.044[a] | |
| | CaCl$_2$ | Pentanol | 0.012[a] | 13.9 |

[a] Results of H. B. Weiser and G. L. Mack, *J. Phys. Chem.*, **86**, 107 (1930).
[b] E. L. Mackor, *Rec. Trav. Chim.*, **70**, 841 (1951).
[c] H. Freundlich and H. Schucht, *Z. Physik. Chem.*, **85**, 641 (1913).

## 15. Summary

It is relevant to ask, in view of the complexity of agglomeration processes, how the results of nucleation, growth, and colloidal instability may be deduced from the morphological features of the precipitate. Until recently, the interplay of these features was thought to be unresolvable. In fact, the older literature abounds (75–80) with the concept that the formation of heteropolar precipitates of low solubility from aqueous solution proceeds through two distinct stages: (1) the formation of primary particles and (2) their agglomeration into secondary structures. This statement is only partially true. It has been seen previously that agglomeration is not generally important in systems where there are fewer than $10^7$ particles/ml (approximately) at any stage of the precipitation reaction. Consequently, any precipitation system which involves heterogeneous nucleation followed by crystal growth is unlikely to involve secondary growth by agglomeration (unless dendritic fragmentation has occurred). Conversely, the system which has undergone homogeneous nucleation will have sufficient particles to undergo agglomeration unless electrical stabilization is feasible.

Since the incidence of heterogeneous and homogeneous nucleation is decided by the supersaturation and interfacial energy, it is not, in general, difficult to make predictions regarding the nature of the precipitate. Some examples are perhaps instructive.

Let us suppose that a precipitate is to be formed by careful direct mixing of reagents in such a manner that the final concentration is $10^{-3}M$, and ask what predictions can be made about precipitate morphology. First, materials which are of solubility $<10^{-6}M$ will in all probability undergo homogeneous nucleation and will show colloidal phenomena, precipitation will depend upon stability, and precipitates will be agglomerated (e.g., very insoluble hydroxides, AgI, CdS, and many salts in nonaqueous solvents). In the solubility range at $10^{-6}$ to $10^{-3}M$ it is instructive to examine AgCl, $CaC_2O_4$, and $BaSO_4$, which are typical of low, intermediate, and high interfacial-energy materials, respectively; each is soluble to approximately $10^{-5}M$. Silver chloride undergoes homogeneous nucleation and is therefore subject to colloidal phenomena. Calcium oxalate is super saturated to a degree which is close to the onset of homogeneous nucleation and hence will give dendritic crystals which may fragment. At higher concentrations calcium oxalate will show agglomeration and electrolytic stabilization. Barium sulfate is considerably undersaturated with respect to the concentration at which homogeneous nucleation occurs and consequently will precipitate as fairly compact crystals with some evidence of dendritic growth. Lead sulfate,

TABLE 5-4
Dependence of Precipitate Morphology upon the Supersaturation and
Interfacial Energy

| Initial supersatura-tion ratio | Interfacial energy | Nucleation | Growth | Morphology |
|---|---|---|---|---|
| 1–2 | High | None | None | — |
| | Low | Heterogeneous | Slow—predom. screw disloc. | Discrete, well-formed crystals, no agglomeration |
| 2–5 | High | Heterogeneous | Slow—predom. surface nucl. | Discrete, well-formed crystals, no agglomeration |
| | Low | Heterogeneous | Dentritic | Poorly formed or dendritic crystals, no agglomeration |
| 10–50 | High | Heterogeneous | Dendritic | Poorly formed or dendritic crytals, no agglomeration |
| | Low | Homogeneous or ancillary | — | Stability dependent, agglomeration evident |
| > 1000 | High | Homogeneous | — | Stability dependent, agglomeration evident |
| | Low | Homogeneous | — | Colloidal |

which is supersaturated only to about $300\%$ at $10^{-3}M$, will produce well-formed crystals with little or no evidence of dendrites.

In consequence, it may be stated that colloidal phenomena can occur only in systems which have undergone homogeneous or extensive ancillary nucleation. [Although there may be exceptions due to large numbers of nucleating impurities ($\gg 10^7$ particles/ml), this situation is likely to be rare.]

Probably then, the most important single feature in determining precipitate morphology is the supersaturation. At low degrees of supersaturation precipitate crystals are well formed, the shape depending on the crystallographic structure and surface energetics. Habit modification is determined by the influence of the solvent and foreign ions and molecules on the surface energetics. At higher supersaturations growth is modified, higher-energy planes emerging and dendritic crystals being produced. At high supersaturations colloidal phenomena are observed. These effects are summarized in Table 5-4.

## References

1. E. Hofer, *Z. Physik. Chem.*, **183A**, 455 (1939).
2. P. H. Egli and S. Zerfoss, *Discussions Faraday Soc.*, **5**, 64 (1949).
3. L. Gordon, J. L. Salutsky, and H. H. Willard, *Precipitation from Homogeneous Solution*, Wiley, New York, 1959.
4. V. K. LaMer and M. D. Barnes, *J. Colloid Sci.*, **1**, 71, 79 (1946).
5. V. K. LaMer, *J. Phys. Chem.*, **52**, 65 (1948).
6. P. E. Pierce and S. H. Maron, *J. Colloid Sci.*, **19**, 658 (1964).
7. M. J. Herak, M. M. Herak, B. Težak, and J. Kratohvil, *Arhiv. Kem.*, **27**, 117, (1955).
8. M. Miura, Y. Tsuchiya and Y. Murekami, *J. Sci. Hiroshima Univ.*, Ser. *A-II*, **26**, 151 (1963).
9. P. P. von Weimarn, *Chem. Rev.*, **2**, 217 (1925).
10. S. Z. Lewin and J. E. Vance, *J. Am. Chem. Soc.*, **74**, 1433 (1952).
11. E. Suito and K. Takiyama, *Bull. Chem. Soc. Japan*, **27**, 121 (1954).
12. J. J. Black, M. J. Insley, and G. D. Parfitt, *J. Phot. Sci.*, **12**, 86 (1964); personal communications.
13. R. Kern, *Compt. Rend.*, **236**, 830 (1953).
14. R. Kern and M. Tillman, *Compt. Rend.*, **236**, 942 (1953).
15. I. M. Kolthoff and B. van't Riet, *J. Phys. Chem.*, **63**, 817 (1959).
16. A. Sover and V. Kriwobok, *Ural'sk. Polytekhn. Inst.*, **5**, 387 (1929).
17. A. E. Nielsen, *Kinetics of Precipitation*, Pergamon, London, 1964.
18. D. D. Saratovkin, *Dendritic Crystallization*, transl. J. E. S. Bradley, Consultants Bureau Inc., New York, 1959.
19. W. W. Mullins and R. F. Sekerka, *J. Appl. Phys.*, **34**, 323 (1963).
20. R. F. Sekerka, *Crystal Growth*, H. S. Peiser, Ed., Pergamon Press, New York, 1967, p. 691.
21. J. W. Cahn, *Crystal Growth*, H. S. Peiser, Ed., Pergamon Press, New York, 1967, p. 681.
22. K. A. Jackson and J. D. Hunt, *Acta Met.*, **13**, 1212 (1965).
23. K. A. Jackson, J. D. Hunt, D. R. Uhlmann, and T. P. Seward, *Trans. AIME*, **236**, 149 (1966).

24. B. V. Enüstün and J. Turkevich, *J. Am. Chem. Soc.*, **82**, 4502 (1960).
25. T. P. Melia, *J. Appl. Chem. London*, **15**, 345 (1965).
26. T. P. Melia and W. P. Moffitt, *Ind. Eng. Chem. Fundamentals*, **3**, 313 (1964).
27. S. S. Brenner and G. W. Sears, *Acta Met.*, **4**, 268 (1956).
28. J. A. Hamilton, J. A. Koutsky, and A. G. Walton, *Nature*, **204**, 1085 (1964).
29. A. G. Walton and J. A. Hamilton, *Nature*, **206**, 819 (1965).
30. I. N. Stranski, *Discussions Faraday Soc.*, **5**, 13 (1949).
31. K. Moliere, W. Rathje, and I. N. Stranski, *Discussions Faraday Soc.*, **5**, 21 (1949).
32. I. N. Stranski, *Z. Krist.*, **105**, 287 (1943).
33. I. N. Stranski, *Z. Physik. Chem.*, **136**, 259 (1928).
34. W. Kleber, *Zbl. Miner. Geol. Palaont.*, **A**, 363 (1938).
35. G. Bradistilov and I. N. Stranski, *Z. Krist.*, **103**, 1 (1940).
36. P. Hartman, *Neues Jahrb. Mineral. Monatsh.*, **1959**, 73.
37. A. F. Wells, *Phil. Mag.*, **37**, 183, 217 (1946).
38. A. F. Wells, *Discussions Faraday Soc.*, **5**, 197 (1949).
39. A. F. Wells, *Structure and Properties of Surfaces*, R. Gomer and C. S. Smith, Eds., Univ. of Chicago Press, Chicago, 1953, p. 240.
40. M. Mehmel and W. Nespital, *Z. Krist.*, **A88**, 345 (1934).
41. S. Z. Lewin, *J. Phys. Chem.*, **59**, 1030 (1955).
42. J. H. Raynaud and J. Pouradier, *J. Chim. Phys.*, **52**, 133 (1955).
43. V. D. Kuznetsov, *Crystals and Crystallization*, Gostekhizdat, Moscow, 1953.
44. T. S. Eckert and W. G. France, *J. Am. Ceram. Soc.*, **10**, 579 (1927).
45. F. G. Keenan and W. G. France, *J. Am. Ceram. Soc.*, **10**, 821 (1927).
46. W. G. France, in *Colloid Chemistry*, Vol. 5, J. Alexander, Ed., Reinhold, New York, 1944, p. 447.
47. P. Niggli, *Z. Anorg. Allgem. Chem.*, **110**, 55 (1920).
48. J. J. P. Valeton, *Z. Physik*, **21**, 606 (1920); **59**, 135, 335 (1924).
49. I. M. Kolthoff, *J. Phys. Chem.*, **40**, 1027 (1936).
50. C. Frondel, *Am. Mineralogist*, **25**, 91 (1940).
51. K. N. Davies and J. Whetstone, *J. Chem. Soc.*, **1954**, 865.
52. J. Whetstone, *Trans. Faraday Soc.* **51**, 1142 (1955).
53. J. Whetstone, *J. Chem. Soc.*, **1956**, 4841.
54. H. E. Buckley, *Crystal Growth*, Wiley, New York, 1951.
55. J. Nyvlt, *Chem. Prumysl*, **12**, 170 (1962).
56. G. T. Stewart, *Nature*, **183**, 873 (1959); **192**, 624 (1961).
57. J. D. Bernal, *Trans. Faraday Soc.*, **29**, 1032 (1933).
58. G. W. Gray, *Molecular Structure and the Properties of Liquid Crystals*, Academic Press, London, 1962.
59. M. von Smoluchowski, *Z. Physik*, **17**, 557, 585 (1916).
60. M. von Smoluchowski, *Z. Physik. Chem.* **92**, 129 (1917).
61. S. Chandrasekhar, *Rev. Mod. Phys.*, **15**, 59 (1943).
62. J. Th. G. Overbeek, *Colloid Science*, H. R. Kruyt, Ed., Elsevier, Amsterdam, 1952, Chap. VII.
63. N. Fuchs, *Z. Physik*, **89**, 736 (1934).
64. E. J. W. Verwey and J. Th. G. Overbeek, *Theory of the Stability of Lyophobic Colloids*, Elsevier, Amsterdam, 1948, p. 116.

65. M. Mirnik and B. Težak, *Trans. Faraday Soc.*, **50**, 65 (1954).
66. W. C. D. Whetham, *Phil. Mag.*, **48**, 474 (1899).
67. W. Ostwald, *Kolloid-Z.*, **85**, 34 (1938).
68. B. Težak et al., *Z. Physik. Chem.*, **175**, 219 (1936); **190**, 257 (1942); **191**, 270 (1942); *J. Phys. Chem.*, **57**, 801 (1953); *Discussions Faraday Soc.*, **18**, 194 (1954).
69. B. Težak et al., *Discussions Faraday Soc.*, **19**, 63 (1955).
70. B. Težak, E. Matijević, and K. Schulz, *J. Phys. Chem.*, **55**, 1567 (1951).
71. B. Težak, E. Matijević, and K. Schulz, *J. Phys. Chem.*, **59**, 769 (1955).
72. J. Kratohvil, M. Orhanović, and E. Matijević, *J. Phys. Chem.*, **64**, 1216 (1960).
73. M. Mirnik, F. Flagsman, and B. Težak, *Kolloid-Z.*, **185**, 138 (1962).
74. W. Ostwald, H. Kokkoros, and K. Hoffmann, *Kolloid-Z.*, **81**, 48 (1937).
75. H. B. Weiser, *Inorganic Colloid Chemistry*, Vol. III, Wiley, New York, 1938.
76. D. Balarev, *Der disperse Bau der festen Systeme*, Steinkopff, Dresden and Leipzig, 1939.
77. O. Hahn, *Angew. Chem.*, **43**, 871 (1930).
78. I. M. Kolthoff, *J. Phys. Chem.*, **36**, 860 (1932).
79. R. Fricke, *Kolloid-Z.*, **56**, 166 (1931); **96**, 217 (1941).
80. J. Traube and W. Behren, *Z. Physik. Chem.*, **A138**, 85 (1928).

CHAPTER 6

# COMPLEX PRECIPITATION SYSTEMS

*Contributed by* Helga Füredi, Ph.D.*

In the previous chapters the mechanism of precipitate formation and growth has been explored in detail. It has been demonstrated that the surface, shape, composition, and structure of a precipitate are determined by the interaction of many processes, such as homogeneous and heterogeneous nucleation, crystal growth, agglomeration, adsorption of constituent or foreign ions on the surface of the precipitate, and coprecipitation. Which processes will be dominant depends on the experimental conditions under which precipitation occurs. Chemical equilibria have also to be taken into account in order to predict whether or not a precipitate is to be formed.

It is not an easy matter, then, to predict the characteristics of a precipitate even in two-component, much less in complex, multi-component precipitation systems. It seems necessary, therefore, to direct studies toward a survey on the influence of changes in the concentration of each individual component in solution. The type of information which might result from such analyses is related to the composition, morphology, and structure of the precipitate. as well as to solubility and complex stability constants.

By means of such systematic surveys Težak and co-workers have unveiled the characteristics of a number of complex systems. The methodology of obtaining, presenting, and evaluating experimental data will be examined next in more detail.

## 1. Experimental Methods and Techniques

Numerous data are required for a survey of the influence of changes in concentration of the components in a multicomponent system, especially when wide concentration ranges are investigated. For this reason fairly simple and time-saving experiments have been devised.

* Department of Physical Chemistry, Ruđer Bošković Institute, Zagreb, Yugoslavia.

The technique of sample preparation and investigation developed by Težak and co-workers (1) consists of the preparation of a series of solutions with various known concentrations of the components of the system under investigation. Usually the concentration of one of the components is varied to produce precipitates while the concentrations of all other components are kept constant. In this manner the maximum concentration attainable before the onset of precipitation may be determined and, hence, the precipitation boundary is established.

Changes in the extent of precipitation and agglomeration, as well as the variation of particle size, may be followed kinetically by turbidity (tyndallometric) measurements.

As previously mentioned (Chap. 2), it is not easy to find light scattering methods which give accurate indications of particle sizes, but a suitable (approximate) method is as follows. For white precipitates the ratio of the extinction coefficients (2) $\epsilon_{\lambda_1}/\epsilon_{\lambda_2} = DQ$ (dispersion quotient) and the turbidities (3) $\tau_{\lambda_1}/\tau_{\lambda_2} = DQ_T$ taken at two different wavelengths $\lambda_1$ and $\lambda_2$ are constant for a given degree of dispersion over a wide range of sol concentrations. It has been shown that a linear relationship exists between the dispersion quotient and the particle size in the range of 50–100 m$\mu$ for $DQ_T$, respectively. For polydisperse systems average particle sizes can thus be estimated by measuring extinction coefficients or turbidities at two different wavelengths and determining $DQ$ or $DQ_T$.

## 2. Evaluation of Equilibrium Constants

Applications of solubility measurements to studies of equilibria in solutions have been extensively discussed by Rossotti and Rossotti (4). These methods will not be discussed further, but an approximate graphical method will be reviewed. This method, which was originally developed for silver halide and thiocyanate complexes (5), has since been shown to yield satisfactory results when applied to precipitation and solubility data from several different systems (6–11). At equilibrium conditions, when no complexes are formed in solution or the composition and stability constants of the complexes are known, the composition and solubility product of the solid phase can be evaluated. On the other hand, when the solid phase is in equilibrium with complex species $B_mA_n$, the charge and, if $m$ is known, the overall (cumulative) stability constants of the complexes can be determined, provided the composition and solubility constant of the solid phase is known. However, the method cannot be applied to distinguish between mono- and polynuclear complexes of the same charge (4,5,9).

Application of the graphical technique to solubility curves and precipitation boundaries must be preceded by a short discourse on the relationship between solubility and complex stability constants where the formation of only one complex is considered at a time. The existence of true thermodynamic equilibrium in all stepwise reactions is assumed in this treatment and the definitions of equilibrium constants are those given by Bjerrum, Schwarzenbach, and Sillén (12).

### A. METAL–LIGAND COMPLEX FORMATION (5,6)

The formation of a solid phase $B_yA_x$ from ionic solution may be represented in simplest terms as follows:

$$yB^{z+} + xA^{y-} \rightleftharpoons B_yA_x(\text{solid}) \tag{6-1}$$

and

$$[B^{z+}]^y[A^{y-}]^x = K_{S_0} \tag{6-2}$$

where the brackets represent ionic activities and $K_{S_0}$ is the solubility product. If the equilibrium activities are plotted on a logarithmic scale,* the slope of the resulting straight line, which is represented by

$$\log [B^{z+}] = -\frac{x}{y} \log [A^{y-}] + \frac{1}{y} \log K_{S_0} \tag{6-3}$$

is equal to the ratio of the numbers of anions and cations forming the precipitate.

The solubility product may be obtained from the intercept of the straight line with the $y$ axis.

If $B_yA_x$ forms a soluble complex $B_mA_n^{(ny-mx)-}$ with the ligand $A^{y-}$, the reaction

$$(m/y)B_yA_x(\text{solid}) + (n - mx/y)A^{y-} \rightleftharpoons B_mA_n^{(ny-mx)-}$$

---

* All log values in this chapter are to base 10, unless otherwise stated.

ensues. Then at equilibrium (6-4)

$$\frac{[B_mA_n^{(ny-mx)-}]}{[A^{y-}]^{n-mx/y}} = K_{S_{mn}} \tag{6-5}$$

or

$$\log [B_mA_n^{(ny-mx)-}] = (n-mx/y) \log [A^{y-}] + \log K_{S_{mn}} \tag{6-6}$$

From Eq. 6-2

$$K_{S_0}^{m/y} = [B^{x+}]^m[A^{y-}]^{mx/y} \tag{6-7}$$

Dividing Eq. 6-5 by Eq. 6-7 gives

$$\frac{[B_mA_n^{(ny-mx)-}]}{[B^{x+}]^m[A^{y-}]^n} = \frac{K_{S_{mn}}}{K_{S_0}^{m/y}} = \beta_{mn} \tag{6-8}$$

where $\beta_{mn}$ is the overall association constant of the complex $B_mA_n^{(ny-mx)-}$.

If the stability constant of the complex is large ($\beta_{mn} \geq 10^3$), nearly all of the $B^{x+}$ ions in solution are in the form $B_mA_n^{(ny-mx)-}$ and log $[B_mA_n^{(ny-mx)-}]$ may be substituted by the logarithm of the solubility. If the composition of the solid phase $B_xA_y$ is known and is constant, the charge of the polynuclear complex $(ny - mx)-$ and the solubility constant $K_{S_{mn}}$ may be derived from the slope and intercept of the straight line described by Eq. 6-6.

If a mononuclear complex is formed ($m = 1$) or $m$ is determined by some other method (e.g., potentiometry), the composition of the complex and the stability constant $\beta_{mn}$ can be also determined (Eqs. 6-6 to 6-8). An essentially similar procedure enables the charge and overall stability constant of a cationic complex $B_mA_n^{(mx-ny)+}$ to be determined.

## B. Metal–Hydroxide Complex Formation (7–9)

The equilibrium between a soluble metal ion hydroxide complex and the corresponding slightly soluble metal hydroxide may be similarly described by Eqs. 6-9 to 6-12.

$$mB(OH)_x(\text{solid}) + (mx - n)H^+ \rightleftharpoons B_m(OH)_n^{(mx-n)+}$$
$$+ (mx - n)H_2O \tag{6-9}$$

$$*K_{S_{mn}} = \frac{[B_m(OH)_n^{(mx-n)+}]}{[H^+]^{mx-n}} \tag{6-10}$$

$$pH = -\frac{1}{mx-n} \log [B_m(OH)_n^{(mx-n)+}] + \frac{1}{mx-n} \log *K_{S_{mn}} \tag{6-11}$$

and corresponding to Eq. 6-8

$$\frac{[B_m(OH)_n^{(mx-n)+}][H^+]^n}{[B^{z+}]^m} = \frac{*K_{S_{mn}}}{*K_{S_0}^m} = *\beta_{mn} \tag{6-12}$$

where

$$*K_{S_0} = [B^{z+}]/[H^+]^z \tag{6-13}$$

The charge of the polynuclear complex $B_m(OH)_n^{(mx-n)+}$ and the solubility constant $*K_{S_{mn}}$ may be derived from the slope, $-1/(mx-n)$, and intercept, $1/(mx-n) \log *K_{S_{mn}}$ of the straight line described by Eq. 6-11 under the same conditions as in the previous case ($*\beta_{mn} \geq 10^3$ and the composition of the solid phase is known and constant).

If $m$ is known, the composition and the cumulative stability constant $*\beta_{mn}$ of the complex may be also determined (Eqs. 6-11 and 6-12).

## C. PROTON COMPLEXES

A similar procedure to the preceding enables the evaluation of the equilibrium constants of a slightly soluble acid in equilibrium with its soluble proton complexes.

$$nH_yA(\text{solid}) + (m - ny)H^+ \rightleftharpoons H_mA_n^{(m-ny)+} \tag{6-14}$$

$$pH = -\frac{1}{m-ny} \log [H_mA_n^{(m-ny)+}] + \frac{1}{m-ny} \log K_{S_{mn}} \tag{6-15}$$

The overall stability constant of the proton complex is then

$$\frac{[H_mA_n^{(m-ny)+}]}{[H^+]^m[A^{y-}]^n} = \frac{K_{S_{mn}}}{K_{S_0}^n} = \beta_{mn} \tag{6-16}$$

where

$$K_{S_0} = [H^+]^y[A^{y-}] \tag{6-17}$$

## D. MIXED SALT FORMATION (10,11)

Chemical reactions leading to the formation of slightly soluble mixed salts with incorporated hydrogen or hydroxyl ions in simplest terms may be represented as follows:

$$p\mathrm{B(OH)}_x + q\mathrm{H}_y\mathrm{A} \rightleftharpoons \mathrm{B}_p\mathrm{H}_r\mathrm{A}_q(\text{solid}) + px\mathrm{H}_2\mathrm{O} \qquad (6\text{-}18a)$$

and

$$p\mathrm{B(OH)}_x + q\mathrm{H}_y\mathrm{A} \rightleftharpoons \mathrm{B}_p\mathrm{OH}_{(-r)}\mathrm{A}_q(\text{solid}) + qy\mathrm{H}_2\mathrm{O} \qquad (6\text{-}18b)$$

where $r = qy - px \geq 0$.

The degree of dissociation of $\mathrm{B(OH)}_x$ and $\mathrm{H}_y\mathrm{A}$ depends on their respective stability constants and on the pH of the solution. The prevailing species in solution are then $\mathrm{OH}^-$, $\mathrm{H}_3\mathrm{O}^+$, $\mathrm{B(OH)}_{x-i}^{i+}$, and $\mathrm{H}_{y-j}\mathrm{A}^{j-}$ ions where $i = 0,1,2 \ldots x$ and $j = 0,1,2 \ldots y$, respectively, depending on the pH. If we then assume that the chemical potential for water molecules is essentially constant in dilute solutions, the logarithmic form of the equation involving the solubility products of both $\mathrm{B}_p\mathrm{H}_r\mathrm{A}_q$ and $\mathrm{B}_p\mathrm{OH}_{(-r)}\mathrm{A}_q$ is as follows:

$$\log \left[\mathrm{B(OH)}_{x-i}^{i+}\right]\left[\mathrm{OH}^-\right]^i = -\frac{q}{p}\log\left[\mathrm{H}^+\right]^j\left[\mathrm{H}_{y-j}\mathrm{A}^{j-}\right] + \frac{1}{p}\log K_{S_0} \quad (6\text{-}19)$$

where the activities of the species $\mathrm{B(OH)}_{x-i}^{i+}$ and $\mathrm{H}_{y-j}\mathrm{A}^{j-}$ are related to the pH of the solution through their corresponding base and acid association constants. Equation 6-19 corresponds to Eq. 6-3, which is valid for neutral electrolytes.

Thus, a knowledge of the activities of the corresponding ionic species in equilibrium with the solid phase enables the ratio of ions forming the precipitate to be determined if it can be assumed that no complexes are formed in solution. If $q$ or $p$ is known, the composition of the precipitate and the solubility product follow from Eq. 6-19. Since in this case various types of reactions may lead to complex formation, a general type cannot be considered at this stage. However, it should not be difficult to obtain the appropriate equations for a particular system in the same manner as Eqs. 6-6, 6-8, 6-11, 6-12, 6-15, and 6-16.

### 3. The Solubility Curve

We now return to the problem of determining constants of the preceding type from solubility and precipitation data. If only one complexing process occurs in solution, variation of the concentrations of the system's components readily enables solubility and complex stability constants to be obtained via equations of the type 6-3, 6-6, 6-8, 6-11, 6-12, 6-15, 6-16, 6-19, and so on. In practice the solubility curve usually reflects many different equilibria. The solubility of $BA_x$ in terms of complex species $B_mA_n$ is given by (4)

$$[B] = \sum_1^M \sum_0^N m[B_mA_n] = \sum_1^M \sum_0^N m\beta_{mn}K_{S_0}{}^m[A]^{n-mx} \quad (6\text{-}20)$$

However, we may construct solubility curves on a log-log diagram and by taking secants or tangents convert the data into an appropriate form for interpretation by means of Eqs. 6-3, 6-6, 6-11, 6-15, and 6-19. Thus, a simple graphical method (5) is available to determine the composition and stability of the various complexes which are in equilibrium with the solid phase.

The solubility curves of silver halides and silver thiocyanate are represented in Fig. 6-1a. Both solubility data, as compiled from the literature (13), and precipitation data (5,14), obtained as described in the first part of this chapter, were used for the construction of the curves. The composition of the solid phase was independent of the solution concentrations* and, thus, the equilibrium constant equations are applicable.

In Fig. 6-1b (5) the solubility curve of silver bromide is approximated by secants, as described by Eq. 6-6. The values of the slopes $b = ny - (mx/y)$ which are indicated on the diagram, determine the composition of the complexes $AgBr_n{}^{(n-1)-}$ and $Ag_mBr^{(m-1)+}$, which are dominant in the corresponding concentration regions. Since the formation of only mononuclear complexes was assumed in this case, $x = y = m = 1$. The various complexes then have $n = 1\text{--}5$ in the lower part of the diagram and $m = 3$ and 4 in the upper part ($m = 1$ and 2 are not shown). The secant with the slope $b = -1$ represents the solubility product $K_{S_0}$ and is thus given by Eq. 6-3.

---

* Assuming an activity coefficient of unity.

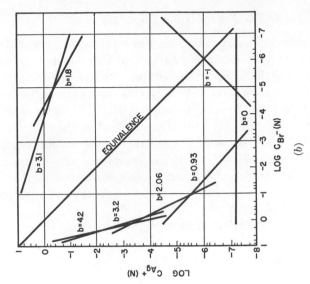

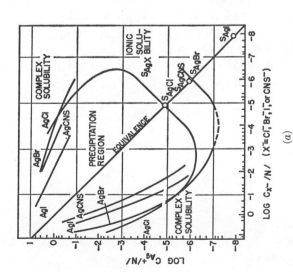

Fig. 6-1. (a) The solubility curves of silver halides and silver thiocyanate in aqueous solutions. (After J. Kratohvil, B. Težak, and V. B. Vouk, ref.5). (b) Solubility curve of silver bromide in aqueous solutions of potassium bromide and silver nitrate approximated by secants. (After J. Kratohvil, B. Težak, and V. B. Vouk, ref. 5)

## 4. The Precipitation Boundary

The precipitation boundary, which may be established by turbidity measurements as described in the first part of this chapter, may or may not coincide with the solubility curve.  The reason for this is the fact that the precipitation boundary establishes the metastable limit of supersaturation for any given system.  We have seen in Chapter 1 that this metastable limit is determined by the presence of impurities and the formation of a critical nucleus which precedes heterogeneous nucleation.  Thus, if no complexes are formed in solution, the precipitation boundary actually reflects upon the characteristics (composition and standard free energy of formation) of the critical nucleus (11).

Ideally, if homogeneous nucleation were involved, the precipitation boundary would be shifted toward higher concentrations of the precipitating components such that the following equations would hold:

$$(^*K_{S_{\mathrm{pptn}}}/K_{S_0})^{1/2} = s^* \tag{6-21a}$$

or

$$(^*K_{S_{\mathrm{pptn}}}/K_{S_{mn}})^{1/2} = s^* \tag{6-21$b$}$$

where $s^*$ is the critical supersaturation and $^*K_{S_{\mathrm{pptn}}}$ is the critical ionic product which could be obtained from the tangents or secants to the precipitation boundary by substituting $^*K_{S_{\mathrm{pptn}}}$ for $K_{S_0}$ or $K_{S_{mn}}$ in Eqs. 6-3, 6-6, 6-11, 6-15, and 6-19.

The relation between the standard free energy of formation of the critical nucleus, $\Delta G^0$, and $^*K_{S_{\mathrm{pptn}}}$, is then

$$\Delta G^0 = -RT \ln {^*K_{S_{\mathrm{pptn}}}} \tag{6-22}$$

Normally, since impurities always initiate heterogeneous nucleation,

$$^*K_{S_{\mathrm{pptn}}} > K_{S_{\mathrm{pptn}}} \geq K_{S_0} \tag{6-23}$$

and

$$s^* > s \geq 0 \tag{6-24}$$

The constant $K_{S_{\mathrm{pptn}}}$ and the supersaturation $s$ are characteristics of the particular system.

If very low degrees of supersaturation are attainable and a stable precipitate is formed, the precipitation boundary may be considered to correspond with the solubility curve and, thus, the same criteria may be applied in equilibrium studies. Substitution of the precipitation boundary for the solubility curve in such cases (5–9) has experimental advantages.

If the two curves do not coincide (11,15,16), the composition of the critical nucleus is determined by the slope of tangents or secants to the precipitation boundary, while the composition of the bulk solid phase may be obtained from the solubility curve. Hence, the comparison of the two curves (11,14) yields the additional information as to whether the composition of both nuclei and the precipitate is the same or the solid phase is formed by a solid-state transformation via a metastable precursor.

## 5. Graphical Presentation of Precipitation Data

Not only the solubility but the physical and chemical characteristics of the precipitate also are largely dependent on the concentrations of all ions in solution. Von Weimarn (17) was among the early authors to report on this subject. He constructed precipitation curves relating the extent of precipitation or the particle size to the concentrations of the precipitating components at equivalent ratio. In order to obtain more information, Težak and his collaborators proposed various other types of graphical presentation of precipitation data, which will be described in some detail.

### A. EVALUATION OF COAGULATION VALUES FROM KINETIC PRECIPITATION DATA (1)

It was shown in Chapter 5 that neutral electrolytes may induce coagulation of stable sols. The critical concentration of an electrolyte necessary to induce coagulation (coagulation value) may be determined from kinetic measurements as follows.

Turbidities and particle sizes, obtained by means of tyndallometric measurements as described at the beginning of this chapter, are plotted as a function of time in terms of time tyndallograms (turbidity vs. time) and time dispersoidograms (particle size vs. time).

In Figs. 6-2a and 6-2b time tyndallograms of a silver bromide sol which was coagulated with various concentrations of potassium

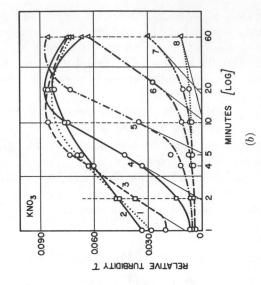

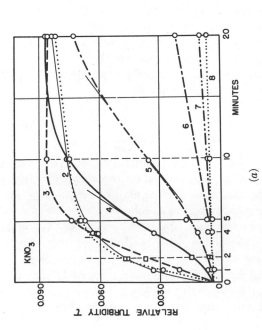

Fig. 6-2. (a) Time tyndallograms (turbidity vs. time, 20°C) of aqueous systems containing silver nitrate ($1 \times 10^{-4}N$), hydrobromic acid ($1.1 \times 10^{-4}N$), and various concentrations of potassium nitrate: the 2-min and 10-min values are marked by dashed lines. (After B. Težak, E. Matijević, and K. Schulz, ref. 1). (b) A semilogarithmic plot (turbidity vs. log time) of the systems represented in Fig. 6-2a: the 2-min, 10-min, and 60-min values are marked by dashed lines. (After B. Težak, E. Matijević, and K. Schulz, ref. 1)

nitrate are represented. From these plots some critical properties of the system may be defined. The slopes $\Delta\tau/\Delta t$ of the tangents to the steepest parts of the coagulation curves in Fig. 6-2a showing the greatest increase of turbidity at a given time are taken as the agglomeration rates. The intersections of the tangents with the abscissa in the logarithmic plot (Fig. 6-2b) are called the critical coagulation times, $t_c$.

If the agglomeration rate $\Delta\tau/\Delta t$ and the critical time $t_c$ are plotted as functions of the concentration of potassium nitrate (Figs. 6-3a and 6-3b), the regions of slow, moderate, and rapid agglomeration may be distinguished.

It is obvious from Fig. 6-3b that in both the regions of slow and rapid agglomeration the process is concentration insensitive; the

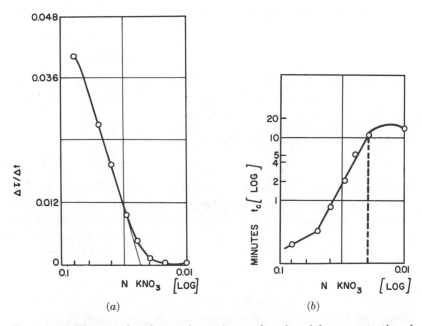

Fig. 6-3. (a) The rate of agglomeration $\Delta\tau/\Delta t$ as a function of the concentration of potassium nitrate for the systems represented in Figs. 6-2a and 6-2b. (After B. Težak, E. Matijević, and K. Schulz, ref. 1). (b) The critical coagulation times log $t_c$, determined from Fig. 6-2b, as a function of the concentration of potassium nitrate. (After B. Težak, E. Matijević, and K. Schulz, ref. 1)

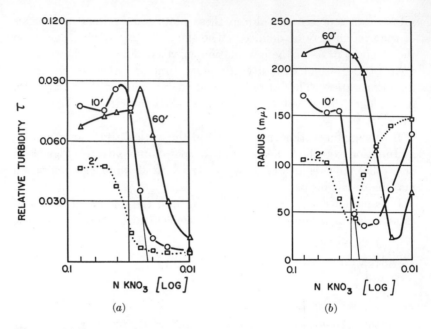

Fig. 6-4. (a) Concentration tyndallograms: turbidity vs. concentration of a silver bromide sol coagulated with potassium nitrate. (After B. Težak, E. Matijević, and K. Schulz, ref. 1). (b) Concentration dispersoidograms (particle size vs. concentration) of a silver bromide sol coagulated with potassium nitrate. (After B. Težak, E. Matijević, and K. Schulz, ref. 1)

reverse is true in the region of moderate precipitation rates. The concentration at the onset of moderate agglomeration is then taken to be the coagulation value of the electrolyte (intersection of tangent and abscissa in Fig. 6-3a, and dashed line and abscissa in Fig. 6-3b). The critical time $t_c$ corresponding to the coagulation value may be read from the $t_c$ vs. concentration plot (10 min, Fig. 6-3b). Once the critical coagulation time is established, further coagulation values may be obtained by plotting turbidities or particle sizes obtained at that time against the concentration of the electrolyte as it is shown in Figs. 6-4a,b. The intersections of the tangents on the steepest parts of the 10-min curves with the abscissa give approximately the same coagulation value for potassium nitrate as was obtained from Figs. 6-3a and 6-3b.

## B. PRECIPITATION CURVES (18–21)

The starting point in the investigation of a complex precipitation system should be the construction of appropriate precipitation curves where the experimental data, reflecting some characteristic feature of the precipitate (turbidities, particle size, quantitative data, and so on), are presented as a function of the logarithm of the concentration* of one of the components in solution at constant concentrations of the others.

The simplest precipitation curve may consist of only one narrow precipitation maximum.  An example (19) is given in Fig. 6-5.  The lower curve is the precipitation curve of the system uranyl nitrate $(10^{-1}N)$–sodium carbonate, while the upper curve shows the corresponding pH values.

If the precipitation region spreads out over a wide range of concentrations of the precipitating components, the corresponding precipitation curve may show various maxima and minima of different origin.  As an example a typical precipitation curve of the system silver nitrate–potassium bromide (18,21) is shown in Fig. 6-6. It actually consists of two curves, which join at equivalent concentrations of the precipitating components.  To the right of this point the concentration of silver nitrate increases at constant concentration of potassium bromide, while to the left of the equivalence point the concentration relations are reversed.  The concentration of the salt is constant and a precipitate was formed in the whole region between the boundaries of complex solubility.  The precipitation maxima and minima stem from agglomeration and stabilization of the sol. (For a treatment of these phenomena, see Chapter 5.)  Thus, at nearly equivalent concentrations of the precipitating components an isoelectric maximum is observed, which is due to coagulation at the zero point of charge.  Both bromide and silver ions, when in excess, stabilize the sol, which accounts for the stability regions on both sides of the isoelectric maximum.  Finally, the negative and positive concentration maxima occur as a result of coagulation of the precipitate when the coagulation values of potassium and nitrate ions are exceeded (compare Fig. 5-17).

---

* The final concentration, which an ion would have after mixing if no reaction had taken place, is plotted in all diagrams.

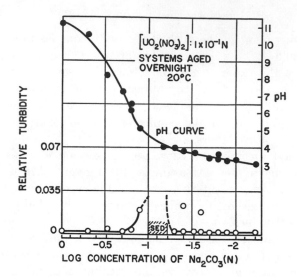

Fig. 6-5. Precipitation and pH curve of the system uranyl nitrate ($10^{-1}N$)–sodium carbonate.   (After H. Füredi, ref. 19)

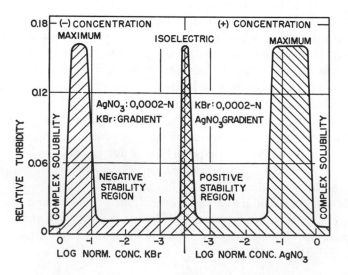

Fig. 6-6. Ten-min precipitation curve of silver bromide: sol concentration $2 \times 10^{-4}N$. (After E. Matijević, ref. 21)

In more complicated systems both physical and chemical processes may interact and give rise to precipitation maxima which cannot be easily explained. A more general characterization of the system may then be obtained by means of more extensive precipitation diagrams and bodies, which follow.

## C. PRECIPITATION DIAGRAMS—TWO-COMPONENT SYSTEMS

A two-component system can be completely characterized by means of a three-dimensional diagram where a convenient parameter, characterizing the precipitate, is plotted on the $z$ axis as a function of the concentrations of both precipitating components, which are plotted on the $x$ and $y$ axes. Such a diagram may be constructed from a number of precipitation curves, each representing a different, constant concentration of one of the precipitating components.

Figure 6-7 shows how a precipitation (lower) and pH (upper) diagram of the system uranyl nitrate–sodium carbonate (19) was constructed. The cross sections are precipitation and pH curves similar to those represented in Fig. 6-5, each of them taken at a different, constant concentration of uranyl nitrate.

The construction of models (21–24) was used by Težak and collaborators to visualize some of the more complicated precipitation diagrams.

The photographs in Fig. 6-8 (22) show the precipitation body of silver bromide representing the precipitation region which is designated in Fig. 6-1a. In order to make full use of this type of presentation, several important cross sections should be examined.

For convenience, a line representing equivalent concentrations of the initially added precipitating components ("Equivalence" in Fig. 6-1) was introduced. This line divides the precipitation diagram into two symmetrical parts; in each part one of the precipitation components is in excess. Any line parallel to the equivalence line represents a different, constant ratio of the precipitating components.

It has been already shown (Fig. 6-1b) that for a symmetric electrolyte the line representing the solubility product $K_{S_0}$ has a slope $b = -1$ and is thus perpendicular to the equivalence. Any line parallel to the one representing the solubility product also represents a different but constant ionic product. The same reasoning, of

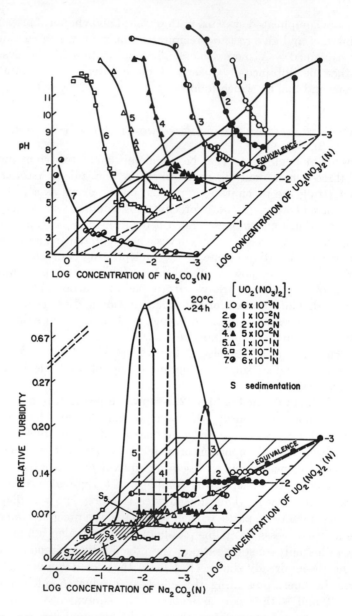

Fig. 6-7. Three-dimensional precipitation and pH diagram of the system uranyl nitrate–sodium carbonate.   (After H. Füredi, ref. 19)

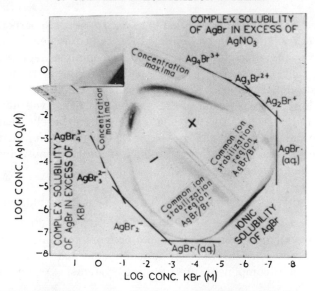

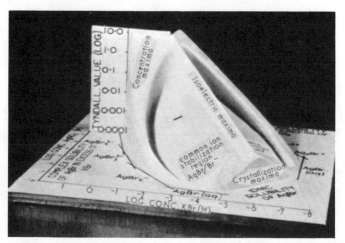

Fig. 6-8. Photographs of a model of the precipitation body of silver bromide. Data obtained in aqueous solution, 20°C, 10 min after mixing. (After B. Težak, ref. 22)

course, is valid for cross sections parallel to any given secant or tangent which may be approximated to the solubility curve.

Precipitation curves are cross sections parallel to either the $x$ or the $y$ axis. The precipitation curve which is represented in Fig. 6-6 consists of two halves—each parallel to one of the axes, perpendicular to each other, and joining at one point of the equivalence line.

The various precipitation maxima and minima represented in Fig. 6-8 may now be easily understood. The isoelectric maximum (coagulation at zero point of charge) nearly coincides with the equivalence line. The positions of the positive and negative stabilization regions and concentration maxima are also immediately clear (compare also the description of Fig. 6-6). The crystallization maximum, which occurs at a constant ionic product, is most probably due to the onset of homogeneous nucleation.

## D. PRECIPITATION DIAGRAMS—THREE- AND MULTICOMPONENT SYSTEMS (23–28)

By convenient combinations of two or more general precipitation diagrams sufficient information may be obtained to characterize complex, multicomponent precipitation systems. As an example,

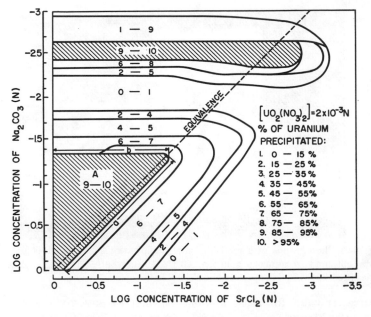

Fig. 6-9. Contour diagram of the precipitation system uranyl nitrate ($2 \times 10^{-3}N$)–sodium carbonate–strontium chloride. In the region marked $A$ (9–10) more than 85% uranium was coprecipitated with strontium carbonate. (After H. Füredi and B. Težak, ref. 24)

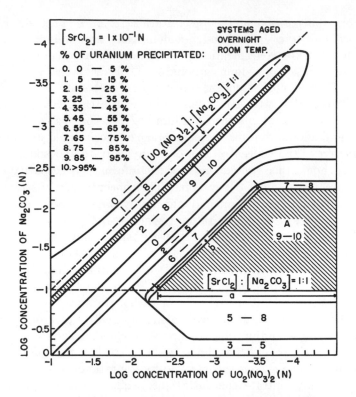

Fig. 6-10. Contour diagram of the precipitation system uranyl nitrate–sodium carbonate–strontium chloride ($10^{-1}N$). In the region marked $A$(9–10) more than 85% uranium was coprecipitated with strontium carbonate. (After H. Füredi, ref. 25)

the precipitation of uranium in the three-component system uranyl nitrate–sodium carbonate–strontium chloride (24,25) will be considered. The percentage of precipitated uranium may be followed as a function of the concentrations of the precipitating components.

In Figs. 6-9 and 6-10 the data are represented by contour diagrams in planes of concentrations of the precipitating components. The contours enclose areas with comparable percentages of precipitated uranium. The regions where more than 85% uranium was precipitated are shaded. In Fig. 6-9 the results are shown as a function of the concentrations of sodium carbonate and strontium chloride, at a constant concentration of uranyl nitrate. Two different maxima of uranium precipitation can be distinguished.

From the position of the precipitation region against the equivalence line it is immediately evident that uranium precipitates mainly when the concentration of strontium chloride is higher than the concentration of sodium carbonate.  [This fact is easily explained by the formation of soluble, complex uranyl carbonates (29).]  It is also evident that with strontium chloride in excess, changes in its concentration do not influence uranium precipitation to a great extent. Another diagram, showing the percentage of precipitated uranium as a function of the concentrations of uranyl nitrate and sodium carbonate, should then provide most of the information necessary for a full characterization of the system.  The concentration of strontium chloride should be constant and sufficiently large to be in excess in the major part of the precipitation region.

The diagram represented in Fig. 6-10, which shows the influence of changes in concentration of uranyl nitrate and sodium carbonate at a constant concentration $(10^{-1}N)$ of strontium chloride, fulfills these requirements.  In this diagram, both the line representing equivalent concentrations of sodium carbonate and uranyl nitrate and the one representing equivalent concentrations of sodium carbonate and strontium chloride are represented.  The contours are parallel to either of these lines, indicating that precipitation of uranium in some regions is controlled by the ratio of sodium carbonate and uranyl nitrate concentrations, while in other regions the ratio of sodium carbonate and strontium chloride is dominant.

The two regions of uranium precipitation which were already mentioned (Fig. 6-9) may be distinguished in this diagram also. After comparison of these with the corresponding pH values, it was assumed that the narrow maximum which occurs at a constant ratio of sodium carbonate and uranyl nitrate is due to hydrolytic precipitation of uranium, while the larger precipitation region is a result of the coprecipitation of uranium with strontium carbonate.  Additional experiments confirmed these assumptions (26).

By using the information which may be obtained from Figs. 6-9 and 6-10, it is possible to represent any given region of precipitation or dissolution of uranium in a system of concentrations of all three precipitation components.  Arbitrarily, the region where more than 85% uranium was coprecipitated with strontium carbonate (shaded regions marked $A(9–10)$ in Figs. 6-9 and 6-10) was chosen as an example. The following conclusions may be derived about this region:

(*1*) When the contours marked *a* in Figs. 6-9 and 6-10 are compared, it is obvious that, regardless of the actual concentrations of the precipitation components, the following requirement must be fulfilled if more than 85% uranium is to be coprecipitated:

$$[SrCl_2] \geq [Na_2CO_3] \tag{6-25}$$

(*2*) The contours marked *b* in Figs. 6-9 and 6-10 indicate that the ratio between the concentrations of sodium carbonate and uranyl nitrate at the boundary of the coprecipitation region has also a constant value in the range of $5 \times 10^{-3}$ to $3 \times 10^{-4} N$ uranyl nitrate.

A more detailed analysis of the results (25) rendered the second requirement for the coprecipitation of more than 85% uranium with strontium carbonate in this concentration range

$$\log [Na_2CO_3] \geq 0.76 \log [UO_2(NO_3)_2] + 0.7 \tag{6-26}$$

Within the limit of their validity, expressions 6-25 and 6-26 generally define the coprecipitation region. The contours at any given concentration of uranium may thus be obtained from their equalities. The data may be plotted in a three-dimensional diagram, as shown in Fig. 6-11. The region where more than 85% uranium was coprecipitated is represented as a body in a system of concentrations of strontium chloride (*x* axis), sodium carbonate (*y* axis), and uranyl nitrate (*z* axis). The cross sections represent the coprecipitation regions at different, constant concentrations of uranyl nitrate. The dotted cross section corresponds to the shaded region marked *A* (9–10) in Fig. 6-9.

## 6. Applications

The outlined methods and techniques have been the basis for extensive studies of precipitation and agglomeration phenomena, which were carried out by Težak and his collaborators (18,22,27,30). The most important of these contributions have been already described in Chapter 5.

The simplicity of the experiments and the convenience of the graphical presentations makes these methods equally attractive for survey studies of complex systems because broad concentration ranges of all constituents can be investigated relatively easily.

We have seen that a simple and time-saving, if somewhat approximate, method is available for equilibrium studies, which gives satisfactory results for many purposes. These results may also be used as preliminaries for a more rigorous treatment, which then may be limited to a smaller set of more exact but somewhat time-consuming experiments.

Apart from extensive studies on the complex solubility of silver halides and thiocyanate, which have been carried out in aqueous solutions (5,14) and mixed solvents (6), contributions to equilibrium studies have included investigations of the solubilities of thorium (7),

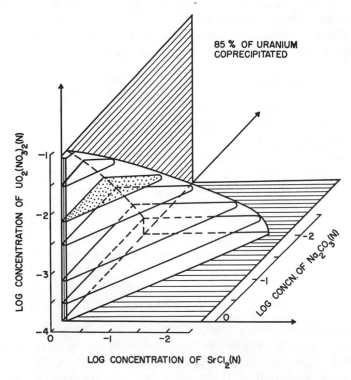

Fig. 6-11. Precipitation body, representing the concentration region, where more than 85% uranium was coprecipitated with strontium carbonate. Dotted plane corresponds to the shaded region marked $A$ (9–10) in Fig. 6-9. (After H. Füredi, ref. 25)

rare earth (8), and zirconium hydroxides (9), carried out in wide ranges of pH and metal ion concentrations. For convenience, the precipitation boundary was substituted for the solubility curve in all the above systems and the results were in fair agreement with data stemming from solubility measurements.

A set of equations similar to Eqs. 6-9 to 6-12 has been derived for the interpretation of the data on thorium hydroxide precipitation (7). The rectilinear parts of the precipitation boundary were used for the computation of equilibrium constants. The solubility constants of the rare earth hydroxides (8) were similarly computed from the logarithmic form of Eq. 6-13. The set of data on the precipitation of zirconium hydroxide (9) was fitted by a least-squares computer program to give the "best" solution for the equation of the solubility curve (Eq. 6-20). All the above-mentioned systems are of considerable importance in nuclear technology.

Progress has also been made in the interpretation of the inorganic function in biological systems. A set of equations similar to Eqs. 6-18 and 6-19 has been derived by MacGregor and Brown (10) for the determination of calcium phosphates in young and adult bone. It was concluded that in young bone octacalcium phosphate and in adult bone hydroxyapatite dominates the equilibrium.

The physiological nucleation of calcium phosphates presents another complicated problem which has been subject to many discussions. This problem should be approached from two aspects: investigations of heterogeneous nucleation of inorganic material on organic substrates or vice versa, and studies of the characteristics of the nuclei of calcium phosphates as a function of all factors constituting a physiological system. The first aspect has been discussed in detail in Chapter 1. The second approach calls for systematic investigations of the type described in this chapter. Some results have already evolved from studies of the precipitation boundary in a wide range of pH and calcium ion concentrations (15).

An interesting method for the detection of the charge of complex ions in solutions ensues from coagulation measurements (31). It was shown in Chapter 5 that the charge of the counterion significantly influences its coagulation value. Thus, if well-defined sols are coagulated with complex ions, their charge would be indicated by their respective coagulation values, which can be determined graphically as described in this chapter. However, this method has its limitations when mixtures of differently charged ions are present in solution because of the much higher sensitivity of ions with a higher charge (see Eq. 5-7).

In biology, geology, the chemistry of natural waters, and so on, often quite complex, heterogeneous equilibrium or metastable non-equilibrium systems are encountered. Some examples have already been given in this and earlier chapters. The solutions of some technological problems also require a knowledge of the various factors influencing precipitation processes. By means of precipitation curves and diagrams such precipitation systems can be mapped, thus locating the concentration areas in which one or more of the constituents determining the composition, structure, and physical characteristics of the precipitates are dominant, and separating different precipitation processes, which can then be studied by more elaborate techniques involving a limited number of samples.

The amount and quality of data to be obtained depends on the particular system and the kind of information needed. In some cases a few precipitation curves may be quite conclusive; in other systems two or more precipitation diagrams are necessary.

A typical example is the survey of the precipitation system uranyl nitrate–sodium carbonate–strontium chloride (19,24,25), which was outlined above. This system, as well as similar ones containing barium, calcium, and magnesium chloride (19,23–26), is of both scientific and technological interest. Diagrams shown in Figs. 6-9 to 6-11 gave general information about the precipitation processes involved, which was then extended by studies of the morphology and composition of the precipitates.

Such diagrams should also be helpful for the solution of technological problems, for instance, when the optimum conditions for the leaching of uranium from high lime ores (32) are considered. Empirical expressions similar to expressions 6-25 and 6-26 could be derived for any given area of precipitation or dissolution of uranium and could be used to adjust the concentrations of the precipitating components to effect precipitation or dissolution of uranium.

Another interesting practical example is as follows. In order to ensure maximum productivity of a cell for the electrolytic reduction of uranium(VI) into uranium(IV) and subsequent precipitation of uranium dioxide (33,34), Pravdić, Branica, and Pučar established the boundary of precipitation of uranium(IV) from carbonate solutions at different temperatures (34). Thus, the conditions under which the electrochemical reduction of uranium(VI) results in stable carbonate solutions of uranium(IV) were determined. The slope of the precipitation boundary indicates that precipitation of uranium-(IV) from these solutions may be achieved by simply diluting them with water.

Further contributions to the chemistry of uranium(VI) and thorium have evolved from systematic studies of the precipitation of alkaline metal and alkaline earth uranates (35), uranyl phosphates with and without addition of alkaline metals (28), and the interaction of thorium nitrate with some dicarboxylic acids (20,36) (phthalic, oxalic, maleic, and fumaric acid). Wide ranges of pH and concentrations of the precipitating components were surveyed and the results are presented in terms of precipitation curves and diagrams showing the regions of precipitation, ionic and complex solubility, and the distribution of the prevalent compounds in the systems. Data on the extent of uranium precipitation (28,35) and on the morphological characteristics and solubility of some complex uranyl phosphates (28) are also available.

## Acknowledgments

I wish to express my appreciation to Professor L. G. Sillén, *Kgl. Tek. Högskol.*, Stockholm, Sweden, and Dr. V. Pravdić, Ruđer Bošković Institute, Zagreb, Yugoslavia, for their consideration of and helpful comments on the manuscript of this chapter.

I am indebted to H. Bilinski, M. Branica, L. G. Sillén, and W. E. Brown for making their manuscripts (refs. 9 and 11) available to me prior to publication.

## References

1. B. Težak, E. Matijević, and K. Schulz, *J. Phys. Chem.*, **55**, 1557 (1951).
2. T. Teorell, *Kolloid-Z.*, **53**, 322 (1930); **54**, 58 (1931).
3. B. Težak, *Z. Phys. Chem.*, **A175**, 219, 284 (1936).
4. F. J. C. Rossoti and H. Rossoti, *The Determination of Stability Constants*, McGraw-Hill, New York, 1961.
5. J. Kratohvil, B. Težak, and V. B. Vouk, *Arhiv Kem.*, **26**, 191 (1954).
6. J. Kratohvil and B. Težak, *Arhiv Kem.*, **26**, 243 (1954); *Rec. Trav. Chim.*, **75**, 774 (1956); *Croat. Chem. Acta*, **29**, 63 (1957).
7. H. Bilinski, H. Füredi, M. Branica, and B. Težak, *Croat. Chem. Acta*, **35**, 19 (1963).

8. Z. Orhanović, B. Pokrić, H. Füredi, and M. Branica, *Croat. Chem. Acta*, **38** 269 (1966).
9. H. Bilinski, M. Branica, and L. G. Sillén, *Acta Chem.*, **20**, 853 (1966).
10. J. MacGregor and W. E. Brown, *Nature*, **205**, 359 (1965).
11. W. E. Brown, Transcript of the First Conference on the Biology of Hard Tissue, Princeton, 1966, N.Y. Acad. Sci. (in press).
12. J. Bjerrum, G. Schwarzenbach, and L. G. Sillén, *Stability Constants of Metal Ion Complexes, Part II, Inorganic Ligands*, The Chemical Society, London, W. 1, 1958.
13. A. Seidel, *Solubilities of Inorganic and Metal Organic Compounds*, Vol. 1, 3rd ed., New York, 1940; J. Kendall and C. H. Sloan, *J. Am. Chem. Soc.*, **47**, 2306 (1925); J. H. Jonte and D. S. Martin, *ibid.*, **74**, 2052 (1952); A. Pinkus et al., *Bull. Soc. Chim. Belges*, **45**, 693 (1936); **46**, 46 (1937); **47**, 304 (1938); I. Leden, *Svensk Kem. Tidskr.*, **64**, 249 (1952); E. Berne and I. Leden, *ibid.*, **65**, 88 (1953); E. Berne and I. Leden, *Z. Naturforsch.*, **8a**, 719 (1953); J. A. Gledhill and G. McP. Malan, *Trans. Faraday Soc.*, **50**, 126 (1954); W. Erber and A. Schühly, *J. Prakt. Chem.*, **158**, 176 (1941); W. Erber, *Z. Anorg. Allgem. Chem.*, **248**, 32, 36 (1941); H. Chateau and J. Pouradier, *Sci. Ind. Phot.*, **24**, 129 (1953); E. L. King, H. J. Krall, and M. L. Pandow, *J. Am. Chem. Soc.*, **74**, 3492 (1952); M. Randall and J. O. Halford, *ibid.*, **52**, 178 (1930); G. C. B. Cave and D. M. Hume, *ibid.*, **75**, 2893 (1953).
14. K. Schulz and B. Težak, *Arhiv Kem.*, **23**, 200 (1951); V. B. Vouk, J. Kratohvil, and B. Težak, *ibid.*, **25**, 219 (1953); J. Kratohvil and B. Težak, *Croat. Chem. Acta*, **29**, 63 (1957).
15. H. Füredi and A. G. Walton, referred to at the Intern. Symp. Nucleation Phenomena, Cleveland, April 7–9, 1965 (to be published).
16. M. M. Herak, M. J. Herak, J. Kratohvil, and B. Težak, *Croat. Chem. Acta*, **29**, 67 (1957).
17. P. P. v. Weimarn, *Die Allgemeinheit des Kolloid-Zustandes*, T. Steinkopff, Dresden, Leipzig, 1925.
18. B. Težak et al., *Discussions Faraday Soc.*, **18**, 63 (1955).
19. H. Füredi, Ph.D. thesis, University of Zagreb, Yugoslavia, 1963.
20. H. Bilinski, H. Füredi, and B. Težak, *Croat. Chem. Acta*, **35**, 31 (1963); H. Bilinski, Z. Veksli, M. Branica, and B. Težak, 2nd Yugoslav Symp. Reactor Materials, Herceg Novi, Oct. 13–16, 1965 (to be published); H. Bilinski, *Croat. Chem. Acta*, **38**, 71 (1966).
21. E. Matijević, *Chimia Aarau*, **9**, 287 (1955).
22. B. Težak, *Discussions Faraday Soc.*, **18**, 223 (1954).
23. B. Težak, H. Füredi, and M. Branica, *Proc. 2nd Intern. Conf. Peaceful Uses At. Energy, Geneva*, 1958, **28**, p. 250.
24. H. Füredi and B. Težak, *Croat. Chem. Acta*, **36**, 119 (1964).
25. H. Füredi, *Croat. Chem. Acta*, **36**, 195 (1964).
26. H. Füredi, Z. Devidé, M. Wrischer, and B. Težak, presented at the 150th Meeting of the American Chemical Society, Sept. 1965 (to be published).
27. B. Težak, R. Wolf, and S. Kratohvil, *J. Chim. Phys.*, **55**, 307 (1958); E. Palić-Schütz, D. Težak, and B. Težak, *Croat. Chem. Acta*, **36**, 133 (1964).

28. E. Matijević and N. Pavković, *Kolloid-Z.*, **159**, 1 (1958); N. Pavković, M. Branica, M. Wrischer, and B. Težak, 17th Intern. Congr. Pure Applied Chemistry (IUPAC), Munich, 1959; N. Pavković, M. Branica, M. Wrischer, and B. Težak, 2nd Yugoslav Symp. Reactor Materials, Herceg Novi, Oct. 13–16, 1965 (to be published).
29. L. A. McClaine, E. P. Bullwinkel, and J. C. Huggins, *Proc. Intern. Conf. Peaceful Uses At. Energy, Geneva, 1955*, **8**, 26 (1956); C. A. Blake et al., *J. Am. Chem. Soc.*, **78**, 5978 (1956).
30. B. Težak and S. Kratohvil, *J. Polymer Sci.*, **12**, 221 (1954); B. Cernicki and B. Težak, *Croat. Chem. Acta*, **28**, 13, 175 (1956); **29**, 7 (1957); **30**, 1 (1958); see also ref. 63 in Chap. 5.
31. B. Težak, E. Matijević, and K. Schulz, *J. Am. Chem. Soc.*, **73**, 1605 (1951); E. Matijević and B. Težak, *J. Phys. Chem.*, **57**, 951 (1953); B. Težak, E. Matijević, J. Kratohvil, and H. Füredi, Symp. Coordination Chemistry, Copenhagen, Aug. 9-13, 1953; E. Matijević, *J. Colloid Sci.*, **20**, 322 (1965).
32. F. M. Stephens, Jr., and R. D. MacDonald, *Proc. 2nd Intern. Conf. Peaceful Uses At. Energy, Geneva, 1955*, **8**, p. 18; J. H. Gittus, *Uranium*, Butterworths, Washington, 1963.
33. V. Pravdić, M. Branica, and Z. Pučar, *Electrochem. Technol.*, **1**, 312 (1963); *Proc. Conf. New Nucl. Mater. Including Non-Metal Fuels, Prague, 1963*, **1**, p. 55.
34. V. Pravdić, M. Branica, and Z. Pučar, "Uranium Dioxide Production. A Survey of Electrochemical Reduction and Precipitation from Carbonate Solution," 3rd Intern. Conf. Peaceful Uses At. Energy, Geneva, Aug. 31–Sept. 9, 1964; *Croat. Chem. Acta*, **35**, 281 (1963).
35. B. Tomažič, M. Branica, and B. Težak, *Croat. Chem. Acta*, **34**, 41 (1962); B. Tomažič, Z. Veksli, K. Popović, and M. Branica, 2nd Yugoslav Symp. Reactor Materials, Herceg Novi, Oct. 13–16, 1965 (to be published); B. Tomažič and M. Branica, *Croat. Chem. Acta*, **38**, 249 (1966).
36. B. Težak, M. Branica, H. Füredi, and N. Šimunović, *Proc. Intern. Conf. Peaceful Uses At. Energy, Geneva, 1955*, **7**, p. 401.

# AUTHOR INDEX

Numbers in parentheses are reference numbers and indicate that the author's work is referred to although his name is not mentioned in the text. Numbers in *italics* show the pages on which complete references are listed.

Abrahamson, E. W., 65, *77*
Albon, N., 54(15), *76*
Aleksandrova, G. I., 126(24), 134(24), *149*
Alexander, A. E., 24(24), *42*
Anderson, W., 140, *149*
Avgut, N. N., 126(47), *150*

Baer, E., 35(43), 36(43), *43*
Balarev, D., 183(76), *187*
Barnes, M. D., 73, *78*, 153, *185*
Beattie, W. H., 73, *78*
Becker, R., 3(2,3), *42*, 51, *76*
Behren, W., 183(80), *187*
Bennett, G. F., 44, *76*
Benson, G. C., 115(4), 116, 117(5), 118, 122(5), 129, *148*, *149*
Berezin, G. I., 126(47), *150*
Berger, R., 140, *149*
Bernal, J. D., 175(57), *186*
Berne, E., 194(13), *214*
Bernett, M. K., 129(20), *149*
Bever, R. J., 68(64), *77*
Bhattacharryya, S. N., 91(21), *111*
Bilinski, H., 189(7,9), 190(9), 191(7, 9), 197(7,9), 201(20), 211(7,9), 213(20), *214*
Bircumshaw, L. L., 60(37), *77*
Bjerrum, J., 190, *214*
Black, J. J., 28, *42*, 156, *185*
Blackadder, D. A., 44, *76*
Blake, C. A., 208(29), *215*
Block, J., 98, *112*
Borosik, M., 109(47), *112*
Bowers, R. C., 145(39), *149*

Boyd, G. E., 83, 84, *111*, 126(48), *150*
Bradistilov, G., 166(35), *186*
Bradley, R. S., 3(5), 13, *42*
Branica, M., 189(7-9), 190(9), 191(7-9), 197(7-9), 201(20), 203(23), 206(23,28), 211(7-9), 212(23), 213, *214*, *215*
Brenner, S. S., 165(27), *186*
Brescia, F., 69, *78*
Bridgers, H. E., 100, 101, *112*
Brown, L. M., 64(49), *77*
Brown, W. E., 189(10,11), 193(10,11), 196(11), 197(11), 211, *214*
Brunauer, S., 137, 139(28), *149*
Bryzgalova, R. V., 91(19,20), *111*
Buckley, H. E., 56(31), *77*, 174, *186*
Bullwinkel, E. P., 208(29), *215*
Bunn, C. W., 54, 60, *76*
Burton, J. A., 100, *112*
Burton, W. K., 45, 50, 51, *76*
Burtt, B. P., 96(28e), *112*

Cabrera, N., 45, 50, 51, *76*
Cahn, J. W., 6(9,10), *42*, 163, *185*
Cave, G. C. B., 194(13), *214*
Cernicki, B., 30(49), *43*, 209(30), *215*
Chandrasekhar, S., 175(61), *186*
Chang, C., 84(7), *111*
Channel-Evans, K. M., 85(12), *111*
Chateau, H., 194(13), *214*
Chessick, J. J., 134(25), 135, *149*
Chlopin, V., 81, 87(23), *111*, *112*
Christian, J., *43*
Christiansen, J. A., 7, *42*, 67, *77*
Claxton, T. A., 118(8), *149*

Collie, B., 129, *149*
Collins, F. C., 27, *42*, 54(20), 62, 63, 67, 68(45), *76*, *77*
Corcoran, B. A., 35(48), 40(48), *43*

Dahlstrom, R., 126(49), *150*
Davies, C. W., 55, 57–59, 68, 69, 70(34), *76*, *77*
Davies, K. N., 174(51), *186*
Dawson, I. M., 47, *76*
Devidé, Z., 206(26), 208(26), 212 (26), *214*
DeWitt, T., 147(51), *150*
Diehl, H., 68(64), *77*
Dinegar, R. H., 27, *42*, 61(42), *77*
Döring, W., 3(2), *42*, 51, *76*
Doerner, H. A., 93, 98, *112*
Doremus, R. H., 56, 68, *77*
Duke, F. R., 64(49), 68(64), *77*
Dunning, W. J., 3(7), 16, *42*, 54(15), *76*
Durham, G. S., 84(11), *111*

Eanes, E. D., 37(45), 39, *43*, 111(48), *112*
Eckert, T. S., 173(44), *186*
Eggertsen, F. T., 145(39), *149*
Egli, P. H., 151(2), *185*
Ellefson, P. R., 65(54), *77*
Emmet, P., 147(51), *150*
Emmett, H., 54, 60, *76*
Enüstün, B. V., 136, 163(24), *186*
Erber, W., 194(13), *214*
Eval'd, G., 87(16), 89(16), 92, *111*
Evans, L. F., 20, *42*

Fabrikanos, A., 68(62), *77*
Feibush, A. M., 96(28b), *112*
Fine, M. E., *43*
Fischer, W. v., 145(39), *149*
Fisher, E. W., 33, *43*
Flagsman, F., 178(73), 182(73), *187*
Fletcher, N., 21, *42*
Fontal, B., 98, *112*
Fowkes, F. M., 125, 128, 132, 133, *149*
Fox, H. W., 129(19), *149*
Fox, P. G., 16(19), *42*
France, W. G., 173(44,45), *186*

Frank, F. C., 46, 47(5), 50, *76*
Frasson, E., 65(53), *77*
Frenkel, J., 3(4), *42*, 51, *76*
Freundlich, H., 182
Fricke, R., 183(79), *187*
Frisch, H. L., 54, 62, 67, *76*, *77*
Frondel, C., 174, *186*
Fuchs, N., 177(63), *186*
Füredi, H., 188, 189(7,8), 191(7,8), 197(7,8,15), 201(19,20), 202, 203(19,23,24), 204, 206, 207, 208(26), 209(25), 210, 211(7,8,15), 31), 212(19,23–26), 213(20,36), *214*, *215*
Fujiwara, S., 87, *111*

Gapon, E. M., 55
Geil, P. H., 49
Gibbs, J. W., 51, *76*
Gillesen, I., 37(45), 39, *43*
Gilman, J. J., 114(1), *148*
Gittus, J. H., 212(32), *215*
Gledhill, J. A., 194(13), *214*
Godycki, L. E., 65(52), *77*
Gordon, L., 27, *42*, 61(39–41), 63, 64(50), 65, *77*, 95(31), 96(28a,28b, 28e,31), 97, 98, *112*, 152, *185*
Gorshtein, G. I., 91(22), *112*
Gray, G. W., 175(58), *186*
Grebeinshchikova, V. I., 91(19, 20), *111*

Haberman, N., 61(41), *77*
Hackerman, N., 126(46), *150*
Hahn, O., 84(6), 87(17), 89(6,17), *111*, 183(77), *187*
Halford, J. O., 194(13), *214*
Halversen, R. A., 146(41), *149*
Ham, F. S., 54, *76*
Hamilton, J. A., 165(28,29), *186*
Harkins, W. D., 126 (48,49), *150*
Harper, R. A., 111(48), *112*
Hartman, P., 166, *186*
Hawkins, J. A., 84(11), *111*
Healy, F. H., 134(25), 135, *149*
Henderson, L., 82, 84(2), *111*
Herak, M. J., 106(44), *112*, 153(7), 154(7), *185*, 197(16), *214*

Herak, M. M., 153(7), 154(7), *185*, 197(16), *214*
Hermann, J. A., 96(28c), 98, 99, *112*
Higuchi, W. I., 56, 74, *77*, *78*
Hileman, O. E., 64(50), *77*
Hilliard, J. E., 6(9,10), *42*
Hirth, J. P., *43*
Hitch, T. T., 114(2), *148*
Hlabse, T., 69(66), *77*
Hofer, E., 151(1), *185*
Hoffmann, K., 182, *187*
Holland, H. D., 109, 110, *112*
Hook, A. van, 55(23), *76*
Hoskins, W. M., 93, 98, *112*
Howard, J. F., 24, *42*
Howard, J. R., 55(25), 59(36), 60(36), 70(36), *77*
Huggins, J. C., 208(29), *215*
Hume, D. M., 194(13), *214*
Hume-Rothery, W., 85(12), *111*
Hunt, J. D., 163(22,23), 164, *185*

II'in, B. V., 126 (24,44), 134, *149*, 150
Insley, M. J., 28, *42*, 64, *77*, 156, *185*

Jackson, K. A., 163, 164, *185*
Jacobs, P. W. M., 124(12), *149*
Jaycock, M. J., 62(43), 73(43), *77*
Johnson, C. E., 24(25), *42*
Johnson, R. A., 25(28), *42*, 68, *77*
Jones, A. L., 55, 69, *76*
Jonte, J. H., 194(13), *214*
Jucker, H., 98, *112*

Kading, H., 87(14), *111*
Kafavova, I. A., 91(22), *112*
Kahn, M., 88, 105, 106(25), *112*
Kantro, D. L., 137, *149*
Karataewa, A., 84(5), *111*
Keating, K. B., 48(16), 54(16), *76*
Keenan, F. G., 173(45), *186*
Keenan, R. G., 139(28), *149*
Kellermand, V. A., 140(30), *149*
Kendall, J., 194(13), *214*
Kern, R., 158, *185*
King, E. L., 194(13), *214*
Kiselev, A. V., 126(44,47), *150*

Kiselev, V. F., 126(24,44,45), 134(24), *149*, *150*
Kleber, W., 166(34), *186*
Klein, D. H., 27, *42*, 61(40), 63, 64, *77*, 98, *112*
Knapp, L. F., 117, *149*
Kokkoros, H., 182, *187*
Kolb, E. D., 100, 101, *112*
Kolthoff, I. M., 30(40), 31, 32, *43*, 84(8), 104, *111*, *112*, 145, 146(41–43), *149*, *150*, 158, 174(49), 183(78), *185–187*
Kossel, W., 51, *76*
Koutsky, J. A., 35(43), 36(43), *43*, 165(28), *186*
Kracek, F., 82, 84(2), *111*
Krall, H. J., 194(13), *214*
Kratohvil, J., 153(7), 154(7), 178(72), 181(72), 182(72), *185*, *187*, 189(5,6), 190(5,6), 194(5,14), 195, 197(5,6,14, 16), 206(27), 209(27,30), 211(5,6,14, 31), *213–215*
Kriwobok, V., 158, *185*
Kuznetsov, V. D., 173, *186*

Laitenen, H. A., 145, *149*
LaMer, V. K., 3(6), 27, *42*, 61, 73, *77*, *78*, 153, *185*
Lange, V. E., 140, *149*
Langer, A., 145(36), *149*
Leden, I., 194(13), *214*
Leineweber, J. P., 27, *42*, 62, 63, 68(45), *77*
Lewin, S. Z., 155, 173, *185*, *186*
Lichstein, B., 69, *78*
Lieser, K. H., 68(62), *77*
Likhacheva, O. A., 126(44), *150*
Lo, H. H., 35(51), *43*
Love, K. S., 139(28), *149*
Lucchesi, P. J., 68(63), *77*
Lygina, I. A., 126(47), *150*

Mabbott, G. W., 85(12), *111*
McCartney, E. R., 24(24), *42*
McClaine, 208(29), *215*
MacDonald, R. D., 212(32), *215*

MacGregor, J., 189(10), 193(10), 211, 214
McIntosh, R., 115(4), 148
Mack, G. L., 182
Mackor, E. L., 182
MacNevin, W., 104, 112
Makavov, L. L., 85, 86, 111
Malan, G. McP., 194(13), 214
Marc, R., 55, 76
Maron, S. H., 73(71,74), 78, 153, 185
Martin, A. W., 95, 112
Martin, D. S., 194(13), 214
Martin, G. R., 35(48), 40(48), 43
Matijević, E., 30(50), 43, 178 (70–72), 179(70), 180(70,71), 181 (71,72), 182(72), 187, 189(1), 197(1), 198–200, 201(21), 202, 203(21), 206(28), 211(31), 213(28), 213–215
Meehan, E. J., 73, 78
Mehmel, M., 172, 186
Melia, T. P., 165, 186
Melikhov, I. V., 87(16), 89, 92, 101, 103, 111, 112
Merkulova, M. S., 87(16), 89(16), 92, 101(39), 111, 112
Merwe, J. H. van der, 13, 14
Mirnik, M., 106(44), 112, 143, 144, 149, 177(65), 178(73), 182(73), 187
Miura, M., 153(8), 185
Moffitt, W. P., 165(26), 186
Moilliet, J. L., 129, 149
Moliere, K., 166(31), 186
Mullins, W. W., 162, 185
Mumbrauer, R., 95(29), 112
Munoz, J., 109(47), 112
Murekami, Y., 153(8), 185
Murkulova, M. S., 87(15), 111
Mutaftschiev, M. B., 143, 149

Nancollas, G. H., 55, 57–60, 61(28), 68, 70(34), 77
Nernst, W., 54, 58, 76
Nespital, W., 172, 186
Newkirk, J. B., 13, 17, 42
Niederhiser, D., 37(46), 43
Nielsen, A. E., 7, 30, 40, 41, 42, 43, 67–69, 77, 78, 158, 163, 185

Niggli, P., 174(47), 186
Noponen, G. E., 84(8), 111, 146(42), 150
Noyes, A. A., 54, 70, 76
Nyvlt, J., 174, 186

O'Brien, A., 145(37), 149
Orhanović, M., 178(72), 181(72), 182(72), 187
Orhanović, Z., 189(8), 191(8), 197(8), 211(8), 214
Oriani, R. A., 72(70), 78
O'Rourke, J. D., 25(28), 42, 68, 77
Ostwald, W., 178, 182, 187
Overbeek, J. Th. G., 176(62), 177(64), 178(62,64), 181, 186
Oxburgh, U. M., 109(47), 112

Palermo, J. A., 44, 76
Palić-Schütz, E., 206(27), 209(27), 215
Panattoni, C., 65(53), 77
Pandow, M. L., 194(13), 214
Paneth, F., 104, 112, 144, 147(52), 150
Parfitt, G. D., 28, 42, 67(43), 64, 73(43), 77, 156, 185
Parker, D. W., 16(19), 42
Parsons, R., 140, 149
Pavković, N., 206(28), 213(28), 215
Pierce, P. E., 73(71,74), 78, 153, 185
Pinkus, I., 194(13), 214
Pohl, H. A., 70, 71, 78
Pokrić, B., 189(8), 191(8), 197(8), 211(8), 214
Polessitsky, A., 84(4,5), 87(23), 89(26), 111, 112
Popović, K., 213(35), 215
Posner, A. S., 37(45), 39, 43, 111, 112
Pound, G. M., 43
Pouradier, J., 173, 186, 194(13), 214
Pravdić, V., 106(44), 112, 213, 215
Prim, R. C., 100, 112
Pučar, Z., 213, 215
Purdie, N., 55(26,27), 58, 59(36), 60, 70(36), 77
Purkayastha, B. C., 91(21), 111

Randall, M., 194(13), 214
Rathje, W., 166(31), 186

Ratner, A. P., 85, 86, *111*
Raynaud, J. H., 173, *186*
Reimer, C. C., 96(28e), *112*
Riddiford, A. C., 60(37), *77*
Riet, B. van't, 30(40), 31, 32, *43*, 158, *185*
Roberts, B. W., 76
Rosenblum, C., 145(39), *149*
Rossoti, F. J. C., 189, 190(4), 194(4), *213*
Rossoti, H., 189, 190(4), 194(4), *213*
Roth, A. E., 37(46), *43*
Rowly, K., 96(28a,28b), *112*
Rundle, R. E., 65(52), *77*

Saad, H. Y., 74(76), *78*
Salesin, E. D., 65, *77*
Salutsky, M. L., 61(39), *77*, 95, 96(28d,31), *112*, 152, *185*
Saratovkin, D. D., 159, *185*
Schiffmann, E., 33(41), 35(48), 40(48), *43*
Schlundt, H., 95, 96(28), *112*
Schucht, H., 182
Schühly, A., 194(13), *214*
Schulman, F., 129(18), *149*
Schulz, K., 178(70,71), 179(70), 180(70,71), 181(71), *187*, 189(1), 194(14), 197(1), 918-200, 211(14, 31), *213-215*
Schwarzenbach, G., 190, *214*
Sears, G. W., 6(11), 37, *42*, 51, 56, *76*, *77*, 165(27), *186*
Seidel, A., 194(13), *214*
Seifert, H., 35, *43*
Sekerka, R. F., 162, *185*
Seward, T. P., 163(23), *185*
Shafrin, E. G., 129(17), *149*
Shaver, K. J., 96(28f), *112*
Shcherbakova, K. D., 126(44), *150*
Shuttleworth, R., 117(7), 120, 124(7), *149*
Sillén, L. G., 189(9), 190, 191(9), 197(9), 211(9), *214*
Simunović, N., 213(36), *215*
Slichter, W. P., 100, *112*
Sloan, C. H., 194(13), *214*

Smoluchowski, M. V., 175-177, *186*
Sover, A., 158, *185*
Spinks, J., 145(38), 147, *149*
Stephens, F. M., Jr., 212(32), *215*
Stewart, G. T., 175(56), *186*
Stites, J. G., 95, 96(28d), *112*
Stow, R., 145(38), 147, *149*
Stranski, I., 51, *76*, 115, *148*, 166, *186*
Stutman, J. M., 37(45), 39(45), *43*
Suito, E., 25(29), 30, *42*, 156, *185*
Suttle, J. F., 98(34), 99(34), *112*

Takiyama, K., 25(29), 30, *42*, 156, *185*
Teorell, T., 189(2), *213*
Termine, J. D., 37(45), 39(45), *43*
Tesla-Tokmanovski, D., 106(44), *112*
Težak, B., 30, *43*, 153(7), 154(7), 177(65), 178, 179(69,70), 180(70,71), 181(71), 182(69,73), *185*, *187*, 188, 189, 190(5,6), 191(7), 194(5,14), 195, 197-200, 201(18,20), 203, 205, 206, 207(24), 208(26), 209, 211(5-7,14,31), 212(23,24,26), 213(20,28,35,36), *213-215*
Težak, D., 206(27), 209(27), *215*
Tillman, M., 158, *185*
Tobolsky, A. V., 84(9), *111*
Tolman, R. C., 142, *149*
Tomažić, B., 213(35), *215*
Tompkins, F. C., 124(12), *149*
Traube, J., 183(80), *187*
Treadwell, W. D., 98, *112*
Tsuchiya, Y., 153(8), *185*
Turkevich, J., 136, 163(24), *186*
Turnbull, D., 7, 8, 13, 17, *42*, 66, 67, *77*

Uhlmann, D. R., 163(23), *185*
Ulevitch, I. N., 73(71), *78*
Upreti, M. C., 9, 15(17), 17(17), 18(17), *42*
Urist, M., 33(41), *43*

Valeton, J. J. P., 174(48), *186*
Vance, J. E., 155, *185*
Van Zeggeren, F., 116(5), 117(5), 122(5), *149*
Vaslow, F., 83, 84, *111*

Veksli, Z., 201(20), 213(20,35), *214, 215*

Verwey, E. J. W., 177(64), 178(62,64), 181, *186*

Volmer, M., 3, *42*, 51, *76*

Vonnegut, B., 7, 8, *42*

Vouk, V. B., 189(5), 190(5), 194(5,14), 195, 197(5,14), 211(5,14), *213, 214*

Wade, W. H., 126(46), *150*

Wagner, C., 87(24), *112*

Walden, G. H., 108, *112*

Wallace, W. E., 84(10), *111*

Walnut, T. H., 27(33), *42*, 61(40), 63, *77*

Walter, Z., 95, 96(28), *112*

Walton, A. G., 3(8), 9, 17(17), 18(17), 19(20), 25(30), 30, 33(41), 35(43), 36(43), *42, 43*, 56, 64, 69, *77*, 108, *112*, 118, 122(11), *149*, 165(28, 29), *186*, 197(15), 211(15), *214*

Walton, G., 108, 112

Wang, J. H., 147

Watanabe, T., 37

Weimarn, P. P. v., 30(39), *43*, 155, *185*, 197, *214*

Weise, C. H., 137, *149*

Weiser, H. B., 182, 183(75), *187*

Weiss, R., 24(27), *42*, 68, *77*

Wells, A. F., 169, 170, *186*

Wert, C., 60(38), *77*

Westwater, J. W., 21, *42*

Westwood, A. R. C., 114(2), *148*

Weyl, W. A., 119

Whetham, W. C. D., 178, *187*

Whetstone, J., 174, *186*

Whitman, D. R., 118(10), *149*

Whitney, W. R., 54, 70, *76*

Wilbur, M., 37

Willard, H. H., 61(39), *77*, 95(31), 96(31), *112*, 152, *185*

Willems, I., 33(42), *43*

Willems, J., 33(42), *43*

Willing, E. G. J., 126 (50), *150*

Wolf, R., 206(27), 209(27), *215*

Wrischer, M., 206(26,28), 208(26), 212(26), 213(28), *214, 215*

Young, G. J., 134(25), 135, *149*

Yun, K. S., 129(21), *149*

Yutzy, H. C., 146(43), *150*

Zener, C., 60(38), *77*

Zerfoss, S., 151(2), *185*

Zettlemoyer, A. C., 134(25), 135, *149*

Zimiens, K., 145(35), *149*

Zipkin, I., 111(48), *112*

Zisman, W. A., 129, 132, *149*

# INORGANIC COMPOUND INDEX

AgBr, 13, 22, 30, 83, 84, 123, 146, 168, 174, 180, 181, 194, 195, 197, 200

AgCNS, 195, 209

AgCl, 13, 21, 22, 27, 28, 30, 56–61, 69, 74, 83, 84, 87, 123, 146, 150, 152, 156, 168, 174, 183, 194, 195

$Ag_2(C_2O_4)$, 90

$Ag_2CrO_4$, 56, 58, 68, 74, 152

AgI, 20, 21, 22, 62, 106, 123, 168, 182, 183, 195

$AgIO_3$, 60, 74

$AgNO_3$, 62, 88, 90, 156, 181, 195, 198

$Ag_2SO_4$, 30, 90

$Al(AcAc)_3$, 94

$Al(NO_3)_3$, 181

$Am_2(C_2O_4)_3$, 91, 96

$As_2S_3$, 152


$BaBr_2$, 80, 81, 88, 89, 90

$Ba(C_2H_3O_2)_2$, 90

$BaC_4H_4O_6 \cdot H_2O$, 91

$BaCl_2$, 24, 88, 89, 90, 95, 96, 212

$Ba(ClO_3)_2$, 90

$BaCO_3$, 94, 96

$BaCrO_4$, 96

$BaF_2$, 118

$Ba(IO_3)_2$, 84

$Ba(NO_3)_2$, 87, 90, 180, 181

$BaSO_4$, 14, 19, 24, 27, 30, 41, 56, 60, 62, 63, 66–68, 69, 74, 84, 96, 98, 104, 118, 126, 133–135, 140, 146, 147, 152, 153, 156, 168, 183

BiS, 152


$CaCl_2$, 182, 212

$CaCO_3$, 13, 19, 87, 109, 110, 123, 126, 141, 152, 166, 167, 168

$CaC_2O_4$, 24, 30, 68, 89, 152, 183

$CaF_2$, 13, 30, 41, 118, 123, 152, 166–168

$CaHPO_4$, 33, 152

$Ca_4H(PO_4)_3$, 33

$Ca(NO_3)_2$, 181

CaO, 33, 138

$Ca(OH)_2$, 123, 138

$Ca_5(OH)(PO_4)_3$, 33, 37–39, 111, 155, 211

$Ca_3Si_2O_7$, 137, 138

$CaSO_4$, 24, 90, 91, 118, 126, 135, 152

$CdCl_2$, 87, 89

$CdI_2$, 47, 49, 168

CdS, 21 70, 71, 152, 168, 183

$Ce_2(C_2O_4)_3$, 96

$Ce(NO_3)_3$, 181

$CoCl_2$, 91

$CoSO_4$, 91

$CrCl_3$, 91

CsBr, 122

CsCl, 85, 122, 159, 166, 167

CsF, 117, 122

CsI, 85, 122

$CsNO_3$, 181

$CsReO_4$, 94

$Cs_2SO_4$, 181

CuCl, 123, 140

$CuCl_2$, 91

CuS, 152

$CuSO_4 \cdot 5H_2O$, 88, 89, 91, 107, 108


$Eu_2(C_2O_4)_3$, 91


$FeCl_3$, 91

$(FeF_6)^{3-}$, 56

$Fe_2O_3$, 133

FeS, 70, 71

$Fe_2(SO_4)_3$, 91


HBr, 181

HCl, 173

$Hf_3(PO_4)_4$, 152
$HgS$, 21, 152, 182
$HIO_3$, 153
$H_2SO_4$, 155

$KBr$, 13, 17, 22, 85, 88, 117, 120–122, 173, 195, 201, 202, 205
$KBrO_3$, 88, 90
$KCl$, 13, 17, 22, 56, 85, 88, 116, 117, 120–123, 140, 158, 172, 173
$KClO_3$, 88, 90
$KClO_4$, 174
$K_2CrO_4$, 167, 168, 171
$KF$, 117, 120–122
$KI$, 13, 17, 22, 85, 88, 117, 120–122
$KIO_3$, 153, 154
$KNO_3$, 88, 90, 170, 174, 181, 198, 199, 201, 250
$KPbCl_3$, 172
$K_2PtCl_6$, 90
$KReO_4$, 94
$K_2SO_4$, 90, 167, 168, 171, 173, 181
$K_2TaF_7$, 94
$K_2TiF_6$, 94
$K_2ZrF_6$, 94

$La_2(C_2O_4)_3$, 89, 91, 98
$La(IO_3)_3$, 153, 154
$La(IO_4)_3$, 96
$La(NO_3)_3$, 153, 180, 181

$LiBr$, 13, 88, 117, 122
$LiCl$, 13, 88, 94, 117, 120–123, 140, 182
$LiF$, 56, 88, 117, 120–123, 174
$LiI$, 117, 122
$LiNO_3$, 181
$Li_2SO_4$, 181

$MgCO_3$, 123
$MgC_2O_4$, 56, 58, 60, 69, 152
$MgCl_2$, 212
$MgF_2$, 30
$Mg(NO_3)_2$, 181

$MgO$, 115, 123
$Mg(OH)_2$, 123
$MgS$, 152
$MgSO_4$, 88–90, 135
$MnCl_2$, 91
$MnCO_3$, 109
$Mn(NO_3)_2$, 181

$NaBr$, 13, 22, 88, 94, 117, 120–122
$NaBrO_3$, 88, 90, 173
$Na_3C_6H_5O_7 \cdot xH_2O$, 153
$NaCl$, 13, 14, 22, 35, 85, 88, 92, 116, 117, 120–123, 140, 158, 166, 167, 173, 174, 182
$NaClO_3$, 88, 90
$NaClO_4$, 182
$Na_2CO_3$, 201, 202, 204, 206–209, 212
$NaF$, 117, 120, 121, 122, 174
$NaI$, 13, 88, 117, 120, 121, 122
$NaNO_3$, 14, 166, 176, 181
$Na_2SO_4$, 24, 88, 89, 91, 173, 181
$Nd_2(C_2O_4)_3$, 96
$NH_4Br$, 88
$NH_4Cl$, 88, 90, 164
$(NH_4)_2Cr_2O_7$, 89, 90
$NH_4I$, 13–17
$(NH_4)_3IrCl_6 \cdot H_2O$, 89
$NH_4NO_3$, 174
$(NH_4)_2SO_4$, 88, 167, 168, 174
$(NH_4)_2TaF_7$, 94
$(NH_4)_2TiF_6$, 94
$(NH_4)_2ZrF_6$, 94
$NiCl_2$, 91, 140
$Ni(HC_4H_6N_2O_2)_2$, 64
$NiSO_4$, 91

$PbCl_2$, 70, 87, 91, 147, 168, 172, 173
$PbCO_3$, 30
$PbCrO_4$, 19, 90, 143, 144, 146, 147, 152, 168
$PbI_2$, 21, 130, 168
$Pb(IO_3)_2$, 84, 153, 154
$Pb(NO_3)_2$, 87, 153
$PbS$, 13, 147, 152, 168

PbSO$_4$, 30–32, 41, 56, 60, 74, 84, 104, 118, 126, 135, 143, 144, 147, 151, 152, 157, 158, 168, 183

$^{210}$Po, 89, 94

RaBr$_2$, 80, 81, 85, 90
RaCl$_2$, 90
RaCO$_3$, 96
Ra(ClO$_3$)$_2$, 90
RaCrO$_4$, 96
Ra(IO$_3$)$_2$, 84, 90
Ra(NO$_3$)$_2$, 87, 90
RaSO$_4$, 84, 90, 96
RbBr, 13, 17, 117, 120–122
RbCl, 12, 13, 15, 17, 85, 117, 121, 122
RbF, 117, 121, 122
RbI, 16, 85, 117, 120–122
Rb$_2$SO$_4$, 88, 90, 181

S, 27
Sb$_2$S$_3$, 152
Sb$_2$(SO$_4$)$_3$, 191
Sc(AcAc)$_3$, 94
Sc$_2$(C$_2$O$_4$)$_3$, 89
SiO$_2$, 126, 133, 138, 151, 176
Si(OH)$_2$, 138
SnO$_2$, 126, 133
SnS$_2$, 152
SrCl$_2$, 90, 182, 207–210, 212
SrCO$_3$, 30, 109, 110, 206

Sr(C$_2$O$_4$), 89
SrF$_2$, 118
Sr(NO$_3$)$_2$, 88, 90, 181
Sr(OH)$_2$, 123
SrSO$_4$, 30, 41, 56, 60, 68, 74, 84, 90, 96, 118, 126, 135–137, 147, 152, 155, 168

Th(AcAc)$_4$, 94
Th(IO$_4$)$_4$, 96
Th(NO$_3$)$_4$, 181, 212
Th(OH)$_4$, 210
TiO$_2$, 94, 126, 133–135
Ti$_2$O$_5$, 94
TlCl, 84, 88, 152
TlI, 21, 123, 130, 131, 143–145

UO$_2$(NO$_3$)$_2$, 201, 202, 204, 207–210, 212
UO$_2$, 213

Y$_2$(C$_2$O$_4$)$_3$, 91, 96
Yb$_2$(C$_2$O$_4$)$_3$, 96

ZnCO$_3$, 109
ZnC$_2$O$_4$, 152
ZnS, 14, 70, 71, 123
ZnSO$_4$, 91
Zr(NO$_3$)$_4$, 181
ZrO$_2 \cdot x$H$_2$O, 94, 126, 210
ZrOCl$_2$, 94
Zr$_3$(PO$_4$)$_4$, 152

# ORGANIC COMPOUND INDEX

Acetic acid, 169, 170
Acetone, 182
Alanine, 37
Allyl chloride, 27, 156
p-Aminophenol, 14
Aniline, 169
Anthranilic acid, 169, 170

Benzene, 21, 22, 126, 134
Benzoates, 57, 59, 70
Benzophenone, 21
Biacetylamine, 64
Butanol, 126
Butylamine, 135
Butyl chloride, 135
Butyl iodide, 135

Carbon tetrachloride, 126
Cetyltrimethylammonium (nitrate),
    57, 59
Chlorobenzene, 126, 134
Cholates, 56
Cholestrol, 25, 30, 33, 38, 56, 175
Citric acid, 174
Cyclohexane, 169

Dimethylglyoxime, 64, 65
Dimethyl oxalate, 96
Dodecylsulfate (sodium), 57–59

Eosin (potassium), 57, 58
Ethanol, 22, 25, 62, 126, 169, 170
(di)Ethyl acetate, 98, 126
(di)Ethyl ether, 62
Ethyl iodide, 62

Fumaric acid, 212

Glycine, 21, 22, 30, 37, 138

Heptane, 135
Hexane, 126, 135
Hexanol, 126
Hydroxylamine, 64

Iodoform, 169
Isooctane, 126

Maleic acid, 212
Methanol, 126, 135, 182
Methyl sulfate, 96

Naphthalene-2-sulfonate (potassium),
    57, 59
Nitrobenzene, 126, 134
p-Nitrobenzoic acid, 14

Octane, 135
Octanol, 126
Oxalic acid, 212

Paraffin wax, 132
Pentaerythritol, 170
Pentane, 126
Pentanol, 182
Pentanyl nitrate, 135
Penton, 35
Phenol, 126, 134
Phthalic acid, 212
Polyacrylic acid, 24
Polyethylene, 35, 36, 132
Polyhexafluoropropylene, 132
Polymonochlorotrifluoroethylene, 132
Polyoxymethylene, 47, 49
Polypropylene, 35, 37
Polystyrene, 132
Polytetrafluoroethylene, 132
Polyvinyl alcohol, 174
Propanol, 126, 182
Propionaldehyde, 135

Sulfamic acid, 96

Tartaric acid, 174
Teflon, 21
Tetraphenylarsonium perchlorate, 64
Thiourea, 14
Trichloroacetates, 96

Urea, 14, 96, 173, 174
Uric acid, 33

# SUBJECT INDEX

## A

Activation energy, for growth, 69
  for nucleation, 4
Adsorption, of compounds, 103
  and heterogeneous nucleation, 9
  of ions, 138–141
  of molecules, 140–141
  of radioactive tracers, 88–90
  rate of, 143–145
Aging, 39, 145–146
Agglomeration, 175–177, 199
Alkali halides, 17, 86
Alum, 173
Amino acids, 35
Amorphous precipitates, 39, 155

## B

Bacteria, 1
Benzene solidification, 22
Bladder stones, 24, 33
Bone growth, 33–36

## C

Calcification, 32–38
Chemical potential and faceted crystals, 171
Cholesterol, 25, 30
Clusters, 1
Coagulation, curves, 179
  time, 177
  values, 181
Coherent interface, 7
Collagen, 33
Colloidal phenomena, 184–185
Complex formation, 190–192
Coprecipitation (and cocrystallization), 79–111, 109, 210
  by direct mixing, 97
  interface models and, 102, 106
  geological, 109
  of miscible components, 80, 89
  in multicomponent systems, 206–209
  by occlusion and entrapment, 108

by PFHS methods, 96
  physiological, 79, 111
  rate of, 98–103
  structural principles of, 86–89
  surface charge and, 106
  of water, 107–108
Counting particles, 74
Critical cluster size, 30
Critical nucleus, 1
Critical supersaturation, 5–13, 17–19, 25–31
Critical supersaturation ratio, 18
Crystal defects, 80
Crystal habit, 166–174
  modification of, by dyes and organic materials, 173
  by ions, 170–171
  by solvent, 169–170
Crystal growth, 45
  screw dislocations and, 46–49
  of seed crystals, 54
  and spiral growth, 47, 49
  surface nucleation and, 45–46, 51–53
Crystal growth rate, 45, 50
  impurities and, 56–57
  surface adsorption and, 59
Crystallinity, 39

## D

Defect sites, 10
Dendrites, 158
  fragmentation of, 163–165
Dielectric constant, 182
Diffuse interfaces, 142
Diffusion theories, 44, 54, 62, 67–69
Dipole moment, 134–135
Dislocations, 46–50
Dispersion quotient, 189
Dissolution, 58, 70
Distortion of crystal lattice, 83
Distribution coefficient (equilibrium), 82–91
  heterogeneous, 93–94

229

Doerner-Hoskins equation, 93

**E**

Edge free energy, 11, 12, 51–53
  cluster charge and, 52
Embryo. *See* Clusters *and* Nuclei.
Elastic modulus, 8, 9, 14
Electrolytic reduction, 212
Epitaxy, 12, 35
Equilibrium, form of crystals, 166–174
  distribution coefficient of, 82–91
Excess free energy of solid solution, 84

**F**

Fragmentation of dendrites, 163–165
Free energy (Gibbs), critical for nucleation, 4
  and excess of solid solution, 84
  of volume, 4
Freundlich isotherm, 139

**G**

Gallstones, 33
Geological cocrystallization, 109
Gibbs adsorption equation, 113
Gibbs-Kelvin equation, 5, 71, 135
Glycine nucleation, 22
Graphical presentation of precipita-
  tion data, 197–213
Growth, diffusion-controlled, 54, 62,
  67–69
  surface-controlled, 55, 67–69

**H**

Habit modifications, 169–174
Heat of crystallization, 4
Heat of immersion, 125, 132, 133–135
Heat of solution, 26, 137
Henderson-Kracek equation, 82
Heterogeneous distribution coefficient,
  93–94
Heterogeneous nucleation data, 17, 21,
  22
  theory, 7–14
Homogeneous nucleation data, 30, 41
  theory, 4, 7
Hydrated crystals, 107
Hydroxyapatite, 37

**I**

Ice nucleation, 20, 21
Induction periods, 7, 31, 41
Impurities, effect on growth rate, 56–57
Interface, coherent, 7
  models for, 102, 106
Interfacial energy, 113
  dispersive component of, 123
    for inorganic compounds, 133
    for polymers, 132
  evaluation of, 129
  and morphology, 184
  and nucleation, 4
  and solubility, 135
  surface distortion and, 130
Interfacial interactions, 114
  and dipole moment, 134
  and hydrogen bonding, 127
  liquid–liquid, 127
  metal–liquid, 127
  polar crystal–liquid, 128
  polymer–liquid, 132
Isoelectric point, 28, 206
  precipitation maximum, 179

**J**

Jump diffusion, 9

**K**

Kaolin suspension, 176
Kidney stones, 24, 33

**L**

Langmuir isotherm, 10, 139
Lattice mismatch, 8, 14
Liquid crystals, 174
Liquid–solid interface. *See* Interface.

**M**

Mica, 13, 16, 17
Mixability of solids, 85
  misfit (mismatch), 8
Mixed crystals, 80
Mixed salts, 193
Morphology, 151
  and interfacial energy, 184
  and PFHS, 154

rate of crystal growth and, 156
solubility and, 151
supersaturation and, 184
Multicomponent systems, 206–215

**N**

Nucleation, 1–43, 51–54, 196
of alkali halides, 17
of benzene, 22
cell for studying heterogeneous, 18
coherent, 10, 12
heterogeneous, 7–38
homogeneous, 4–7, 30, 41
of ice, 20–21
incoherent, 10, 12
inhibition of, 23–24
kinetics of, 39–41
rate of, 5, 6, 9, 11
solvation and, 3, 40
of sparingly soluble materials, 30
Nuclei, size of critical, 1, 30
Nylon, 35

**O**

Ostwald ripening, 71–72
Oyster shell, formation of, 38

**P**

Penton, epitaxy of, 35
PFHS (precipitation from homogeneous solution), nucleation and, 9
growth kinetics and, 61–64
Phospholipids, 33
Physiological cocrystallization, 111
Physiological nucleation, 33
Polyethylene, epitaxy of, 35–36
Polynuclear complexes, 191
Polypropylene, epitaxy of, 35–37
Precipitate stoichiometry, 193
boundary, 196
Precipitation, of chelates, 64
diffusion-controlled, 62, 67–68
interface-controlled, 67–68
kinetics of, 61–64, 66–69
of metal hydroxides, 191
Precipitation curves, 66, 201
for two-component systems, 205–208

for three- and multicomponent systems, 208–211
Precipitation rate, factors influencing, 75
Proton complexes, 192

**R**

Radioactive tracers, 88–90
adsorption of, 146–147
Rate of growth, 45, 50
Rate of nucleation, 6
Rayleigh scattering, 73
Ripening, 71–72

**S**

Scaling, 23
Sclerosis, 33
Screw dislocations, 46–50
Seed crystal growth, 54
Silica, 21
Silicosis, 33, 35
Solid–liquid interface. *See* Interface.
Solid solutions, 82–83
Solidification, of benzene, 22
of water, 20
Solubility, and interfacial energy, 135
and morphology, 151
and particle size, 135–136
Spherical crystals, 154
Spiral growth, 47–49
Stability (colloidal), 177–182
dielectric constant and, 182
ion charge and, 179
ion radius and, 181
solvent effect on, 180
Stability constants, 192
Stability of lattice, solvent molecules and, 107
Stirring, and rate of precipitation, 60, 76
Stoichiometry, 39, 191–193
Supercooling, 15
Supersaturation, 2, 5
critical, 6, 9
Surface, adsorption, 56–59, 170–174
and growth rate, 59
defects, 10

diffuse, 142
diffusion, 9
enthalpy, 137
  values for, 138
exchange, 143
instability, 162–163
nucleation, 45–46, 51–53
Surface energetics, and heat of immer-
    sion, 125, 132, 133
  and surface interaction, 125
Surface energy, of alkali halides, 117,
    122
  atomic interaction and, 116–128
  calculation of, 115
    empirical methods for, 122–123
    for ionic surfaces, 115
    for organic crystals, 124
  experimental measurement of, 114
  of faceted crystals, 121
  of fluorite-type crystals, 118
  of orthorhombic sulfates, 118
  of separation of components, 123
  of solids, 114–125
  sublimation energy and, 124
  surface charge and, 117
  surface relaxation and, 116, 119

Surface tension, relation to lattice
    energy, 121
  relation to molecular volume, 120

**T**

Temkin isotherm, 139
Turbidity, expressions for, 73, 189
Tyndallograms, 198
Two-dimensional nucleation, 9–12, 51

**U**

Uranium salts, precipitation of, 203

**W**

Walter-Schlundt equation, 95
Water, crystallization of, 107
  solidification of, 20
Whiskers, 165

**X**

X-ray, determination of crystallinity
    by, 39

**Z**

Zeldovich rate factor, 9